SOUTH *of* DARKNESS

JOHN MARSDEN

SOUTH *of* DARKNESS

MACMILLAN

Pan Macmillan Australia

First published 2014 in Macmillan by Pan Macmillan Australia Pty Ltd
1 Market Street, Sydney, New South Wales, Australia, 2000

Cataloguing-in-Publication entry is available
from the National Library of Australia
http://catalogue.nla.gov.au

Typeset in 12.5/18 pt Fournier MT Regular by Post Pre-Press Group
Printed by McPherson's Printing Group
Internal text design and endpapers by Debra Billson
Endpapers map by Thomas Bowen (1749–1790) / National Library of Australia

Papers used by Pan Macmillan Australia Pty Ltd are natural, recyclable products made from wood grown in sustainable forests. The manufacturing processes conform to the environmental regulations of the country of origin.

To Kris, with memories of those quiet days in that vast room,
in the beautiful stillness of winter . . .

Chapter 1

Having been asked by the Revd Mr Johnson to jot down a few notes about my upbringing and the manner of my arrival in the colony, I will attempt to do so, but I should say at the outset that I have little of interest to relate. I have not contributed much of worth to the world, as will no doubt become obvious in the pages that follow, and indeed I sometimes wonder that I even survived the trials and tribulations of my earliest years.

I will begin, however, by relating my present situation. I do so in order to get my thoughts assembled in some way, for I confess I am loath to go back over some of the more painful memories that have accompanied me to this place. Verily, it seems easier to write about what I see outside my window than what I see when I look to the interior, at the dark rooms of the past.

Around me, then, are a few cleared acres, with trunks of trees piled here and there. These were fired the day before yesterday and are still smouldering. The smoke steals into everything, making my eyes water and my cough even worse. If a man wakes in the middle of the night he sees the red glows in all directions, and though he can be thankful for the warmth, he still shivers at the thought of that infernal flame to which a great number of the men and women who inhabit this place may expect to be consigned when the awful knell sounds.

Beyond the beginnings of Mr Cowper's farm lies the endless grey-green forest of this land. My fellow convicts, not to mention the soldiers, marines, emancipates and free men, were and still are for the most part uninterested in what they see as its strangeness and monotony. When I first arrived I regarded it with much the same distaste. Yet gradually I have fallen under its spell. To wander through it is to be struck by both its immensity and at the same time the delicate details that I fear generally escape the notice of my compatriots. As a boy and young man I believe I lacked the capacity to notice its finer features, for attention to detail comes only with age. As time passed, however, I did have quite singular opportunities to get to know it at close quarters, and perhaps those early experiences laid the foundations for my current appreciation of its qualities.

I feel I have at least been able to venture some small way into its mysteries.

At first one is struck by the absolute peculiarity of the native creatures. I remember vividly the first time I surprised kangaroos at rest. They were in the middle of a stand of trees, in a clearing with sufficient grass for them to rest comfortably. The sun was at its height. The first they knew of my presence was when I emerged from a dense stretch of eucalypts at the edge of the glade they had adopted as their home. They were as startled as I was. In a rather ungainly way they scrambled to their feet and bounded away, scattering in a variety of directions. Kangaroos are one of the few wild creatures who do not move quietly, when in flight at least. They pound the ground with the heavy spring of their rear legs, so I could hear them for a considerable time.

In spring, the little prickly beasts known as echidnas are everywhere, sometimes in a line of three or four. I believe they can be compared to the hedgehogs of home, but I have seen these latter only in books. The koala bears are rather less common, and are seldom seen on the ground. Men say they never need water, but I have observed them several times lapping from pools. In their trees, where they spend the greater part of their lives, they are slow and ponderous, moving from branch to branch with the solemnity of a judge at the Old Bailey. Unlike those awful dispensers of justice, however, the koalas, with their babies clinging to their backs, make a charming spectacle.

It must not be thought that it is just the creatures of this country which give the forest its beauty. Sprinkled through it, in the spring particularly, are brightly coloured flowers which would be lauded were they to grow in the woods and heathlands of England. Here they are disregarded, because they come into bloom for brief intervals only, and because they are not easily evident in the endless expanse of trees and grasses. Some are indeed among the tiniest and most delicate of God's creations, but are they to be crushed under the careless boot of a soldier or convict for that reason alone? They too have their place. To be insignificant in Man's eyes says nothing of the way we are viewed by the Supreme Being who, despite the vicissitudes of my life, I still believe made me, and everything else, and did so for a reason.

In my time I have been somewhat insignificant, and exactly why God took the trouble to create me has been difficult to imagine, though I can hardly be compared to a flower. A rank weed perhaps. Yet I too have felt the crushing boot of my uncaring fellows.

Perhaps it is time, though, that I complied with Revd Mr Johnson's charge, to describe a little of my tale.

My name, then, is Barnaby Fletch. To the best of my knowledge I have no middle name and cannot say of whom I am the son, or of whom my father's father's father was the son. I can hardly give the story of my birth let alone my pedigree, unlike the gentlefolk who are able to say, 'My great-great-grandfather fought with . . . at . . .' or 'On my mother's side I am descended from the Duke of . . .' Would that I could. Alas, my origins are shrouded in mystery, and the only mother and father I can summon are wraiths. On occasions I have invoked these phantoms in my mind, attempting to give myself succour in times of loneliness or sorrow, but the images I have conjured, which I am convinced are manifestations of the imagination alone, have provided little in the way of comfort, and I can only pray that all will be revealed when I am summoned to the Judgement Seat, for it is not likely to happen during my mortal existence.

My earliest memory is of being pulled aside in a crowded and narrow street that I surmise must have been in London, for I have no memory of ever going outside that town until I was thirteen years old. I believe I was about to be run over by a grand carriage, perhaps in the manner in which the aristocrats of France cared not whom they crushed under their wheels in the days before the recent revolution in that country. It may have been merely a cab; I cannot say at this distance. I recollect huge wheels and the great noise they made on the cobblestones, and my arm being nearly wrenched out of its socket and a voice bellowing at me in anger at my carelessness. Some shiny bauble had attracted me and I think I had trotted out into the path of the carriage to collect it. I know not what manner of thing it was, for the arm pulled me head over heels, and by the time I regained my balance, the shiny object was gone. Perhaps it was just a beam of sunlight reflecting from a puddle. I had not cried at the violent pulling on my arm, nor at my near escape from death, nor at being turned upside-down on the roadway, but I cried at the loss of the bright hope represented by the gleam on the cobblestones.

Perhaps the man who snatched me clear and then roared at me was my father. There are wisps of memory of a big bearded man who shouted a lot, and a woman who held me tight at certain times and pushed me away at others. These are the wraiths to which I can give no earthly form. Likely they have now gone to their rest and I can only pray that they know God's love and forgiveness in their eternal home.

Chapter 2

A THREAD THROUGHOUT MY CHILDHOOD was the great church in the district known to the local people as Hell, down by the north bank of the river. I apologise to my readers for inflicting this distasteful word upon their sensibilities, but it was the name commonly used by its denizens, although I believe that maps of London refer to it by the less offensive epithet East Smithfield. However, even at this distance, having seen what I have seen, Hell still seems to me an apt enough name for this den of iniquity. The proper name for the church was St Martin's, though again that was not how it was known among the local folk. Respect for my readers' sensibilities causes me to refrain from recording its popular name here.

St Martin's stood like a fortress among the insect life which teemed around its perimeter. Though the human termites made their burrows and consumed with avid mouths all that was soft and corruptible, the church could not be eroded. Its massive buttresses were implacable; the saints in its stained-glass windows turned their backs on the hordes in the streets and gazed upon the pious with tender eyes. Those outside could not see in, and those inside were insulated from the human transgressions which rolled endlessly against the walls, as the waves of the ocean roll against the rocks of the shore. They became blind and deaf to the swell of sin. The silence in the church was almost absolute; only the occasional whispers of a member of the clergy or a parishioner, or the puny efforts of the organ, interrupted the vast stillness.

I'm not sure at what point in my life I began to sneak into St Martin's to spend my nights within the safety of its walls. Perhaps I was four years old, perhaps I was five. But it frequently served as my refuge in times of trial. I had several hiding places. One was under the altar itself, though as I grew older I feared the wrath of God for treating the holy sanctuary with such irreverence. I dared not go near it when certain clergy were on duty, for if they were to catch me I feared their wrath would be as awful as that of the Lord. Another, somewhat colder bolthole, was behind a statue of St Peter, though eventually I grew too big to fit into the little space between him and the wall. But I liked St Peter's kind face, and I talked to him sometimes at night, when I was alone there in the dark.

The other safe spot was the high pulpit, used by the clergy only on the most solemn occasions. It contained a small prayer cushion, which made a pleasant pillow, and it was nearly as warm as under the altar. Many a time I curled up in there and waited for the night to pass.

In time I learned the habits and idiosyncrasies of the holy men who served the Lord in St Martin's. The rector was the Revd Mr Cartwright, a Christlike man indeed, who moved about the church shrouded in such an air of piety that few dared approach him. He had a fine and haughty face, and stood in the high pulpit on Sundays like an eagle on a crag, gazing through the air as though taking no notice of anyone, yet at the same time giving the impression that he saw every detail of every life of those doomed and sinful souls seated before him. Oh, the congregation paid him such attention. They dared not look away. He preached a fine sermon, even though I rarely understood a word of it, so grand was his eloquence and so elevated his thoughts.

I doubt that the Revd Mr Cartwright had any more real regard for us poor folk than he did for the mouse who lived in the vestry and made his meals from the crumbs in Revd Mr Haddock's cupboard.

Revd Mr Haddock was always at food, which was the salvation of the mouse, for he would not have survived otherwise. Many a time it was my salvation too, for he not infrequently left unfinished food on a low wooden ledge below his cupboard. I had to compete with the mouse for these suppers, and if I was a little late I had to brush his little black pellets away before I could consume the victuals.

As time went on I noticed that Revd Mr Haddock left food behind only when he was the last to leave the church at nights, the one charged with locking the building. I did not know why he was so careless on these occasions, but to a child with an empty stomach, alone in the great dark building, the comfort derived from a few slices of bread, a piece of sausage, or a couple of baked potatoes was like a benediction from the Lord himself.

Revd Mr Haddock was a big man, which was not to be wondered at, but he moved about the church quickly and quietly, with a surprising energy. I felt that the people laughed at him a little, for his ways were eccentric, and he was rarely charged with preaching a sermon or administering important services. Matins and Compline often fell to his lot. Yet he was always kind. Sometimes at night when he believed he was alone he would talk to himself, in a voice louder than one was accustomed to hearing in that place of silence. Perhaps he did it because he was lonely and even a little afraid, for at such times he often spoke words of comfort.

Five minutes or more might elapse between each sentence, as though he pondered long and deeply over every remark. His words rumbled towards me out of the darkness. 'Though the way be cold and cruel, yet there is always hope,' he would say. 'Know that even the least among us has a friend, and that friend is closer at hand than we might realise. You are here for a reason and God will make the reason clear to you one day, if that be His will. The Lord knows of your suffering and the Lord will reward those who try, no matter how many times they fail.'

Certainly the Revd Mr Haddock failed many times, if the disapproval of the Revd Mr Grimwade was any indication. Revd Mr Cartwright may have been the rector of the church but a visitor could have been forgiven for thinking that Revd Mr Grimwade held this appointment. A lean man with a thin mouth, Revd Mr Grimwade would have cowed Satan himself had that malefactor dared set foot inside St Martin's. He used words like the cracking of a whip, and one short sentence from him could leave a scar to last a lifetime. Grim he was by name and by nature.

If I saw him in the church when I slipped in through one of its many doors I often left again. If I was in one of my hiding holes when he entered, I cowered in fear and tried to make myself as small as the vestry mouse.

I confess now to the sin of hatred for one of the Lord's anointed, for there were times when I hated Revd Mr Grimwade, and even more when he tongue-lashed Revd Mr Haddock or one of the curates. It offended my sense of justice. Revd Mr Haddock was, it must be said, somewhat clumsy at times, whereas Revd Mr Grimwade spoke and moved with such precision that it was difficult to imagine him ever making a mistake. At one Good Friday service Revd Mr Haddock put the wrong numbers on one of the hymn boards, which meant that half the congregation was trying to sing 'There is a green hill far away', while the other half, and the organist, were attempting 'Guide me O thou great Jehovah'. The way Revd Mr Grimwade spoke to Revd Mr Haddock afterwards, in the vestry, as I listened from the curved staircase leading to the belltower, was a shame and should never have been allowed. 'You make a mockery of Holy Orders,' he said in his cold flat voice. 'I notice the Bishop is seeking to appoint a chaplain to St Luke's Asylum. That might suit you better, for there is no place for buffoons here.'

But the time when Revd Mr Haddock dropped the chalice as he went to administer Communion to the first parishioner kneeling at the altar rail . . . that was Revd Mr Grimwade's opportunity to sting with all the venom at his command. To be sure, it was a shocking sight, to see the blood of Christ spilled on the floor and dripping down the steps, and the parishioners backing away as one, with fear and horror in their eyes. Some made the sign of the Cross, which I knew even at my tender age would not please Revd Mr Grimwade, who regarded it as a contamination from the Papacy. There were three clergy officiating on this particular morning, Revd Mr Grimwade and Revd Mr Haddock and a young curate whose name I never learned and who did not stay at St Martin's long. They and the two altar boys stood as if paralysed by the awful and sacrilegious spectacle. I don't think anyone knew how to clean up the wine without committing further offence. Revd Mr Grimwade was the first to recover his wits, and although there was a gasp of horror from the congregation at the action he took, I had to admire the strength of his thinking. He removed the tippet from around his neck and, working calmly and methodically, used the holy garment to soak up the holy wine.

Revd Mr Haddock tried to help him but was waved away. The parishioners soon began to recover, and at a gesture from Revd Mr Grimwade moved around the stain on the floor and resumed their places at the altar rail. Revd Mr Haddock stepped forward to continue the administration of the Communion, but with a nod of the head and a lifted eyebrow Revd Mr Grimwade consigned him to a chair on the far side of the sacristy, where the big young man remained for the rest of the service to contemplate his errors, which assignment, judging from his despairing expression, he carried out to an extent that would have satisfied any but the most merciless inquisitor.

Unfortunately Revd Mr Grimwade was a man to whom mercy was unknown, and in the vestry after the service he subjected his inferior to such an excoriation as I had never heard before, which was followed by Revd Mr Haddock's being forced to practise moving a jug from the vestry windowsill to the little wooden table and back no fewer than five hundred times, on the pretext that he needed to rehearse the action.

After Revd Mr Grimwade left, I believe I heard, from my perch on the staircase, the muffled sobs of a man crying. I did not intrude by peeping down to see who it was, but instead inched further up the steps, thereby moving a little closer to the realm of One whom it is hoped is not so harsh a judge as may be some of His representatives on Earth.

Chapter 3

THE GREAT COLD STONE exterior walls of the church of St Martin's had
been blackened over the centuries by the cooking fires and chimney
smoke; that same smoke which stung my eyes as I groped through the
dark and foggy streets. Having traversed the endless eucalyptus forests
of New South Wales, it is now my conviction that every boy should
be raised in the countryside. Truly, space is the greatest luxury mortal
man can experience, and I speculate that the noblest families in their
tapestried apartments cannot know the sense of joy that possesses the
man who stands in the middle of the forest breathing its pure air and
knowing he is free to wander in any direction his fancy determines.

Such was not the nature of my childhood. It was scarcely possible
to take a step without bumping against one of my fellow creatures, or
tripping over someone's feet, or dislodging an item displayed on a street
stall. I seemed to spend my early years in a deluge of curses and imprecations, so that I was saturated by them. I do believe they soaked into
my very soul. Oftentimes I am sure the words meant little enough to the
people who flung them at me; no doubt they were, on most occasions,

forgotten by the perpetrators within moments, but the effect on my impressionable self was to believe that every man's hand was raised against me, and every man's face distorted by a scowl. Aye, and every woman's too.

Thus I spent my formative years like the vestry mouse, learning to find protection in holes and crevices, practising stealth and deception, fearing at all times the sudden pounce of the cat or dog. The man whom I believe saved my life by plucking me from under the wheels of the coach in the crowded street was doing me a kindness no doubt, but when kindness is wrapped in a cloak of harshness it is hidden from a child. Thus, all I remember of him is his anger.

I was taught to steal by a girl slightly older than I. I don't know who she was, and perhaps I had been stealing before then, without any moral awareness of the nature of my act, but I remember the girl instructing me and another boy about my age. She taught us how to brush against shop counters in such a way that objects fell into our pockets. She taught us how to look around, to be aware of the gaze of the shopkeepers without seeming to notice them and without attracting their attention. And she taught us how to leave a shop with full pockets but without exciting any interest.

She also taught us how to look 'respectable', as best we could in the tattered bits and pieces we called clothes. We learned to wash our faces and hands in the gutter water, to use our fingers to comb and part each other's hair, to walk with our heads up as though we were as entitled as gentlefolk to be in a fine shop.

For all that, though, we were thrown out of half the businesses we attempted to enter. This did not disconcert our young female companion in the slightest. She would merely toss her head, shout some insult at the shopkeeper, and march out, saying to us: 'Well boys, we'll know not to spend our money here when we come into our fortunes.' Then she would lead us into the store next door.

I was probably about five years old at this time. The other boy's name was Quentin, and we met when I took shelter from a rainstorm under a footbridge and found him huddled there, curled up like a little mole. I was afraid of him at first, because he had a huge red birthmark covering half of his face, and I had been told this meant he was possessed by the Devil. But I was afraid of getting cold and wet too, so when he moved over and made a space for me I crawled into it gratefully. There was not much room, because so many other of London's poor had chosen the same refuge. Just a foot away was a huge man lying on his back asleep, snoring as loudly as the thunder, his hand resting on an empty brown bottle. I had seen him around the streets often enough; he was known to everyone as Uncle Bert. I was not afraid of him when he was asleep, but when he was awake I kept my distance, for he had a violent temper.

As we waited for the storm to ease, Quentin told me a little of his origins. 'I was left on the doorstep of a convent when I was born,' he said, almost proudly. 'Because of this, I suppose,' he added, touching his birthmark.

'Have you always had it then?' I asked, for I knew nothing of birthmarks, or of anything for that matter.

He nodded solemnly. 'That's why my father and mother didn't want to keep me,' he explained. 'Leastways, it's what the nuns told me.'

When the rain stopped we left our shelter. No sooner had we got out from under the bridge than Quentin showed me a large bread roll. His expression was one of triumph.

'Where did you get that?' I asked, amazed, for I was sure he had not had it a few moments before.

'It was sticking out of Uncle Bert's pocket,' he giggled.

'Will you share it with me?'

He shared it willingly, and so our friendship was cemented.

Just a few hours later, however, he sauntered past a fruit stall and I was startled to see him pluck an apple from the top of a pile and attempt to dart away down an alley. This was before the lessons with the older girl; she would have scorned such an amateurish approach. Quentin ran a dozen steps, but in looking around at the stall to see if he was being pursued he failed to notice a massive obstruction: to wit, the back of a large and prosperously dressed man, of a type we seldom saw in Hell. He was standing in the middle of the alley, gazing searchingly around him as if wondering how he came to be in such a place. Quentin ploughed straight into the man and staggered back, holding his nose. The man whipped around. He had a cane and he raised it high above my companion. 'What are you doing?' he shouted. 'Vagabond! Be off!'

The collision gave the stall owner the time he needed. He had seen the theft, and now he seized Quentin and dragged him away behind his horse and cart. Fearing for my friend's safety I hastened around there, in time to see the man belabouring Quentin with a stout stick. The blows landed on Quentin's back and shoulders as the boy fought to break free. But the man was too strong and had too good a grip. There was nothing I, a puny child, could do. He only stopped when a gaunt old woman loading a cart behind him screeched: 'Leave him alone, you great oaf! What's he done to you?'

'He's a thief,' the man retorted. But he ceased his flogging of the boy.

'Yah! As if you don't steal from every customer you short-change. Anyway, what have you got that's worth stealing? Your mouldy old apples? I wouldn't feed them to my horse.'

'You'd better feed the nag something or he'll end up as skinny as you, you old bag of bones.' But he laughed as he said it. With a quick twist Quentin was out of his arms and gone. 'Leave my fruit alone or you'll get worse next time,' the man shouted after him.

There in the mud and horse excrement I saw the stolen apple, dropped and forgotten in the clamour. I picked it up and went in search of Quentin.

Back then such incidents were common enough for we children who lived by our wits in the crowded streets of London's poorer areas. I don't know if much has changed since. Watchmen or constables, let alone the Bow-Street Runners, whom we called the Robin Redbreasts, were rarely seen in Hell, unless it was to raid a molly house or a place of prostitution, or to close the shops of those working on the Sabbath, or some other activity that had little effect on our lives. Punishments were rough and ready. I believe in the countryside the ducking stool was still in use. A judge could sentence a felon to be hung, drawn and quartered, though in practice the sentence was always commuted to hanging and decapitation. The streets were dark and dreadful at night, especially in winter, for the wonderful innovation of gas lighting was not yet used to illuminate a single thoroughfare.

Before I met Quentin I lived largely on the scraps left on the ground when the markets closed and on hand-outs from the occasional kind soul. Then there were the little suppers left behind by Revd Mr Haddock, and payment of food for jobs I performed from time to time. Of course in my youngest days I could do few jobs that were of use to anyone, yet to some extent I was compensated for this inadequacy by the fact that people were more inclined to show pity to the youngest children. As I grew older I was tossed fewer and fewer scraps, but I was employed more and more to run errands, guard stalls or clean windows.

I still consider it something of a miracle that I survived, for of course most children did not, and during my infant years I came upon more than one little body in the streets.

Under Quentin's tutelage, and later that of the nameless girl of whom I have written, I became a more skilled thief and not a day passed that I did not steal something. The girl made us give her a lot of what we took, but we were able to conceal a great deal from her. One day, however, she disappeared. We were supposed to meet her at a statue of a man on a horse, and when she did not turn up we soon drifted away. People were always coming and going in our lives. Yet she did not turn up the next day, or the day after that, and in fact we never saw her again. Perhaps she had been arrested. We soon forgot her, but we continued to practise the lessons she taught us.

Strangely, I always had a feeling of sickness as I did so. I do not know whether this was from the fear of punishment, or the stirrings of the conscience that God has given all but the most benighted. Perhaps it was a little of each. Certainly I had good reason to fear punishment, for numerous times I was chased and not infrequently caught, my little legs not being strong enough to outrun a determined pursuer.

I resolved from an early age not to cry when I was beaten and I gradually became more stoic on these occasions, taking pride in my inner strength, which sometimes elicited ejaculations of wonder from onlookers. Yet it was not always possible to maintain this appearance of stoicism. My worst thrashing came at the hands of a footman from a rich house, when Quentin and I ventured further from Hell than was our usual practice. We were in a back lane when a commotion broke out in one of the buildings. A bewigged old man threw open a window on the second floor, poked out his head, and cried, in a surprisingly powerful voice: 'Fire! Fire!' A stream of white smoke issued from the adjoining window as he spoke. A moment later, the back door burst open and a woman in cook's uniform ran out into the laneway, looked up, saw her master and the smoke, uttered a scream and ran back up the steps into the house.

Quentin and I, excited by the prospect of this spectacle, and, I can say with certainty in my case at least, with no thoughts of larceny, followed her up the steps. We found ourselves in a large and grand kitchen, the warmest room I had ever known, hung with pots and pans. A dresser stretched almost the full length of the wall. The vast table in the middle of the kitchen was laden with food the like of which I had never seen outside a shop. And the smells! I felt dizzy with the aromas of baking bread and roasted meat and frying bacon and cooked onions. It was as though I were in a delightful dream. I had been wafted away from the putrid smells of rotting meat in the markets, the corpse of a horse abandoned in a street at the edge of Hell, and the channels and puddles of human sewage that festooned the alleys and laneways of our usual surroundings. And the best of it was that the room was completely deserted. We could hear squawks and screeches from upstairs as the denizens of the house confronted the fire. Evidently it had engaged the attention of all. Quentin and I immediately forewent all interest in the fire. He looked at me with sparkling eyes, and without a word exchanged, we set to gathering all we could carry. In my case, an entire chicken in one hand, two potatoes in the other, a loaf of bread under my arm, and best of all a large biscuit crammed into my mouth. For Quentin a large brown bowl of rice pudding, two or three pastries and a long bread stick.

Out the door we ran, straight into the arms of a man in servant's uniform, blue and silver, who was entering all in a rush. 'Oh ho ho,' he laughed. 'What have we here? Take advantage of our situation, would you? Well, we'll see about that.'

He dragged us back into the kitchen. He had my head under his left arm, lodged in his smelly armpit. I dropped the chicken and potatoes, and spat out the biscuit, and fought to get free. When I had no success in prising his arm loose, I bit him as hard as I could, through his jacket. I don't think I had much effect, but he grunted, 'Oh, that's your game is it?' and hit me across the head. In doing so, I believe he lost his grip on Quentin, because he suddenly lurched across to his right, as though grabbing at someone. For a moment I had a chance to break free but I could not quite manage it, and an instant later he was holding me more tightly than ever. 'You can have the punishment for two then,' he snarled. 'That'll learn you.'

With that he pitched me forward, into I knew not what. A door slammed behind me, the room became instantly dark, and I heard a key turn in a lock. I was imprisoned in a tiny windowless space that seemed empty. All I could think of was the fire upstairs, and the fear that the house would burn down with me in it took me over, chasing away my stoicism, so that I screamed in fear and begged through the door for help. There was no response. The sound echoed back at me in a dead way that made me think my thin voice was incapable of penetrating the heavy wood. Yet I continued to shout until my voice gave out, and then I sobbed in frustration and despair.

I do not know how much time passed before the door was opened. My tormenter stood before me, and as my eyes adjusted to the light I saw a mocking smile on his face that did not bode well for me. Behind him stood another man, in powdered wig, wearing a red waistcoat trimmed with gold lace. He glanced at me disdainfully.

'The fire . . .' I sobbed but they ignored me.

'Here he is, sir, the little wretch,' the servant said. 'Shall I take him to the magistrate or would you have me deal with him myself?'

'Oh, I can't be bothered with the magistrate,' the man said. 'Not today of all days, with the shambles upstairs. You can inflict justice, I'm sure, Thomas.' He turned away as he finished his sentence: a man who obviously had too much on his mind to be concerned with an urchin from the gutters.

'Oh I can, sir, depend on it,' the servant gloated.

He slammed the door shut and locked it again, but this term of imprisonment lasted only a few minutes before I heard the key turn and he flung the door open once more. I trembled to see a whip in his hands. It was a kind I had seen rich men use on their horses: black leather, with a rigid handle and a short hard piece for striking. I cowered into the corner of the little room but he grabbed me by the back of the neck and hauled me out, despite my kicking and wriggling. Then he picked me up and tucked me under his arm as before, and marched down into the cellar.

I will always remember the smell of that dark and damp room. Around me, stretching into the distance, were barrels and chests, and hanging from the walls were any number of dead beasts, awaiting, I suppose, the day the lord of the house ordered them for his table. The natural stagnant smell that one finds underground blended with the fresh smell of death from the recently hung animals and birds, and in turn was supplemented by the sour smell of wine from the barrels and bottles.

The smell mingled with the fear in my stomach, and I felt the rush of saliva into the mouth that generally presages an extrusion of vomit. I tried to hold the bile back as the footman placed me across a low bench, holding me with one hand pressed into the small of my back and pulling my britches down with the other. Then he set about flogging me with his whip. No matter how I tried to protect myself I was unsuccessful:

when I got a hand behind my back to cover my buttocks the blows fell on my arm, and when I jerked my hand away in pain the blows resumed their assault on my rear portions. I have always been lean, having had little choice in the matter, and of course I was a bony underfed thing back then, with no fat to protect me from the brute's blows.

He did not hold back; I do not know how many times he lashed me, but I passed at last into that place beyond pain, a place most convicts know all too well. The pain encompasses the whole body until nothing but pain is known, and yet at the same time one transcends the pain and floats away from it. It is a kind of death, I believe, where one lets go of part of oneself that is mortal; it is also a surrender. Not necessarily a surrender signifying submission to the one who is administering the punishment, but a surrender to a greater power.

At some point I vomited, and I think some of it splashed onto his elegant black shoes, for he swore, thrashed me another half-a-dozen times very quickly, then stamped away up the stairs.

I lay there in a state resembling insensibility. After some time I heard footsteps approaching and saw the glow of a lamp reflecting from the dark walls. I feared that it was the man returning, but a woman's voice gasped, and I heard her say: 'My God, what's he done to you?' I attempted to twist around so I could get to my feet, but it was difficult to move, and before I could succeed I felt her hands on my nether regions, cool and soft on the burning flesh. 'Stay there,' she said, and went away again. When she returned it was with some sort of ointment, which she spread onto me. The ointment was soothing but any contact with my body was painful. Still, I endured it, and when she had finished I got to my feet, though not without some difficulty. With even more difficulty I hauled up my pants and shuffled towards the staircase, determined to escape this house of horrors.

The woman helped me up each painful step. I emerged into the kitchen, the place which had for a few moments promised Quentin and me such riches. Seeing the door to the street I made for it. 'Wait,' the woman said. Up until now I had not glimpsed her face but I stopped and turned to look at her. 'Thank you for your kindness, ma'am,' I said, perceiving her to be an older woman, plump, with small eyes, and dressed in the uniform of a cook, but not the same woman I had seen run out into the street at the cry of 'Fire!'

'Oh Lord,' she said. She glanced up at the door, which I surmised led to the main part of the house. She seemed frightened. She pushed away the grey hairs that straggled down under her cap. 'Wait,' she said again. She went into some sort of storeroom and emerged again within a minute, holding a substantial cloth-covered bundle. 'Quick,' she said, thrusting it at me. 'Begone with you, before he comes back. He's got a black heart, that one. Be off with you now.'

'Thank you, ma'am,' I said again, but it was not easy for me to make a quick escape, as I could hardly walk. I shuffled awkwardly to the door. She was there before me and opened it. I noticed that her eyes were full of tears. I laboured out into the street and hurried away as best I could. I turned around once only, to see if the woman was still there, but she was gone, and the door was closed.

Chapter 4

A ND SO QUENTIN AND I got our feast after all, half a chicken instead of
the whole one I had tried to purloin, and a loaf of bread, and some
sweet biscuits. I did not get as much enjoyment from it as I had hoped, for
I felt sick, and pain had the freedom of my body to go where it wished.
It made merry play with me too, running up and down my legs and my
back, spreading to every part of me, so that I was nothing but pain. My
buttocks burned and burned. There was blood through my clothes, and
every time I passed water it was red with blood. Quentin said the skin on
my rump was broken in many places. He fetched Uncle Bert, for Uncle
Bert had the reputation of being a healer, and the big man tut-tutted over
me and made up some mixture from herbs growing along the banks of the
river, which Quentin painted onto me three or four times a day. I believe
it consisted mainly of comfrey, and it may have done some good.

As the bruising healed, Quentin said it was as good as a painting to
see all the colours change. Orange and blue and green and purple, laced
of course with red and black – I was sorry I could not twist around
enough to get a full view of the exhibition for myself.

Gradually I was able to move more freely again and the time came when I could walk almost normally. I hobbled around Hell, finding it a little more difficult for a while to avoid collisions and accidents. Quentin never left my side and I came to appreciate his kindness and the devotion he showed in nursing me, for without him I know not how I would have fared. Neither of us ever made reference to the fact that the beating I received may have been more severe as a result of his escape, but perhaps it helped explain the fidelity of his attentions. I didn't care; I was just glad he had not been subjected to such a terrible experience.

From gratitude I showed him my hiding places in St Martin's, but he did not like the church much. To me it was a sanctuary; to him it was too quiet. He complained that it gave him bad dreams. So for the sake of keeping company with him I spent fewer nights there after this deepening of our friendship.

However, there were still many periods when Quentin and I were separated, sometimes for several days, and on those occasions I continued to use the church as my refuge. I remember distinctly one spring morning when I listened to a sermon by the Revd Mr Haddock, who was preaching in a side chapel to an early morning congregation of five or six people: not an unusual number at that time of day, in the middle of the week, when only the most devout could be expected to attend.

I cannot in all conscience call myself devout, for my motives for being in St Martin's had, as I have made clear, little to do with an attraction to the Christian virtues preached therein. However, I was curled up in the high pulpit, an eyrie never used for these Matins services, and an eyrie never graced at all by Revd Mr Haddock, who was rarely invited to preach anyway. It was no doubt thought by his ecclesiastical superiors to be a challenge beyond his intellectual or spiritual powers, or perhaps they considered him simply too dangerously clumsy to be entrusted with such a responsibility.

He started his sermon with a story. From my earliest years I have never been able to resist a story, so I listened quite attentively. It was the story of Job. I had heard his name before, at funeral services especially, when his utterances were frequently read from the Book of Common Prayer: 'Naked came I out of my mother's womb, and naked shall I return thither: the Lord gave, and the Lord hath taken away; blessed be the name of the Lord.'

Or, 'Man that is born of a woman is of few days, and full of trouble. He cometh forth like a flower, and is cut down: he fleeth also as a shadow, and continueth not.'

From the mouth of one such as Revd Mr Grimwade these words were full of woe indeed and I fear gave little comfort to those who had come thither to mourn friends or relatives recently departed. But Revd Mr Haddock spoke quite differently, and in simple words that even I at my tender age could understand. He told the story of Job: how he had been the wealthiest and most powerful man in the land of Uz, with seven sons and three daughters, seven thousand sheep, three thousand camels, five hundred oxen, and many other beasts and servants. He was an upright and God-fearing man who served the Lord with devotion. One day, when Satan visited God, the Lord said to Satan: 'Have you observed my servant Job, and are you not impressed by his purity and sanctity?'

And Satan said to God: 'It is easy for Job to be pure and sanctified when you have showered such blessings on him. Take the blessings away and see how he will curse your name then, aye, curse you to your very face!'

So God said: 'You are wrong, and I will prove it! I will grant you the right to test Job by doing whatsoever you like with him and with his possessions, only provided that you do not hurt the man himself.'

Armed with this power Satan visited fearful torments upon Job, destroying his ten children with a great wind that caused a building to collapse upon them, burning all his sheep with a fire from Heaven, and having enemies slaughter his servants and carry off his camels and oxen.

Job was torn apart by grief, yet he maintained his faith in the Lord and his devotion to Him.

When Satan returned to visit God again, God said to him: 'Now do you see what a perfect and upright man this is?' But Satan sneered and said: 'He remains steadfast only because he himself has not been harmed. Let his bone and flesh be smitten and you will see him turn upon you.'

So now God said: 'I tell you, nothing will shake his faith, and I will prove it to you. I grant his body to you also; do with him as you will, only you must not end his life.'

Satan caused Job to be covered with boils, so that he suffered greatly, but he still would not renounce the Lord, even though his own wife told him to curse God. Job responded by saying: 'We cannot expect to receive nothing but good from the Lord; we must expect dark times as well.'

Curled up in the pulpit I nodded; yes, dark times, it was true. Life for such as those who lived in Hell had a tendency to be full of trouble.

Revd Mr Haddock went on to describe how God then spoke to Job from inside a mighty storm. He roared forth like a tempest, asking Job if he truly understood the power of the Lord. 'Where were you when I laid the foundations of the earth, while the morning stars sang together, and all the sons of God shouted for joy? Who shut up the sea with doors, when it brake forth? Who said to the sea "Hitherto shalt thou come, but no further: and here shall thy proud waves be stayed?"'

Again and again He spoke to the man of His powers, saying to Job: 'Have the gates of death been opened unto thee? Or hast thou seen the doors of the shadow of death? Hast thou perceived the breadth of the earth?'

He spoke of the war horses, asking Job: 'Is it you who has given the horse strength? Hast thou clothed his neck with thunder? Canst thou make him afraid as a grasshopper? The glory of his nostrils is terrible. He paws in the valley, and rejoices in his strength: he goes on to meet the armed men. He mocks at fear, and is not affrighted; neither turns he back from the sword. The quiver rattles against him, the glittering spear and the shield. He swallows the ground with fierceness and rage: neither believeth he that it is the sound of the trumpet. He says among the trumpets, Ha, ha; and he smells the battle afar off, the thunder of the captains, and the shouting.'

Thus did God instil in Job a terrible fear of His awe and majesty, so that Job fell down upon his knees, recognising that the universe was infinitely more powerful and far-reaching than he had ever conceived. And that the One who had brought it into being could be held account-able to no mere mortal. Job expressed his humility, saying: 'I know that Thou canst do everything, and that no thought can be withholden from Thee. I uttered things that I understood not; things too wonderful for me, which I knew not. I had heard of Thee before, by the hearing of the ear: but now mine eye sees Thee, wherefore I abhor myself, and repent in dust and ashes.'

And so God rewarded Job for his new and more profound under-standing by restoring him to his previous station in life, doubling the wealth he had earlier possessed and granting him ten new children, seven sons and three daughters as before, but this time his daughters were described as the fairest in the land.

If Revd Mr Grimwade had preached upon the story of Job, he would doubtless have abjured the congregation to approach the Lord in fear and trembling, lest His wrath be visited upon them. This was not in the nature of Revd Mr Haddock, however. He was a mild man, and he spoke mildly upon this occasion, saying simply that we must conduct ourselves modestly, aware that the infinite power of the Lord surpasses our understanding. 'This is a proud God,' he said, 'a God who on this occasion entered into an arrangement with Satan to test a seemingly devout man to his very limits. We cannot hope to understand our Creator's motives, nor should we presume to do so. We can only be aware that when suffering descends upon us, when we are struck down by a seemingly malign fate, God is acting according to His own reasoning. He who is proud requires from us not pride but humility.'

I am sure that Revd Mr Haddock did not intend the visible members of his congregation, let alone the invisible one crouched like a lion cub in the den waiting for succour, to be terrified by God's behaviour towards the devout. Yet for the first time in my life, a great fear, seemingly of the universe itself, came over me as I considered this story. Unlike Job, I was riddled with sin, and my soul was black indeed. If God was willing to enter into a covenant with Satan whereby a righteous man could be punished so mightily in order for God to demonstrate the full reach of His majesty, what hope was there for one such as me? I felt that I was a helpless cub indeed, and that at any moment the heavens might be rent apart by a great thunderclap and the huge weight of God's wrath fall upon me. As the eagle pounces without mercy upon the unprotected lion cub, so it seemed God was likely to crush me without regard to justice or reason.

I did not lose my faith, but from then on I saw myself as nothing more than an insignificant creature crawling across the face of the world, liable to be extinguished in the blink of an eye, with God capable of deliberately staying His hand rather than protecting me.

Chapter 5

I WAS NOT ABLE TO articulate even to myself the new understanding revealed to me by Revd Mr Haddock's exposition on the Book of Job. The views I have described were only dimly perceived by me in the years of my childhood. Yet perceived in some shape or form they were. I already, as a result of my early experiences, had a jaundiced view of human behaviour. Although I had been pleased to recognise kindness when I found it, I never trusted fully in the goodness of humanity. Now I sensed that God, like so many of His servants on Earth, was capable of inflicting casual destruction. I could not rely on the New Testament promises of God's mercy. The occasional kindnesses of others were not enough to change my sense that we are subject more to capricious impulses and behaviours than we are to immutable universal laws. Not quite '*Jeder fur sich und Gott gegen alle*' ('Every man for himself and God against all') but 'Every man for himself and take your chances with God'.

In the crush of the streets of Hell I could be snatched to safety from under the wheels of a carriage which threatened to annihilate me, but equally I could be pushed under the wheels of another by a casual passer-by. Indeed, one evening I annoyed a bigger boy, a lout of eighteen or so, by knocking into him as he was about to take a swig from a bottle. The bottle fell to the ground and shattered, spilling his gin across the cobblestones. With a snarl of rage he turned, picked me up and flung me, as one might fling a stone, across the wall that separated the path from the river. I spun as I travelled through the air, got a confused view of faces and upside-down bodies and a tree and a boat, then landed in the river and sank quickly in its depths. The foul limpid water swallowed me as it had swallowed many bodies before mine, and did so with complete indifference. As I sank further and further I felt that I would never reach the bottom because it had no bottom. Something soft and huge caressed me. Although I opened my eyes, the water was so filled with muck that I could not tell what manner of thing it was, but then its head bumped mine and I realised it was the corpse of a horse. The horror of this apparition caused me to go into a frenzy of movement, and although I had no more idea of swimming than a fish does of walking, I somehow fought my way up again.

My head broke the surface and I opened my mouth to draw breath, only to find myself in a large pool of turds slowly making its way down the river. I struggled to get into a clean patch of water but my clothes were waterlogged and my strength was going from me already. I could see a piece of wood – half of a door possibly – floating a few yards away and I struck out for it but could not close the gap between me and it. It seemed to be in a faster current and it soon drifted away.

I had seen bodies being dragged out of the river on more than one occasion and I was now a fair way to joining their company. A glance at the bank showed no one taking the slightest interest in my plight – the gin-drinking boy and his friends had disappeared already.

I knew then something of the despair of Job. I wondered idly how it was that Job's ten dead children could be replaced by another ten, and whether God believed that thus could Job's misery be assuaged. Was that how the world worked? Did the beauty of Job's three new daughters console him for the loss of his first three? Who would replace me?

I started trying to swim towards the bank, with a feeble paddling motion, but almost immediately a large swell washed over my head and under I went. Up I came, although I fancied I would not survive another such dunking. Another wave quickly followed the first one, with the same result. This time, although I waved my arms and kicked my legs, I could not rise. I found myself going down instead of up, into the endless depths.

Something hard poked into my back, prodding at me as though pushing me down even further. I could not resist it, even as I wondered what it could be. Then quite suddenly, like a scrap of food picked up by a seagull, I found myself rising at great speed. I burst out of the water and hung in the cold night air, coughing and spluttering. Something slimy had draped itself across the top of my head and was trailing down my forehead; I tore it away. It dropped into the water and as it disappeared I realised it was a dead rat. Behind me I heard a loud guffaw and a man's voice exclaiming: 'Now there's a good catch: two dead rats with one poke.'

It took me several more moments to understand that I was hanging in the air at the end of a long boathook. The waves which had washed me under were caused by an approaching boat, and a man in the boat had fished me out. He pulled the pole in, with me on the end of it, my rags miraculously holding together long enough to enable the hook to keep me safe.

He dropped me onto the floor of the boat. 'Good fishing, Silas,' another voice said. It sounded like a younger man. I lay there shaking and trembling and no doubt looking very much like a fish that had just been landed and was twitching its life away. However, my position was somewhat different. My life had just been saved.

Someone threw a blanket over me and I clutched it gratefully, but I seemed unable to stop shaking. I was dimly aware that the boat was in motion once more and that the men were conversing in occasional grunts, but I could not make out the words. In time the comforting fragrance of pipe tobacco drifted into my nostrils, but I remember little else until the boat bumped against some obstacle and I was commanded to get to my feet. I found myself unable to do so, managing only to roll over and get onto my hands and knees, but a strong arm hauled me up and presently, still wrapped in the blanket, which indeed I was unwilling to forego, for it seemed like my best friend, I was carried along some sort of jetty, onto land and up a steep hill.

The next thing I knew was the warmth of a room and a couple of lamps burning and a woman bending over me. She seemed dreadfully old and ugly, with a large mole on her nose that had hairs growing from it. I wondered if she might be a witch.

'Pooh, the stink of it,' she said. 'It's brought the river with it and no mistake. What in the name of God did it think it was doing, going for a swim at this time of night?'

A man whom I could not see laughed and said: 'Aye, queer thing to be doing.'

Indignantly I tried to explain that I had been thrown into the river, but she poked me in the chest and said: 'There, there, don't be distressing yourself, it's only teasing you we are.'

She said to someone else, 'What is it then, a boy or a girl?' at which I felt further indignation, but was too tired and felt too strange to attempt another answer. But the man told her: 'Why, it be a boy I reckon.'

'Oh well then, it might be some use,' she said with a cackle. 'Fetch me something dry of Johnny's to be putting on him.' She unwrapped the blanket and peeled me as though I were one of those funny little mandarin fruits. It was a relief to be relieved of the wet clothes, but the cold still pressed in on me. She rubbed me hard with the blanket, and although I tried to protest the rough treatment, it did help get my blood moving. A big bearded man, whom I thought I recognised from the boat, handed her a pair of pants and a pullover, both of them too big for me, but I was pleased to be able to cover my nakedness, and I felt a little warmer in the clothes.

'Get rid of them,' she said to the man, and he took my wet rags, holding them at arm's length, and threw them outside somewhere. Another, younger, man, with vivid red hair, followed him as he came back into the cottage. I thought he was probably the second man from the boat.

'Here, I've got what he needs,' this new arrival said in a cheerful voice. I did recognise him now, by his voice. He was the one who had said, 'Good fishing, Silas' earlier. He came over to me. I began to realise that I was lying on a table. The redheaded young man proffered me a bottle and pushed the neck of it between my shivering lips. I took a gulp and immediately coughed and spluttered, spraying half of it out again. But some of it ran down my throat, sending a burning heat through me. I had drunk gin before, on the few occasions when I could procure it: gin was known to us as Hell water, and for those who could afford it was a better and safer drink than the water from the pumps or the river. But this was different from gin. It was as if a hot cat with sharp claws was rushing through every inch of my body, yowling with terror because its fur was on fire. I sneezed any number of times, and felt as though hot cat fur was coming out of my nostrils.

'It's terrible muck,' said the young man, watching me and laughing at my discomfort. 'She calls it brandy, but it tastes like she distils it from pigs' piss. It'll scald your insides, that's for sure.'

'There now, hush your mouth,' cried the old woman. 'Don't be giving him any more, whatever you do. You haven't plucked him from the river just to drown him with that poison. Put him to bed now. Put him in Johnny's bed.'

'Johnny's bed?' asked the young redheaded man, turning serious in a moment. 'Are you sure?'

The old woman shrugged. 'Yes, yes, it's a good use for it. This one's been brought back from the grave tonight, so yes, it's a good use for Johnny's bed.'

It was true I had been brought back from the grave, but during the next few days I could easily have been returned to it at any moment. I fell into a kind of feverish illness, no doubt brought about by my immersion, or by the foul water, or both. I had moments of lucidity, but I do not believe that they lasted more than a few minutes each time, and even in those moments I was only dimly aware of my circumstances. Frequently when I awoke it was to vomit, and I know that on more than one occasion I fouled the bed with bowel motions that ran like water from me. I reached the stage where I felt that there was nothing left inside my body but the vital organs, and even they could not be trusted to continue to function. But most of the time I was unconscious or in a delirium. I do remember one night waking to the flame of the candle burning at the foot of my bed, and believing it to be a giant fire threatening to consume me I started up and leapt at the candle, and it took both the men to wrestle me back under the covers. Another time I thought I was in bed with a dead horse, no doubt recollecting in some part of my diseased mind the encounter with the corpse at the bottom of the river, and I fought like a madman, screaming and beating my fists, and again I believe it was one or both of the men whom I was actually fighting.

I also remember the old lady constantly at my side, wiping my face, replacing the blankets which I often kicked from me in my thrashing-about, and all the time muttering words of solace. I wondered that I had ever thought her ugly, because she came more and more to resemble a ministering angel. There were times when her eyes were bloodshot and rheumy and she smelled of alcohol, and at such times she often called me Johnny, but even then I clung to her and I believe to this day that she was the lifebuoy that saved me from drowning a second time.

One morning, as the grey light spread across the sky on the other side of the river, I awoke. I found myself looking at a wooden carving hanging from the wall. It was a replica of a new moon, but the moon had been given a nose and lips and a red-edged eye that made the face look both curious and determined.

I knew at once that I had passed out of the valley of death and re-entered the green kingdom of the living. The old lady was sitting on a chair beside my bed, as I suspect she had been doing almost without cessation since first my illness began, and now she smiled at me and said, 'Why, you may be restored to us yet. Silas,' she called, 'fetch a cup of tea.'

'I just made you a cup,' he called back from the other room.

'It's not me that's wanting it,' she answered him. 'It's the lad, God be praised.'

Silas appeared in the doorway in an instant. 'Well now, look at you,' he said, smiling down at me from his great height. 'If I'd known how much trouble you were going to be I'd have left you in the river, but at least now maybe I won't have to dig a hole to bury you in.'

'We could have just thrown him back in the river,' said the young redheaded man, appearing in the doorway at Silas's side. 'There's plenty who do. Anyway, catch a great lazybones like you digging a hole? Not likely! I would have been the one with that job.'

'Fetch the cup of tea and stop your fooling about,' the old woman said. 'And make it strong. And while you're at it, you can be mindful that I'll have no jokes about digging graves in this house.'

Both the men looked ashamed. 'I'm sorry, Mother,' said the big man, Silas. 'We meant no harm, nor no disrespect.'

She looked at me bleakly. 'There's been graves dug in this family all too often. But men forget. Women never do.'

Chapter 6

S O NOW I WAS to experience kindness of a sustained and consistent nature. I had learned the lesson of Job, and indeed the lessons of life, well enough to have no faith in the permanence of it, but while it lasted I basked in it like a cat in the front window of a shop, soaking up the warmth of the sun through the glass. The tiny cottage, I soon learned, was set a few hundred yards back from the river and had three residents: wife, husband and son. The big black-bearded man was named Silas, as I had already ascertained; the old lady's name was Abigail; their redheaded young son was Thomas. The family name was Piggott.

They made their living by fishing and by pulling salvage out of the river. As I regained my strength, they found me some clothes that fitted well enough, and which I believe belonged to the missing Johnny, whom I deduced to be now occupying one of the graves of which Abigail had spoken. I conceived this to be a delicate subject and so asked no questions about it.

The clothes may have been poor but were of much better quality than my discarded rags. They were all too big for me, by a considerable margin, but I rolled up the bottoms of the trousers, rolled back the cuffs of the shirts and tied a length of twine around my waist, and felt well satisfied with my new wardrobe.

Silas and Thomas started taking me out in their boat, and I assisted them by baiting their lines when they were fishing and helping haul in their catches. As well, my eyes soon proved to be sharper than theirs, and I took pride in my ability to see possible salvage that had escaped their view. On one of the first days I accompanied them I drew their attention to an object floating in the water, and persuaded them to investigate it. They rowed there reluctantly, against a strong tide, and it turned out to be a sailor's trunk, so heavy that it was already almost completely submerged. It took the three of us to haul it on board. I was excited to see what was in it, but it was padlocked, and Silas and Thomas did not have the tools on the boat to open it. It was not until we got back to the jetty after dark and dragged it up the path that we were able to explore its contents. The men were delighted by what they found: a set of tools, from a ship's carpenter no doubt, including saws, planes, adzes, hammers, chisels, braces and bits, and a great variety of nails. 'Aye, someone'll be ruing the day he lost this lot,' said Silas, running his hand along the teeth of the biggest fret saw. 'There's years of collecting gone into it, and it would have sunk in another minute. Poor fellow. If I could return it to him I would, but we'll never find him. He'll be a miserable man this night, and for many a night to come.'

'Never cry over something that can't cry over you,' said the old lady.

'Well, he may be shedding tears, but it's our good fortune, and thanks be to our lucky charm here,' said Thomas, alluding to me.

'Aye, but why does one man's good fortune have to be purchased at the cost of another's misery?' Silas asked. 'We climb to happiness on the backs of our fellow man.'

Although Silas was a kind-hearted fellow, as evidenced by his saving me from the river and his care of me afterwards, he was given to melancholy at times. They were all kind folk, but Mother Abigail ran the household and did so on stern lines. She had a severe tongue in her head.

Whilst I was ill with the fever I did not of course question my place in their house, for I was too far beyond reason to think of such abstractions, but now that I was recovered I began to wonder how long they would allow me to stay. For the first time I was experiencing the way countless of my fellow Britons lived, under the same roof year in, year out, patching up holes and stopping leaks, gradually collecting furniture and suchlike around them, planting and harvesting their vegetables. The Piggotts asked me where I lived, so that they could assist me to return to the bosom of my family, but I told them I had no place to stay at present, as my family were farm labourers who had gone to the country in search of work. Some sort of discussion took place around the kitchen table that night, where I believe my position was discussed. They supposed me to be asleep. Strain as I might, though, I could not hear much of what was said, but they did not raise again the topic of my leaving.

Their life was conducted at such a calm and even pace that while I was convalescent, I found it restful. It was Thomas's job to get up first in the mornings and light the fire, after which Mother Abigail would appear, wearing a huge purple nightcap which, with a button on one side but not on the other, had a strange resemblance to a malevolent one-eyed cat. She made porridge each day in a great black saucepan on the fire. When it was ready we sat in a line on a wooden bench while Silas said a long prayer invoking God's blessing on the food. As might be supposed from this, they were a pious family, who lived their lives according to the injunctions of Holy Writ. After that we tucked into the porridge, which, when money was in the house, was embellished with sugar or honey.

Very good was Mother Abigail's porridge, and most heartily did we eat it. After breakfast was over Silas said another prayer, of thanks, and Thomas took the dishes outside to clean them, which was the prelude to other domestic chores.

The only variation to this routine occurred when booty from salvage had become scarce. During these periods, Silas and Thomas would go fishing in the dark early hours of morning, so as to be on the river at dawn when the fish were at their hungriest. On such days, breakfast was delayed until they returned.

When my recovery was more or less complete, I started, as I have described, going out in the boat with them, during daylight at first, and later, on some of their early morning fishing trips too.

We'd be on the river most of the day, until after dark. When we got home, as hungry as horses, there'd be an evening meal, perhaps pease soup, white soup, pottage, fish stew or Irish stew. Mother Piggott was a good cook, who managed to add extra delicacies to most dishes, often from herbs growing in her garden. These gave the food a piquant flavour which placed it outside my previous experience but which I came to enjoy.

After dinner, Silas read from the Good Book, and we had more prayers. Then he sat beside me at the table to give me lessons in reading and writing, for he had soon ascertained that I was interested in my letters. I am sure I do not know how it was that I had acquired the ability to read. It seemed to come naturally and quickly to me, as I believe it does to some. I have memories of different people teaching me my letters and numbers when I was but a wee lad, though I do not know who they were. But I remember at the age of six venturing out to the Strand, where every house bore signs at every window on every floor, proclaiming the occupation of those who resided within, whether dressmakers or jewellers or haberdashers or ironmongers or confectioners, and I could read every sign pretty well, which caused people to marvel that one of such a tender age could do so.

Because I had picked up what little learning I possessed from here, there and everywhere, I was consequently advanced in some respects and backwards in others. Still, I was a quick study according to Silas, and he was not the first to have said it, so I had hopes of becoming proficient enough one day. And Silas was a good teacher, patient and thorough.

Whilst he and I sat at the table the other two generally sat in front of the fire, Thomas sipping at ale and Abigail at her foul home-made brandy, until slumber crept upon them. Ale made me sleepy, but even without much of it I was usually the first to take to my bed, especially after Silas's lessons, which I found the most taxing part of the day.

The only worry which niggled at my mind was my abandonment of Quentin, whom I imagined to be lonely and miserable on his own in Hell. I had no way of knowing his situation, of course, but he had come to be considerably dependent upon me. I would dearly have loved for him to share my new good fortune, but I dared not broach the matter with the Piggotts, as I could not confess my deceit with regard to the story I had told them. I had formed the view that they were intolerant of falsehoods, or indeed of any breach of the Commandments.

After several months of this life, however, I started to feel bored and restless when we were not out in the boat. As I recovered from my fever, Mother Abigail set me to domestic tasks the like of which I had never done before, and much vexed she was at the standard of my work, for she often considered my ignorance to be idleness. One day out on the river, as he rested on his oars for a few moments, Silas spoke into the air, saying: 'Barnaby, you know Mother was aggrieved something awful with you this morning, over the emptying of the chamber-pots. What on earth possessed you, lad, to tip them out the window? You made a nasty-smelling mess right in the garden, and fouled a couple of the chard plants.'

I dropped my head, for already I hated to be in the wrong with him. 'I don't know,' I mumbled. 'I thought that was what you do.'

'It's maybe what they do in the city,' Thomas interjected, 'but down here we know better.'

'They do it all the time in London,' I offered. 'When you go past the huge tall houses in the mornings you have to be quick on your feet if you don't want a shower of the stuff.'

'But then yesterday,' Silas went on, 'you were meant to scatter the seeds for the chickens and you put them all in a heap, where the birds fight over them and tread them into the mud, so that half of them are wasted.'

'I didn't know any better,' I said in a low voice.

'But it's everything you're a-told to do, lad. You don't know how to make a bed or clean a window or scrub a floor or chop wood for the fire. I mean, some of it's lasses' work, fair enough, but it does no harm for a lad to do it, and both ours did and no complaint.'

'No complaint?' Thomas said with his usual cheeky grin. 'I seem to remember hiding up the beech tree once or twice when it was my turn for chores.'

'Aye, and you got a switching for it more than once or twice,' his father said grimly. Still resting on his oars he said to me earnestly: 'Now Barnaby, what's the truth of the matter? You say your family are farm

43

labourers and they've gone to the country. I want to know what manner of family is it that they teach their son nothing, and then go off leaving him on his own in a city as wicked as London? At your age?'

'Yes, and the rags you was dressed in when we pulled you out of the river,' Thomas added. 'What kind of dress is that for a child from a respectable family?'

'I never said I was respectable,' I said darkly.

'You've been welcome here, of course,' Silas said, 'but it can't last. You must have people somewhere we should be sending you to. It's not right to keep you away from them. We know what it's like to lose a child. It's the greatest grief of all. Nothing can compare to it.'

I guessed he was referring to the mysterious Johnny, whose bed I had been occupying. I stayed silent. I feared that as soon as I told them the truth they would throw me back out onto the streets, as a vagrant not fit to be under the same roof as decent people. I wished I could invent a family who would somehow send word to the Piggotts that they were welcome to keep me for as long as they cared.

'Why did your folks not take you with them when they went away to the countryside?' Thomas asked.

'Don't you have grandparents or uncles or aunts or cousins?' Silas asked. 'Do you have brothers, lad, or sisters?'

When I didn't answer he shook his head and bent his back to the oars once more. As we got under way I trailed my hand in the water, wondering how much longer the Piggotts would put up with my ignorance and bad habits.

Chapter 7

IT DID NOT TAKE long to find out. Four days after the conversation in the boat Abigail, Mrs Piggott, found I had been stealing food and hiding it under my bed. Unfortunately – I had not anticipated this – rats found the food and ruined it, and then Mrs Piggott found the rats.

I am ashamed as I write these words, for the Piggotts had been so good to me, sharing their home and their food, and even putting clothes on my back. I don't know why I kept taking food, for they were good providers and shared all they had. Yet something within me seemed unable to resist when I opened a cupboard or jar and found bread or cheese or sausage inside. It was as though I had to have it, and some demon made me stretch out my arm, take it, and scurry to my bed like I was a rat myself, to secrete my ill-gotten gains.

It seemed that of all the creatures in the world the ones Mrs Piggott could least abide were rats, and she went to great trouble to keep them out of the house. When three fled from under my bed one morning, the screams of the good lady could be heard down by the river, where Silas and Thomas and I were caulking the boat. We ran up to the house and in through the door, me some distance behind the two men, because I did not of course have strength in my legs to equal theirs. When I arrived Mrs Piggott was standing on the kitchen table and pointing at my bed. Thomas was already peering underneath it, and a moment later, in front of my stricken eyes, he pulled out the remains of my hoard.

'How could a rat drag so much food in there?' Silas asked in simple bewilderment.

His wife turned to me. 'There's the rat,' she screeched. 'I thought we was missing food all the time. The ingratitude of it. Stealing food from under our very noses.'

Silas looked at me, horror stricken. Watching him through eyes of shame I saw grief slowly stealing over his face, replacing the horror. 'Why would you do such a thing?' he asked slowly. 'Didn't we take you in? Didn't we nurse you through your sickness? Didn't we fill your belly morning and night?'

I nodded. 'Indeed you did all of those things,' I whispered. 'I'm sorry, Silas. I'm sorry, Abigail. I don't know why I took the victuals.'

Shaking her fist at me Abigail said: 'The eighth commandment. Thou shalt not steal.' She folded her arms and marched into the next room.

Silas shook his head. 'I think it's time you be leaving us,' he said. 'You can keep the clothes. I'll row you down the river and set you off at the place where we picked you up.'

And so I left the house, in disgrace and ignominy, with Mrs Abigail Piggott's back turned to me. 'Shall I be coming with you?' Thomas asked his father, but Silas replied: 'No, there's no need. It's a heavy load I'm taking, to be sure, but a light one, if you know what I mean.'

Thomas shook his head sadly at me as I departed. 'You'll end up on the gallows,' he said. 'You had better mind yourself.'

I sat in the boat despondently as Silas let the current carry us down the river, just taking an occasional stroke with the oar to keep us straight. Would that my life could be kept straight so easily, I reflected bitterly. But my thoughts were interrupted by Silas. He had the habit of speaking as if to himself, when he intended his words to be heard by others, and so he did on this occasion.

'There's no doubt Mother can be easily upset,' he said. 'The trouble is, not many get to know her. Not many know the goodness in her heart. And her heart has stayed good, despite the troubles she's seen. Ah, life, it's a hard affair for such as us. We've buried three infants, Mother and I, that the Lord saw fit to take. And then there was Johnny, what a lad he was, the apple of her eye, and no wonder. He was the darling of all who knew him.'

'What happened to Johnny?' I asked tentatively. I had always wondered.

Still without looking at me, Silas responded to my question. 'He fell in love with Madame Geneva. That were the real story of his downfall, though his mother won't have it at any price.'

I knew well who, or rather what, Madame Geneva was. It was one of the names people in Hell, and no doubt various other places, used for gin. Along with Hell water, strip-me-naked, bunter's tea, blue ruin and meat-drink-washing-and-lodging. And a dozen others.

I had seen many men and women in love with Madame Geneva, whatever alias she went under, and she did not serve them well.

'Yes,' Silas went on. 'He took to it like a babe to mother's milk. Night after night he came home reeking of it, staggering in his walk, and day after day I pleaded with him to keep away from grog shops and the low types who patronise them. And then one night he didn't come home. Before dawn I went out looking for him, and found no trace of him until three days later, when I was nearly mad with despair and loss of sleep. A young barmaid I had spoken to several times during my search finally took pity on me and told me what she had seen. Mind you, she had to do it some ways from her place of work, for she would have lost her position had they known she was snitching on them. Johnny had been plied with gin by a press-gang who were in league with the owner of the place, and when they had him so he didn't know which way was up and which was down, they put him in their cutter and rowed him away into the darkness. And he were only seventeen years old.'

'What's a press-gang?' I asked.

Silas looked at me directly for the first time. 'It's the way they have of manning His Majesty's ships. Evil creatures roam the streets of the city looking for young men they can steal away for the Royal Navy. It's a foul trade indeed.'

'And have you not heard any news of Johnny since?' I asked.

'Oh we heard news all right,' Silas said heavily, looking at me again. 'We had a fine letter from the Admiralty, done up in a ribbon with the seal of the Secretary for the Navy himself upon it, informing us that Able Seaman Jonathan Piggott had been lost overboard in a storm off the coast of Scotland, and they could not recover his body. And the Secretary conveyed his deepest sympathy, but mentioned as how we could be consoled by knowing that Johnny had died serving his country.'

'Not much consolation, sir,' I ventured, not sure how my remark would be received.

Silas shook his head dolefully. 'None at all,' he said, looking up at the clouds. I had the feeling he did so to prevent tears spilling from his eyes. 'And later, a good deal later, they sent us a parcel containing his possessions, of which there were precious few. But to his mother they were precious indeed, and she pored over them day after day. His bed, too, remained untouched until you arrived, drenched and half-drowned and feverish and lost.'

His words brought home to me the enormity of my betrayal. I felt I had not been worthy to occupy the bed which was previously Johnny's.

We arrived at Horse Ferry Stairs, and Silas had the goodness to shake my hand as I disembarked. 'God be with ye,' he said. 'He saved your life for a reason, be sure of that.'

He was a righteous man, who did his best to live as the Lord ordained, and he could not understand one such as me. My heart was too full to answer him, but I stood watching as he rowed away up the river, bending his back and applying his great strength in the battle against the current. I knew that I would be unlikely to meet anyone better. I just wished I could be as sure as he of God's having a special plan for me. God's taking of Johnny's life seemed reminiscent of the way He had treated Job. It was hard to discern any special plan in anything.

When Silas was out of sight, I turned and toiled up the steps, back into the familiar streets of Hell. The noise and smells and zigzag movements of the people and animals and vehicles drew me in as though I had never been away. I sometimes had the odd feeling that London, or this part of it at least, was about to vomit a great excrescence of rotting food and stinking water and faecal matter and disease all over itself. I had a fancy that there would be a great convulsion of the city, causing a giant water spout of corruption to flood over its inhabitants. Perhaps I was casting my mind back to Revd Mr Grimwade in the pulpit at St Martin's, quoting Leviticus to the congregation in his cold voice: 'Do not defile yourselves with any of these things; for by all these the nations are defiled, therefore I visit the punishment of its iniquity upon it, and the land vomits out its inhabitants. You shall therefore keep My statutes and My judgements, and shall not commit any of these abominations, either any of your own nation or any stranger who dwells among you, lest the land vomit you out also when you defile it, as it vomited out the nations that were before you.'

There was much that was vile about London, and it is the vileness I tend to remember, though if I look back honestly, without a jaundiced eye, I have to say there was much also that was enticing and attractive. Every day my life on the streets showed me human nature at its best and worst. Tragedy, comedy, history, pastoral, as the playwright described, and romance as well, which he omitted from his list: they were all there in the open; little was concealed. The tragedy of seeing a boy about my age pinned to a wall by the wheel of a carriage driven too wildly down a narrow alley, his stomach torn open, and his insides spilling onto the cobblestones as he gasped his last breath, was that mitigated by the people who gathered around him and held him and wept over the pitiful sight, and by the rage of those who chased the coach driver and had to be restrained from lynching him there and then? Comedy there was too, in abundance for those who had eyes to see, from the sight of Uncle Bert dancing drunkenly to the music of a piano accordionist on a street corner, to the magician who could make pennies come out of my ears, to the strange lady dressed in black who always walked sideways along the street. Or was there tragedy too in her story?

Wonders there were in plenty, including Hector the Performing Pig, who could do arithmetic by tapping his trotter when his master named the right answer to a sum, and the Spotted Man, whose skin was white with dark spots, a marvellous thing to behold. But nothing was the equal of the menagerie at the Tower of London, which Quentin and I travelled to one Sunday afternoon. Getting there was neither comfortable nor pleasant, as we had to pass through the foulest display of butchers' stalls I ever had seen. It was not so much that the sights and smells were worse than we were used to in Hell, but that there were so many of them, and they covered a vast area. The road was slippery with the secretions from the guts that were tossed onto the cobblestones with indifference, there to be trodden underfoot by the passers-by.

Nevertheless, we survived the ordeal of the butchers' stalls and arrived at the Tower gates. There we met with disappointment. We had not known that it cost four pence each to gain entrance, and having not a penny between us we were refused entry. As we turned away in disappointment a kind gentleman dressed in the finest of clothes, with a top hat on his head, took pity on us. 'Lacking the wherewithal, lads?' he said cheerfully. 'Here you are,' and he tipped us sixpence each.

Thus we gained entrance to the most marvellous and wonderful sight I had ever been privileged to see. Lions stalked up and down in their enclosure, and cheetahs too, and leopards. We watched as a keeper threw a dead dog to the savage beasts and they fought over it. I overheard a gentleman remark that a person's admission to the Tower could be gained by tendering a dead dog or cat, knowledge which Quentin and I wished we had possessed before setting out on our trip. We could have laid our hands on a couple of each and the owners would have been none the wiser. I wondered why they did not simply bring in baskets of animal guts from the streets outside.

An elephant, with small eyes on top of its head, and waving its extraordinary trunk, made a noise that set the ladies shrieking. The keeper remarked to the crowd that for six months of the year the elephant had to be given wine, as it was unable to drink water during that time. This information occasioned much merriment among the onlookers.

Ostriches, the most peculiar of birds, too big and heavy to fly, ran around their enclosures. They are able to eat metal, an oddity which sets them apart from all other of God's creatures. When I saw the emu-bird in New South Wales I thought they were very alike, but I could not imagine an emu-bird eating metal.

Yes, there was plenty to marvel at, despite the stench, which hung over the place like a shroud and was as bad as the stench from the butchers' stalls outside. It made Quentin nauseous, although I have a strong stomach and did not suffer the same symptoms.

Really though, when I think back, every day that we survived in Hell was something of a marvel, if not a miracle. Plenty our age or younger did not survive; the churchyards were so chock-a-block with bodies that people like us were buried in poor pits, three or four lined up abreast, then more piled on top until they were at least seven deep, twenty or thirty bodies altogether, and only then would they fill in the hole. Pooh, the smell! You'd try to stay a block or more away, especially in summer.

A boy had to keep his wits about him if he were to survive in these convulsing streets. I threaded my path along the laneways, ducking under the elbows of the gossiping women, manoeuvring around the whores and stepping over the drunks, trying to avoid the pools of muck, keeping one eye on the heavy shop signs hung out into the street on iron bars: signs that were notorious for falling in strong winds and crushing any unfortunate soul standing beneath.

It had taken me a day and a half after my precipitate eviction from the Piggotts' to find Quentin again. He looked at me in some confusion when I appeared at the end of an alley where I had been told I might find him. He was engaged in a game of hopscotch with a couple of other boys, neither of whom I knew. Quentin gazed at me as if unsure of who

I was. Then he approached me, saying cautiously: 'Barnaby. I thought you was drowned.'

'I very nearly was.'

He thought about this for a few moments. 'Do you want to play hopscotch?'

'All right.'

Once we had played the game for a time he seemed to become more comfortable with me again, and from then on we resumed our friendship, going around together much of the time.

Chapter 8

AT AGE TWELVE OR thereabouts, for I could never fix my age with certainty, I got my first regular employment. Up until then I had been earning what I could where I could, which meant mostly doing odd jobs that I picked up in the streets, such as standing at the heads of horses and holding their reins while their owners went into a tavern, or sweeping the footpath out the front of a shop, or running errands for people who had stalls along the marketplaces. Then an apothecary called Mr Ogwell started to pay me some attention. I cleaned his windows quite often, and having been taught by Mother Abigail, I was now a good deal more proficient at such tasks. Several times Mr Ogwell came out onto the footpath and stood watching me at work, and finally one morning he said to me: 'Well young Barnaby, I am inclined to engage you as a delivery boy, for you know Ralph has been missing two weeks now, and I fear we must give up hope of his returning, for the time being at least.'

Ralph was about eleven or twelve, a nice kind boy whom I knew a little. One day he had not come home from work, and he had not been glimpsed since. I believe he lived with his parents down past the park. I had seen his distressed mother and father walking the streets day after day, searching for their boy, but as Mr Ogwell said, there was neither hide nor hair to be seen of him.

I took the job gladly, although the pay was only sixpence a day, which considering bread was tuppence a loaf, and cheese tuppence or more a pound, was never enough to live on, but it was something, and I could supplement my income by the usual means.

Mr Ogwell handed me a list of names and addresses which I had to read to him, to prove that I knew my letters, before he would confirm my employment. He seemed impressed by my reading, which had been reinforced by my lessons with Silas Piggott.

And so I became the delivery boy for Mr Ogwell's business. I knew that should Ralph return I would lose the position, but he never did so, and eventually his parents gave up their search. Mayhap he had run away to sea, as boys sometimes did, for he was too young to be press-ganged.

I quite enjoyed my new-found respectability. I particularly enjoyed the time spent bustling along the streets with my basket, searching for the addresses of the customers. At first it was difficult, because my master, Mr Ogwell, expected me to make more deliveries than seemed possible, but although I knew the streets and alleys and lanes well, or so I thought, it turned out that Mr Ogwell knew them considerably better. So when he made out the delivery schedule, he did so with a particular route in mind. Not knowing this, I rearranged the schedule upon leaving the shop, unwittingly giving myself a longer path to travel. With many premises, Mr Ogwell knew of back doors or side doors which could be reached by expedited means; I only knew of the marked doors, at the front, and I quickly found I was given a frosty welcome at those in the better class establishments. Angry servants, resenting my presumption, would tell me to take myself to the trade entrance, which oft-times required a detour of half a block.

Armed with my basket and my list of customers, I found myself exploring parts of London that had previously been outside my familiar territory. So much of London life was lived below street level, and time and time again I found myself descending grimy, greasy staircases as if to Hell itself, except that the temperature dropped quickly during my descent, instead of rising as one might expect if truly entering the satanic realms. Groping through the darkness trying to find the right door, being cursed when I found the wrong one, quenching my nausea at the stench of sickbeds, holding grimly onto the medicines until the exact money was counted into my palm . . . I often felt I had entered an underworld indeed.

Twice I arrived too late with Mr Ogwell's medicines. The first time was in an attic room, at the top of countless flights of stairs. The building was so rickety that the higher I went, the more I became afeared that it might collapse. It seemed to shudder and sway even at my light tread upon the steps. When I reached the door to which I had been directed, it stood ajar, and when no one answered my knocks I pushed it open and went inside. It was a cramped space with hardly room for a bed and dresser, but there they were, along with a small table and two stools. In the bed lay a man, and I could see at a glance that he was dead. His eyes were open but he stared at nothing. His mouth was open too, and as I stood gazing in horror a large bluebottle flew slowly out of it and came towards me. I turned and fled, jumping down the steps five or six at a time, not caring whether I might send the whole building toppling to its doom. I ran from the house without even telling anyone that the man in the attic was deceased. I told Mr Ogwell when I got to the shop; he merely shrugged and without a word took the bottle of pills and emptied their contents back into one of his large jars.

The second time was, by strange coincidence, in the next house to the one occupied by the corpse in the attic. The scene here was very different. I descended instead of ascended, for I was told that the person I sought was in the basement. However, as I arrived at her door, a woman flung it open before I could knock. Her face was contorted by strong emotion, and when I said, 'Pills for Mrs O'Rourke from Mr Ogwell,' she cried, 'No use to her now!' and pushed past me, bursting into sobs as she did so. Glancing into the room I could see another woman tearing at her hair and lamenting, as she crouched over a woman lying on the bed, so I went away quietly and informed Mr Ogwell that another customer would have no further need for his medicines.

By and large I believe I served Mr Ogwell well enough, and he seemed satisfied with my work, though he never said a word of praise, being more inclined to criticise my every defect. He was a man entirely without humour; indeed, the very notion of humour seemed to make him angry. One day, as the rain poured down unceasingly for the third consecutive day and the streets ran wet with mud and slush, a big red-faced man came lurching into the shop, remarking: 'A drop of rain is just what we need, to dampen the dust out there.' Mr Ogwell responded, in his usual cold voice, 'Facetiousness is the mark of a petty mind, sir,' at which the man's laughing face turned in an instant to a scowl and out he stamped again, without making a purchase.

On the second day of my employment, I told Mr Ogwell how I had seen nothing less than a gold sovereign lying in the street that morning, and I and two or three others had all started for it at the same time. A beggar sitting paralysed at the corner, his crutches beside him, his hand outstretched as he entreated passers-by for money, saw it too.

He leapt to his feet, dashed across the street to the coin and picked it up, ran back, grabbed his crutches, and was off down an alleyway, leaving us all dumbfounded.

I told it as a funny story but Mr Ogwell listened without a flicker of expression and said merely: 'There is a Judgement Day coming for all such as he,' and continued mixing his potions.

Every time I entered the shop I felt a kind of gloom steal over me, so it was a relief to go on my delivery rounds and escape the oppressive atmosphere. The only exception was when Mrs Ogwell brought in their little daughter, which she did about once a week. The child, whose name was Josephine, brightened up the whole street. She was about three or four years old. These were the only occasions when I saw Mr Ogwell smile. Even if he did not, the little girl smiled enough for two. She was the opposite of her father, a sunny little thing with golden ringlets cascading to her shoulders. The mother seemed timid and hardly spoke a word, not to me at any rate. It was as though I did not exist; she looked through me as if I were the air itself. I don't think it was anything special about me; she seemed too scared of life to speak to anyone. Every time the door opened she looked apprehensively over her shoulder. This was in the days before the London Monster, the fellow who went around pushing needles and knives into women, but from the look of her you could have been forgiven for thinking she was expecting the London Monster at any moment, years before anyone else.

Mrs Ogwell spoke with a thick accent which made her difficult to understand; I believe she may have been Norwegian or some such.

For some reason the child took a fancy to me, rough spoken and rough in my ways though I was. She took to running to me and wanting my attention as soon as she arrived in the shop. I am bound to say that, as time went on, she seemed almost to fancy spending more time with me than with her father, of whom, as best I could judge, she appeared to go in some fear, despite his treating her with more warmth than he did anyone else.

I got in the habit of making little dolls for her, tiny things I whittled with a knife in the evenings. I became quite a dab hand at it. Before I gave her the first one I of course asked Mr Ogwell for his consent. He looked at it long and hard where it lay in the palm of my hand, picked it up and scrutinised it with one eye, sniffed it, turned it over and over, and studied it from about sixteen different angles. I wondered if he were about to take to it with his microscope, or even dissect it maybe, but finally he said, 'I suppose there's no harm in it,' which was about as close as he ever went to paying a compliment.

When I gave it to the child, saying, 'Here, miss, I made this for you,' it was like giving her the Crown Jewels. She seemed hardly to believe that such a thing as a doll was possible. I felt well rewarded by her expression of wonder and astonishment. As if that were not reward enough, she then threw her arms around me and, before either of her parents could intervene, gave me a kiss to my cheek. Mr Ogwell started forward with an ugly look on his face, which I did not like at all. There was no harm in what she did; she was just a child. Mrs Ogwell called out, 'Josephine, come here at once,' but there was no need for that, because she was already running to her mother, saying, 'Look, Mama, look, see what the boy gave me.' She did not even know my name.

I gave her five dolls all up, but after the fifth one Mr Ogwell said to me: 'My daughter has enough dolls now; she has no need of any more.' So that was the end of dolls for Josephine. But not for me entirely, because Quentin persuaded me to make more so we could sell them to the fine folk who promenaded along the Embankment.

I made a baker's dozen of the little things, and one bigger one, and went with him on a fine Sunday afternoon to try our luck. I left it to Quentin to do the selling, as he was better at talking than I, but we had no luck. People drew away when he approached them, and some waved their walking sticks or rolled-up umbrellas to drive him off. After nearly two hours we had not a single sale. The discouraging thing was that they were not even looking at the dolls. Then Quentin said to me: 'I need to go for a piss, Barnaby, you take over.'

I didn't want to, but he pushed the basket at me and ran off like he was about to burst. So I approached a couple who were walking along slowly, a little girl following behind. To my astonishment they peered closely at the dolls and the lady said to her husband: 'Oh they're lovely, George, let's get her one.' And it was the big one they took! I couldn't believe my eyes, and as they walked on I stood there holding the money in my hands like a fool.

I tried three more lots of folk without success, then sold another one, and a couple of minutes later another one again. I thought Quentin was taking a long time about his pissing, but then he came back. I knew something was wrong the moment I saw him. His lips were shut tight but they hung down like a crescent moon tipped over sideways. 'What ails you?' I said to him. 'Look at this now, I've sold three of the little blighters.'

'Aye, I thought as much,' he said. 'I knew you would. I've been watching.'

'What do you mean, you've been watching?' I said. 'I thought you went to piss in the river?'

'I didn't need to piss,' he said. 'I went and hid in the garden over there to see what would happen when you set out to sell them. I know why they wouldn't buy from me.' He touched his birthmark. 'Respectable folk won't have naught to do with me. It's not so bad in Hell, they're used to anything there. But respectable folk, they see this and they think it's the Devil's mark, or I'm the spawn of a witch, and they don't want me near their children.'

I'd known Quentin for so long that I hardly noticed his birthmark any more. I conveniently put aside my own thoughts when I had first met him, for I knew by now that there was nothing demonic about him. I was sorry for him, that folk could believe such nonsense. Yet the evidence of their convictions was in my pocket, in the form of the ten pence we'd made from selling the dolls.

Chapter 9

THINGS WENT FAIRLY KINDLY for me for a while. Quentin and I agreed that he would make clothes for the dolls, for he was a dab hand with a needle, having learned it in the convent. Putting clothes on the dolls meant we could double our prices, and when the weather was favourable we generally sold a dozen or more.

When the weather was bad we sold none.

I still stayed in St Martin's occasionally, with Quentin when I could persuade him. He was gradually becoming better reconciled to the delights of my great cold stone refuge. Other nights we'd sleep under a bridge or in a dosshouse, or sometimes behind the stalls in the markets, but the markets were not our first choice, as we had to be up and out of there early, given that many of the stallholders were at their work by five in the morning.

Mr Ogwell treated me well enough and by now I had learned the tricks of the trade and could get around the streets with sufficient speed to satisfy him, insofar as he could ever be satisfied. One brave day I asked him for a pay rise. He looked at me bleakly and said: 'The day you ask that question again will be the last day you work for me.'

So, Quentin and I still had to use our wits and our light hands to survive. By that I mean we continued to steal in order to keep our bellies somewhere near full. In a good week the money from the dolls and from Mr Ogwell might have been enough to get us through, but not every week was a good one. And besides, when we had money, I have to confess we sometimes lacked the moral character to spend it wisely. We were not always strong enough to resist the temptations that life in London threw our way. When we were cold or tired or feeling miserable we were as likely as not to waste money on sweetmeats, biscuits and ices, for we both had a terrible partiality to sugar. One afternoon we stood in front of the Pot and Pineapple, the establishment of Mr Domenico Negri, the Italian confectioner, in Berkeley Square, and the juices ran in my mouth at the sight I beheld there: a whole garden laid out in sweetmeats, with glass fountains and porcelain swans and gravel made of sugar. Sadly, after just a few minutes, we were chased away by the doorman.

At every opportunity we paid a visit to a fair. The best of these was Bartholomew Fair, staged at Smithfield every September, where we could see the prize fighters going at it hammer and tongs, and the strong men lifting weights that seemed marvellous to us with our puny little limbs. We saw the tallest man there ever was, the Glasgow Giant, Mr Hamish Dunhill, seven foot three inches. And oh, there were so many things: puppet shows, African savages, gymnasts, and a man who could fold himself away in a barrel that looked as though it would barely accommodate little Josephine Ogwell. We were, I am afraid to say, bloodthirsty little creatures, and at every opportunity we watched the bear-baiting and cockfights, half in horror, half in fascination.

We liked going to the New Spring Gardens, to watch the slack rope vaulting and the jugglers, the wire dancing and the hot air balloons, or to Ranelagh Gardens, to see the Chinese Pavilion and the fountain of mirrors. At night-time the pretty lights of Ranelagh were a marvel to behold. When I was older and read Mr Tobias Smollett's *The Expedition of Humphrey Clinker*, although I was by then in New South Wales, I recognised Mr Bramble's description of the crowds at Ranelagh 'devouring sliced beef, and swilling port, and punch, and cyder' for I fear Quentin and I were in that very crowd, but I believe Mr Bramble was unkind to say that those who went there were 'possessed by a spirit, more absurd and pernicious than anything we meet within the precincts of Bedlam'. I thought it a wonder to see the white pavilions, the lush lawns and the artificial waterfalls, the statues and the paintings. These entertainments illuminated our lives as the infinite lights of Ranelagh illuminated the night sky, but they were expensive, and seldom enough were we able to sample them. More usual for us was the daily challenge of staying alive, trying not to sink to the bottom of London's society, though it was clear to me that we were not far from it. We could dream of being lords and dukes, but dreams did not put clothes on our backs or food in our bellies.

I remember well – how could I not? – when my life took a savage turn for the worse. Like Job I had no warning. I would not presume to compare myself to that benighted soul in other ways, for he was a righteous servant of God and I could make no such claim for myself, but the blow fell on me with something of the same suddenness and heaviness. It was a Thursday morning, some time late in July I believe, and the only thing out of the ordinary was that Mr Ogwell was late in opening the shop. Such a thing had never happened before, and I sat on the step, in the sunshine, waiting for him to arrive. The bells of St Martin's struck eight and little did I know as I counted them that they were ringing doom for me. As the last chime sounded through Hell I perceived

Mr Ogwell coming along the street, looking most agitated. He was hatless and wore neither coat nor tie, and his hair was as though he had been running his hands through it until it pointed in all different directions. I did not immediately realise that he was accompanied by a number of other men, but I soon became aware that he was at the head of a group of half-a-dozen, which included two Bow-Street Runners.

I stood as they approached but no sooner was Mr Ogwell within twenty yards of me than he sung out: 'There he is, gentlemen, that's the boy.'

The two Robin Redbreasts came at me at once, looking very important at their business. I did not know what to make of this but soon enough realised that I was being accused of something, and the Lord knew, there was plenty I could be accused of. The situation had an aspect that looked altogether too serious for my liking, and I turned to make a run for it, but I had left it too late and barely covered five yards before they seized me and dragged me back to my employer and his confederates.

'What do you mean by it, you foul creature, to despoil such as her?' Mr Ogwell shouted. It was as though he were half-mad, or fully mad more like it. I had never seen this in him before. He was always so controlled.

As I stood gaping at him, held by the arms, he suddenly produced a knife from inside his shirt and lunged at me, aiming to run the blade through my chest. My legs went from under me with terror and I pushed backwards against the Runners. The only thing that saved me was that my captors gave a little with the suddenness of my movement, and Mr Ogwell in turn overbalanced in his attempt to reach me. The knife stabbed into me sure enough, but lower than Mr Ogwell was aiming, and not as deep. Nevertheless, blood spurted from below my ribs and it was more scarlet than the waistcoats of the Runners and it scared me mightily to see it falling on the cobblestones, for I did not know how badly I was hurt.

'Now then, that's enough of that,' one of the men with Mr Ogwell said, and they dragged him back. 'That won't help matters, sir,' the man said to him. 'The boy must stand trial and the law will deal with him as is fit and proper.'

I did not know who this man was but he seemed to be in charge. Mr Ogwell sagged suddenly in the grip of his attendant. He looked at me as if he blamed me for cheating him of his satisfaction, but they took the knife off him and the man came forward and inspected my wound. 'That is your shop I believe?' he said to Mr Ogwell, who signified his assent with a nod. 'Very well, sir, you must have bandages in there, fetch one at once, and God willing we'll save this boy's life and you will not have to answer to my brothers on the bench for your rashness.'

Mr Ogwell looked so furious now that had he still been in possession of his knife I believe he might have run the two of us through. He showed no sign of obeying the man, who, it seemed, was a magistrate, but the gentleman said, 'Now then, sir, look sharp, do as I say,' and he had such an air of authority that even Mr Ogwell had to obey.

In truth, by the time he came back with a bandage the bleeding had almost stopped and I was fairly confident that my life would not immediately be forfeit, but I did not like the way things stood, and wondered if my life was soon to be forfeit in another and most uncomfortable way. The magistrate applied the bandage himself and did so with such skill that I had the feeling he could probably do anything, from skinning a rabbit to making a macaroon that would rival those of Mr Domenico Negri's.

As he finished the bandaging I asked him in a low voice: 'What is it I'm supposed to have done, sir?'

His head was bent over my wound as he secured the dressing, but he glanced up at me sharply and stared at me for a long moment. Then he went back to his work, saying nothing. Yet I had a strangely comforting feeling as I looked into his eyes, as though he at least would not condemn me out of hand.

Some strength was coming back to my limbs, but there was no getting away, for the Runners continued to hold me tight, as though I were the most dangerous criminal in the whole of London. I became aware that quite a crowd had formed. They stood in a ring around our group watching and speculating and taking the greatest interest in the proceedings. I suppose were I not the one under arrest I would have been looking on with the same rapt attention. It did not take much to attract a crowd in Hell.

Once it was ascertained that I was not about to die from loss of blood, and that my vital organs were probably undamaged, I was marched away. A deadly terror had taken possession of me by then, for I had no idea of the accusation against me, but I knew my habitual stealing was not the issue; such a force of men would not have assembled for the theft of a loaf of bread, or a shilling from a rich man's pocket.

I was ushered into a cab at the end of the street. It was the first time I had been in such a conveyance, and although I had often yearned to ride in one, I had not imagined doing so in these circumstances. The journey was a longish one, and the men spent their time looking out the windows, only occasionally addressing remarks to each other. They completely ignored me. The exception was Mr Ogwell, who sat the whole time staring ahead of him, conversing with no one, like a man of ice. I wished I could ask him for details of the predicament in which I found myself, for it had clearly moved him to a passion so great that he had wished to assassinate me, but I was too deterred by his attack with the knife to address any questions to him. I feared another attack even as we sat there, and wished that the Bow-Street Runners had searched him for weapons before we got in the cab together.

My greatest fear, apart from being murdered by Mr Ogwell, was that I would be taken to Newgate, which had recently been rebuilt after the mob tore it down during the riots against the Roman Catholics. I had heard prison stories from the old lags who made their homes under the bridges where Quentin and I sometimes took shelter. The way they described life in Newgate made me wonder that anyone came out alive. And they claimed it was little improved since the rebuilding. But others maintained that one prison was much the same as another, and others again were adamant that Marshalsea was the worst. For me it had been a hypothetical argument until now, but suddenly it looked likely to assume considerable importance in my life.

Chapter 10

I HAD NOT BEEN AWARE that there would be an intermediate step before I was thrown into a place of detention, but it turned out that I had to be taken before the magistrates, to determine my status. Our destination was the Bow Street Magistrates' Court, near Covent Garden, where I was placed in a cell somewhere underneath the building. This was the first time in my life I had been confined in such a way, and desperate feelings threatened to overcome me as the realisation sunk in that I had lost my freedom. No matter how much I begged or pleaded or bargained with the gaoler, I could not leave this tiny room.

To make matters worse, an old man in a cell opposite took great delight in telling me how I would find conditions in prison, whence, without knowing anything of me, he was confident I would be consigned after my arraignment before the magistrates. I do not know what satisfaction he derived from his taunting, but he was not to be silenced. Observing my tears, which I could not prevent, he sneered: 'Cry at this, would you? Why, this is nothing! When they take you to Newgate there'll be thirty of you in a space like the one you've got now.

You won't be able to lie down, that's a fact. Why, it's not so long ago that three women suffocated in one night, in a cell bigger than that one you've got there.' He grabbed the bars and shook them. 'Oh, you'll know all about it by tonight, yes you will. Why, you'll have rats running over your face, and be thankful if you wake up in the morning without your face half-eaten.'

At this a voice from another cell shouted: 'Shut up, you old fool. I'd like to see a rat eat your face away, and your tongue with it.'

But another voice shouted: 'It happened all right, to that army fellow, and not long ago either.'

Then another voice joined in, and shouts came from everywhere, until I felt that I was in the middle of a hellish chorus. Among them I heard one man say: 'The army fellow was dead when his face was eaten away,' from which I took some comfort, but only a little.

When there was a lull, the old man resumed his ranting. Seizing the bars of his cell with both hands again, he stared at me across the corridor with fierce eyes and shouted: 'You'll be ironed and bull pizzled, and they'll set on you with the cat-o'-nine-tails, you'll get bezels and handcuffs and chains, and if all that don't do for you, the gaol fever will finish you off.'

I did not understand half of what he said, but felt so sick and close to fainting that when the gaoler came to take me up into the court, I could hardly move.

It was a very different atmosphere up there, though, with all the beautiful woodwork and the quiet of it and the way it was so clean. I was placed in a little compartment that I later found was called the dock, with the Bow-Street Runners behind me, and there I waited for about twenty minutes before a man came in and called on us all to stand, which we did. Then two men entered from the back of the courtroom and took their places upon the bench. I recognised one of them as the man in charge of the group who arrested me, the one who had stopped Mr Ogwell from doing his worst.

I saw too as I looked to my right that Mr Ogwell had come into the court, and he now took up a place at the front, below the magistrates' bench. He looked even paler than he had before, if it were possible. It almost seemed that he was the one who had lost blood.

The proceedings began and in my befuddled state it was all I could do to understand a word, but gradually I found myself able to listen with more concentration. The first part seemed to be just a whole lot of long sentences read by a small grey-headed man sitting to the left of the magistrates. It was about the King's warrant being granted to the court or some such thing. Then it was my turn. The grey-headed man stood up and said to me: 'Barnaby Fletch, is that your name?'

'Yes, sir, it is,' I said.

'Stand up, Barnaby Fletch.'

I did so, on legs that shook beneath me.

'Are you known by any other names, Barnaby Fletch?'

'No sir,' I stammered. 'I don't believe so.'

'Well then, Barnaby Fletch, you are charged that on this day just past, in the night-time, not having God before your eyes, but being moved and seduced by the instigation of the Devil, in the peace of God and our lord the King, feloniously, wilfully, and of your malice aforethought you did make an indecent assault with force upon one Josephine Inga Ogwell, being a child of this parish, and that in so doing you acted against the peace of our lord the King, his Crown and dignity. How say you, Barnaby Fletch, are you guilty or not guilty of this felony whereof you stand charged?'

Very nervously I said: 'I'm sorry, sir, for my ignorance, but I don't really understand what you're saying.'

'Come now,' said the other magistrate, the one I did not know, who was a very fat man and looked bored by the proceedings already. 'I think you understand well enough. Is it true that you pressed yourself upon this child? That you behaved indecently with her?'

The room blurred before my eyes and I felt I should fall. With the greatest difficulty I stammered: 'No, sir, no such thing. No, sir, never.'

'I understand that to be a plea of not guilty,' the other magistrate said to the grey-headed man who had read out the charge. 'Let us get on. You may sit down, prisoner. Mr Ogwell, is it your intention to go ahead with a prosecution in this case?'

Mr Ogwell looked up briefly and whispered: 'Yes, sir, it is.' Then, just as the magistrate seemed about to say something, he added: 'What was done to my little girl is a terrible thing.'

There was a pause in the courtroom. A few people looked at me as if to their eyes I was clearly the person who had done this terrible thing. The magistrate who had led the arrest spoke again to Mr Ogwell. 'Are you, sir, a member of a prosecution association?'

Mr Ogwell seemed to have trouble remembering what that was. I had a memory of his saying something about being in a prosecution association – I had the idea that it was some kind of insurance scheme for shop owners, so they could afford to prosecute cases at law. As Mr Ogwell had not answered the magistrate, I tried to be helpful and said: 'You are, sir, you told me so.'

Mr Ogwell did not look at me, but he nodded to the magistrate as if to confirm that I was correct.

The magistrate gave me another of his sharp glances. Then he said to my master: 'You recollect, sir, that I told you to bring your wife and daughter to the court?' When Mr Ogwell nodded again, the magistrate, in his peremptory style, to which I was quickly becoming accustomed, said: 'Well, sir, have you done it? Where are they?'

Mr Ogwell stood and turned to the rear of the court. I looked in the same direction and saw Mrs Ogwell sitting there. She had her handkerchief to her eyes, so I could not see her face well. If Josephine were with her she must have been hidden by the back of the seat in front of her.

The magistrate said: 'Come forward, madam, if you please, and take your seat here.'

It took her a goodly time to get to the witness box, but at last she was sitting there, looking down at her lap. The grey-haired man stood in front of her and gave her a Bible and asked her to swear on the Holy Book that she would tell the truth. Still hanging her head she muttered something, at which the fat magistrate asked her sharply to speak up. In a louder voice she said: 'I swear by Almighty God to tell the truth, the whole truth, and nothing but the truth.'

The grey-haired man indicated that she should kiss the Book, which she did, whereupon he snatched it out of her hand, rather rudely I thought, and sat down at his place again. Mrs Ogwell looked up then for the first time, at her husband. Everyone looked at him. He said nothing for a moment, then in a weak voice he asked his wife: 'Just say what happened this morning.'

Speaking very quickly, in her accented English, she said: 'I was awoken by my child's screams. I went to her room. She came running out of the door just as I got there and flung herself into my arms. At first I thought she was having a nightmare, but when I took her back to our bed and lit the candle I could see blood on her legs. I then examined her and saw that she was . . . injured. She had scratches around her privates, and I thought a bruise was starting to form. When you came in, I told you that she was injured. You seemed much put out. At first you did not believe me, but then the old lady from next door came in and she looked at Josephine and agreed with me and said we must send to Bow Street. And then the lady from downstairs came in also and she said she would get the magistrate and the Runners and off she went.'

There was a long silence. I felt stricken that such a terrible thing would happen to the beautiful and happy little girl. I found it hard to associate myself with what had happened. There seemed no connection possible between me and such ugly matters.

The fat magistrate said to Mrs Ogwell: 'How old is the child, ma'am?'

'Just turned four, sir.'

The other magistrate asked: 'At what point did you conceive the boy Fletch was responsible for this outrage?'

'I kept asking her, sir, asking her who had hurt her. She did not answer for a long time. Finally she said it was the boy who gave her the dolls.'

'And that was the defendant FLETCH?' said the fat man. He said my name very loudly and glared at me at the same time, then looked around the courtroom as if to be sure everyone had noticed.

'Yes, sir,' Mrs Ogwell said.

'Have any other boys given dolls to your daughter?' the other magistrate asked.

'No, sir.'

The same magistrate then said to Mr Ogwell: 'Have you any questions you would like to put to your wife?'

Mr Ogwell shook his head. Then the magistrate asked me: 'Have you any questions you would like to put to the witness?'

I was stricken with embarrassment and blurted out: 'I don't know, sir, I don't know what I'm meant to do.'

'Were you at this person's house this morning?'

'No, sir, I don't know where Mr Ogwell lives, sir.'

He paused and gave me one of those piercing looks again, as he had done in the street. I looked back at him frankly. I was terribly frightened, but there was something about him that made me feel I could trust him, that he might even be on my side. Then he said: 'I will put a question on your behalf.' To Mrs Ogwell he said: 'Did there appear to be intromission?'

She flushed very red. 'I really couldn't say, sir. As I say, there seemed to be some injury. Perhaps not very . . . far.'

'Did you observe any evidence of emissions upon the child?'

A great silence fell upon the courtroom. Mrs Ogwell looked overwhelmed, huddling even lower in the witness box. I did not understand what the question meant. The magistrate said to her: 'Do you understand the significance of the question? Given the age of the defendant in these proceedings? His . . . capability, so to speak.'

'Yes, I do, sir. Yes I do. But I'm not sure of the answer . . . I can't say whether there was or there wasn't.'

'What about the bedding? Did you examine the bedding?'

'Not in any detail, sir, I didn't. I was too upset.'

'The night attire? Did you examine that?'

'In a manner of speaking, sir. There may have been something . . . what you said . . . I really couldn't say for sure.'

The two magistrates conferred for a few moments. Then the one who seemed to be in charge said, to no one in particular: 'We will need to hear from the child now.'

Mrs Ogwell straightened up. When she spoke, her voice was suddenly strong and quite loud. 'It can't be, sir. She was that upset I didn't bring her here, I couldn't. Mr Ogwell's sister is looking after her.'

No one responded, and after a minute she continued: 'Begging your pardon, your Honours, and no offence, but I'd rather not continue with the prosecution than bring her to this place.'

The magistrates conferred again. Then the main one looked straight at the Bow-Street Runners behind me. He said to them: 'We need to examine the bedding, and the child's night attire. Go with this lady now and fetch it all, and we will adjourn the case until you return. Make sure no one interferes with the articles that you are fetching. Be very mindful.'

Both the magistrates got up, though it was a struggle for the fatter one. The grey-haired man called: 'All rise.' Everyone in the room obediently stood as the magistrates left, through the same door by which they had entered. The Runners went to Mrs Ogwell, and after a short discussion they too left, with her. Mr Ogwell had already gone. Perhaps he did not want to be near me a moment longer than necessary. Then a guard appeared and fetched me back down to the cells.

Chapter 11

THIS TIME I FOUND myself sharing a cell with three others, all a good deal older than I. The old man had disappeared from the cell opposite, for which I was grateful.

The three men knew each other, and it emerged they were taken for the same crime, a case of arson. They were well dressed, spoke like gentlemen, and seemed quite sanguine about their prospects. It was evident that they were familiar with the procedures of the magistrates' court, and indeed, I suspected, many other courts. They took a keen interest in my case and listened closely to my account. They explained, with ribald laughter, the kind of evidence the Robin Redbreasts had been sent to seek, which brought a blush to my cheeks. Then they commented on the magistrates. 'You've been lucky and unlucky,' one said. 'The fat one is Sir Bennett Cousins, and everyone he trials is guilty as far as he's concerned. But the other one is Sir Henry Matthews. If he takes a set against you, you're for the gallows, boy, and no mistake. But on the other hand, if he thinks you've been taken unjustly, he'll hang the rule book before he hangs you.'

'What about benefit of clergy?' one of them, a very tall man, asked.

'Aye,' laughed another. 'Take your glove off and show him your thumb.'

The tall man blushed and hid his thumb away. 'Ah, that's no good to the boy,' said the third man. 'When they cut out the branding, they took the benefit away for all the really worthwhile crimes.'

They laughed long and hard at this, as though he had said a very merry thing. Their conversation was completely beyond my comprehension. I did not know then of the plea of benefit of clergy, by which a person could have his sentence greatly eased. Later I learned that in the old days a first offender could, in the case of most crimes, plead the benefit, at which his thumb would be branded, with a T for Thief, or an M for Murderer, or an F for Felon. He would then either be set free or sentenced to a year or so of incarceration. Sometimes he might be transported to North America as well, although not of course after the disgraceful Peace of Paris and the loss of that colony to a ragtag army of mercenaries, ruffians and Frenchmen. It was by way of the benefit of clergy that many a man, and some women too, saved themselves from the gallows; until 1779, when the Government did away with branding and at the same time stopped felons pleading the benefit for most offences.

When their mirth had subsided, the tall man, blushing even more, set them off again by saying: 'I could have had the whole alphabet on my thumb,' and they all fell about laughing.

They laughed with everything they said, but I was too frightened to ask how seriously I should regard their talk of the gallows. I knew well enough that boys my age or younger had taken the drop before this.

'You have no money, I suppose?' one of them asked, and that made them all laugh at the mere thought of it. I was becoming irritated by their constant merriment and wished that I could pull out a fat purse and astonish them by spilling a pile of gold sovereigns onto the floor. I sank into a corner of the cell, thinking bitterly that it always came down to money in the end. The rich either bought themselves a life of comfort in prison, or bought their way straight out the gate. The poor were left to rot.

The men lost interest in me. They started talking of arson. 'It's a funny thing,' the most talkative one said, 'how when you don't want a fire it's no trouble at all to start one, and when you do want one, you can be at it an hour before it'll light.'

'Aye, you should have brought flints for all of us,' the tall man said, by which I deduced they were guilty of the crime with which they had been charged.

After a little longer, when they had tired of talking, one of them crouched beside me and said in a more serious tone: 'Do you have anyone who can speak to your character? It can make a big difference in a case at law.'

'Only my employer, sir, and he's now my accuser.'

'There's no one else?'

'No, sir.' The man shook his head and whistled through his teeth, then turned back to his companions. He had failed to bring me any comfort.

After some time they were taken up to have their case heard and I did not see them again. Despite my predicament I was now feeling weak with hunger, having been there many hours. It was not until darkness began to settle over the city that a gaoler handed a small bucket through the bars, which upon investigation I found contained a type of soup, or gruel. There were a few slivers of meat in it, which I particularly savoured, and some onions, and some potatoes roughly cut and not fully cooked.

It has been my life's experience to take quite a number of meals in prison, and I would say now, looking back, that this first one was by no means the worst; indeed, I had on occasions suffered worse meals when free and living in the streets of London.

As the night went on, more men were admitted to my cell. All seemed to be drunk, several snored prodigiously, and two vomited all over themselves and their neighbours. The stench became so fetid that I began to feel nauseous myself and so stood as close as I could get to the window grille, giving up any thought of sleep in favour of as much fresh air as I could breathe.

I welcomed the first smudges of grey light in the sky, as the prelude to another day. How wretched must a man be if the coming of dawn fails to ignite hope in his heart? No matter the awfulness of the circumstances in which we find ourselves, the morning light is Nature's reminder that a new day brings promise. I wondered whether a condemned man in his cell, hearing the stirrings of the first spectators arriving to witness his execution, and waiting for the awful tread of the chaplain proceeding down the corridor, still welcomed dawn's light. It would be understandable that he might not.

Despite the lack of space in the cell, I sat down against the wall, my knees drawn up, and dozed a little before some bread and water were brought us for breakfast.

It was somewhat puzzling to me that there had been no further progress apparent in my case. When the Runners left the court with Mrs Ogwell the day previously I had been under the impression that I would be summoned back within an hour or so, when they returned with the objects they had been commanded to fetch. That had not happened, and I still waited in vain for someone to come for me. The day's hearings had evidently commenced in the courtroom above, because as the morning wore on gaolers took various of the malfeasors who had been admitted during the night. The traffic backwards and forwards was considerable, but I sat languishing against the wall most of the time, getting up restlessly at intervals to prowl around the small space. It seemed inconceivable that anyone could exist in such a place for more than a day without going mad. Yet soon enough I estimated that a full day had elapsed since my imprisonment, and still the hours continued to pass. The hope that had risen in me at the dawn bid fair to be extinguished again as the day dragged towards its weary close.

Hunger gnawed at my vitals for most of the morning and all through the afternoon. I was no stranger to hunger, but there was so little else to think about, sitting there in the gloom, that it was difficult to concentrate on any other topic.

Late in the afternoon I was alone again in the cell, which I preferred. Across the corridor this time were a couple of boys not much older than I, who ignored me most of the time, except for an occasional jeering comment flung in my direction. Then I heard the now-familiar heavy tread of the gaoler coming down the corridor, and the rattling of his keys. I hoped he was coming for me, because, after just a day and a half, I had reached the stage where I thought I would prefer to be the recipient of bad news than be left languishing any longer. Indeed he had come for me. He flung open the door as though in a bad temper. 'Get yourself up there,' he said.

I scurried past him and made my way along the same route as the day before. Within moments I was back in the dock, with this difference, that the magistrate was already sitting there, in position. It was the man they called Sir Henry Matthews, the one who had led my arrest. I was relieved to see that the fat one was not there and Sir Henry was on his own.

Sir Henry was writing and did not look up. Minutes passed. I dared not sit down. I glanced around the room and saw only a few people, but no one I recognised. At last Sir Henry placed his quill in its well and leaned back in his chair. He glared at me. 'Has anyone made the boy aware of the developments in his case?' he asked the courtroom.

As hardly anyone was present, I was not sure to whom his question was addressed. But the grey-headed man spoke up. 'Not so far as I know, sir,' he said, rising and bowing to the bench.

'Well then,' Sir Henry said, turning his piercing gaze back to me. 'There have been developments, there have indeed.'

I gulped. I did not know whether this presaged good or ill for me. Sir Henry leaned forward. 'When the officials of the court went with the mother of the child to their premises to secure the bedding and night attire, as per my instructions yesterday, to which I believe you were privy . . .'

He stared at me and I realised I was expected to respond, so I said: 'Yes sir, I do recall.'

'. . . they found that all the articles they sought had disappeared.'

I reeled, and had to clutch the railing of the dock for support. What mystery was this? Was I now suspected of stealing the bedclothes of the little girl? I stared at the magistrate. I could read nothing in his face.

'This morning the father of the unfortunate child was seen throwing certain items into the river. They have now been retrieved and have been identified as the missing bedding and nightclothes. As the father, who has proved elusive throughout the day but has just been discovered, seems unable to provide a satisfactory explanation for his activities, he has been taken into custody and will be appearing before me within the hour.'

I gaped at him. I must have looked like an idiot. He said to me in the most threatening tone: 'Do you have any further light to shed on this affair?'

'No, sir,' I said. 'I still don't understand a single thing about it.'

'No,' he said. 'I thought not. I am dismissing the charges against you. You are free to go.'

Chapter 12

THUS ENDED MY FIRST encounter with the law, and greatly did I respect Sir Henry Matthews in consequence. However, I was now in a parlous state, not only without a position, considering the arrest of Mr Ogwell, but also soon to find that every man's hand was turned against me, and every woman and child's too. For I found that my acquittal mattered naught to the folk in Hell. In that den of iniquity, where the angels could search in vain for one soul that was not foully corrupted, I, who had been declared innocent by the law of the land, was found guilty of some unspecified crime by a jury whose numbers vastly exceeded twelve and whose reputation for vice was rich indeed. When I walked down the street, people turned their faces away in evident contempt, and those who turned towards me did so only to spit.

I was bewildered and frightened by this change to my life, which was as unexpected as the arrest and hearing had been. I did not know which way to turn, or whom to trust. Within a couple of days I was spending most of my time skulking in St Martin's, experiencing a new kind of solitude.

Quentin, only Quentin, stood by me. He had even less comprehension of the crime I was supposed to have committed than did I, but he was steadfast and would have been so, I am convinced, had I been guilty of high treason, piracy, murder, and armed robbery on the King's highways. He was himself no stranger to injustice, having been summarily evicted from the convent when blamed by another boy for spitting on the consecrated wafers. Although Quentin knew the other boy to be the perpetrator of this misdeed he was unable to convince the nuns, and so, out into the streets he had gone.

As abruptly as I had become notorious, however, things changed again, suddenly and quite soon. One morning Quentin came to me in a state of high excitement, waving a broadside of the type that frequently infested the streets. Quentin could barely read, but I had been teaching him his letters and he was making good progress. 'Barnaby,' he cried, 'here's a name you know.'

I took the sheet from him. It was one of the penny publications printed in haste when a public execution was to take place. I read it with a growing sense of horror and dread. It had been about six weeks since the arrest of Mr Ogwell, and the broadside proclaimed in detail the events attendant upon his capture.

On Saturday afternoon, the Recorder made his report to the King in Council, concerning the unhappy man who was capitally convicted at the last Old Bailey sessions. Isaiah Mayhew Ogwell has been ordered for execution on Friday next at Newgate.

The prisoner pleaded not guilty to three indictments, of rape upon his own daughter, a four-year-old infant, of attempted murder of a lad employed by him in East Smithfield, and of wilfully destroying evidence.

The horrible crime of Rape was discovered by the unfortunate mother of the victim whose attention was attracted by the crying of the child one morning and who, upon going to her aid, found her much distressed and with injuries upon the nether regions which could only have been inflicted in an attack by one with the most evil intentions. The case was prosecuted by Serjeant Stevens who told the jury that upon hearing the evidence they would have no doubt of the guilt of the accused, who had compounded his crime by attempting at first to lay the blame for the offence at the door of an innocent lad employed by the defendant, a boy who had previously shown goodwill towards the child by making keepsakes for her in the form of dolls. What bitter thanks for he who had acted only from the purest of intentions! For the prisoner, having led the magistrate, no less a personage than Sir Henry Matthews, accompanied by the Bow-Street Runners, to the lad, thereupon launched a savage attack upon him, which was undoubtedly intended to put an end to his life and to prevent him establishing his innocence. The name of the unfortunate boy would have been forever tarred with guilt, for a crime committed by his would-be murderer!

Ogwell's attack was thwarted thanks to the swift action of Sir Henry and the Runners, but the boy was immediately arrested and taken before Sir Henry, assisted by that renowned jurist Sir Bennett Cousins. Sir Henry, having the gravest doubts as to the boy's culpability, and doubting that one of such a tender age could be capable of the injuries complained of, acted in his usual decisive fashion and ordered the seizure of bedclothes and nightwear belonging to the victim, to be examined for evidence of the age of the perpetrator. Bow Street officers proceeded to the prisoner's house in company with the prisoner's wife and found the property inexplicably missing. A neighbour to the prisoner was interviewed, however, who had observed the prisoner fleeing with the desired articles just before the Runners arrived. This occasioned much astonishment, as it was the first time suspicion had fallen on the father of the victim. The prisoner was subsequently pursued by the Bow-Street Runners but not found, evidently having become aware of the search for him, and finding refuge in a place unknown.

In the morning, the prisoner was observed throwing bedclothes and a child's nightwear into the River Thames, which were then retrieved by a couple of boatmen, in no fit state to be examined, as all possible evidence had been destroyed by the actions of the river. The defendant being apprehended by the Runners later that day hiding in the basement of his shop was taken up by the Runners, conveyed to the magistrates' court, and there arraigned for trial by Sir Henry Matthews.

Serjeant Stevens produced witness MRS ELIZABETH ADAMS, who swore that she had seen the prisoner hurrying from the premises with an armful of bedclothes shortly before the arrival of the court officials and that he had knocked her aside in his rush. Witnesses MR THOMAS PURCELL and MR ADAM MCADAMS testified that they had seen the defendant engaged in throwing the articles into the water, and they subsequently identified the defendant in court. The prisoner upon being invited to question the witnesses asked only one question, to Mrs Adams, to wit, 'How do you know it was me and not someone else you saw with the bedclothes?' to which she replied, 'Why I've been your neighbour for eight years. I should think I'd know you well enough by now.'

The Old Bailey jury, having heard the evidence last Thursday morning, took just twenty minutes to return a finding of guilty. The prisoner appeared stricken and in a state of collapse following the announcement of the verdict. When asked whether he had anything to say, he remained mute. The judge, Mr Baron Farrow, then addressed the prisoner, saying that he was a most wicked and unhappy man who *had committed a crime which would cause the utmost feelings of revulsion in all honest men, and he must look now to He who alone has the power of forgiveness if he is to have any hope of eternal life. His Honour advised the wretched man that he must henceforward think of himself as one no longer of this earth, but must do all that was within his power in his short time remaining to cleanse his soul and prepare to meet his Maker. Mr Baron Farrow then pronounced sentence of death, ordering that the prisoner be taken to the place of execution next Friday and there hanged by the neck until he was dead, and his body afterwards to be dissected and anatomised pursuant to the statute.*

Upon the sentence being pronounced, an awful silence pervaded the court, which was crowded with spectators. The wife of the prisoner was not in the court but is believed to have removed herself to the home of her father and mother, which is in Dover, where she is attending assiduously to the child who was the subject of the outrage.

A large concourse of people attended the Condemned Sermon last Sunday given by the Revd Mr Ambleside who preached from Ezekiel xviii 24: 'But when the righteous turneth away from his righteousness, and committeth iniquity, and doeth according to all the abominations that the wicked man doeth, shall he live? All his righteousness that he hath done shall not be mentioned: in his trespass that he hath trespassed, and in his sin that he hath sinned, in them shall he die.'

The condemned man has been an apothecary in the city of London with his own premises these fourteen years past, and up until these events has borne a good character, which however, as according to the words of the prophet Ezekiel so tellingly pronounced by the Revd Mr Ambleside, doth avail him not in the light of the terrible attack made upon his own child. He is now to be submitted to the awful mercy of his Creator, and

let his fate be a warning to those who deviate from the paths of right-
eousness. O sinner, every day you are spared is but one day of respite
to you. There is one whose all-seeing gaze is witness to our every act,
and His retribution is swift but certain! BE SURE YOUR SIN WILL
FIND YOU OUT.

I had seen these broadsides with their dying statements many a time
and must admit had perused them avidly, sometimes even reading them
aloud to Quentin, but now I flung this one from me with disgust and
vowed never to look at such a thing again. Yet wherever I went that
morning I saw crowds of people reading copies of it and talking over the
contents, and suddenly I found that I was redeemed, that however I had
been reviled before, so was I lauded now, and everywhere I went people
were anxious to tell me how ill-used I had been and how they had never
for a moment doubted my innocence. Thus I learned the power of the
printed word, and learned too, if I had not known it before, the fickleness of humanity.

Chapter 13

THE THOUGHT OF MR Ogwell being hung from the neck until death haunted me. I could hardly credit that a man so strictly insistent upon the highest standards of behaviour, and apparently living a moral and Christian life, could end his days dangling ignominiously from the gibbet while the usual crowd of ruffians and drunks hurled rubbish and insults at him.

Though I had, as I said, read Dying Declarations, as the broadsides were called, many a time, yet I could not reconcile the kind of villains described in them with what I knew of Mr Ogwell. He was, to the best of my knowledge, not a Sabbath breaker nor a bad liver. In fact, far from being a Sabbath breaker, he attended church two or three times on a Sunday. In the dark reaches of London that we inhabited, he stood out for his righteousness.

I had never myself been to a public execution, shrinking from exposing myself to such brutality. Something within me retained some sensitivity of feeling I suppose, despite the degraded circumstances in which I lived. I thrilled to sports like cockfighting but the thought of watching men, and women too, being marched up to the drop and having the noose put around their necks before being consigned into Eternity sent a coldness coursing through my body which perhaps in some way mirrored the last moments of these poor benighted souls. And so, as the tide of humanity coursed through the streets towards Newgate on the days of executions, I had invariably beaten against it. It was more than enough for me to hear the roar of the crowd as the deed was done – which, on occasions, amounted to as many as six or seven separate roars when a number of executions were undertaken on the same morning.

Though I had been exposed to much that was sordid and untimely in my short life, I had, thanks to my youth, only a limited ability to conceive of the nature of the act perpetrated upon the little girl Josephine Ogwell. I did not allow myself to dwell upon it; I only knew that it was an act which must challenge even the Divine to exercise His mercy. Similarly, I did not allow myself to dwell upon the way in which Mr Ogwell had attempted to implicate me in the dreadful deed. It bewildered me that Josephine had apparently named me as her attacker; I could only surmise that in her state of terror she could not bring herself to point an accusatory finger at her father, who indeed had a powerful and dominating manner, even to his customers, and certainly to me, his employee. To his wife and daughter then, how much more powerful and dominating must he have seemed?

My time as an assistant to the apothecary having come to such a brutal and unexpected end, I reverted to the ways of my former life. After experiencing the malevolence of the public countenance, I now experienced its benevolence, but the latter proved to be as short-lived as the former. New scandals and other matters of interest came along, and it seemed that among most people the memory of Mr Ogwell quickly faded. Within days I found I was being treated no better and no worse than I had always been.

My main legacy from my time in the service of Mr Ogwell was many months of frightful dreams, during which I saw all too often the sight I had avoided on the Friday of the execution. In these visions I saw him mounting the steps, not bravely and in hope of the Lord's mercy, as the broadsides led me to believe many had done before, but always being half-carried up there because his legs would not support him. And I saw the clergyman approach him with the Good Book in his hands and Mr Ogwell unable to hear the words of exhortation and repentance. And I heard him invited to address the crowd but turning his head away, for he always had a certain delicacy and disdained the common herd, which must have made doing business in a place such as Hell particularly repugnant to him. Not for him, I surmised, the fine speeches made by many about to go to their doom, saying as how although their body was to suffer upon the gibbet yet they hoped their souls would be admitted to Heaven, and admonishing reprobates and Sabbath defilers to mend their ways lest they meet a similar wretched fate.

In my dreams I saw him then escorted to the scaffold, shaking the hands of those who offered them, having the cap placed over his head and the rope around his neck, then the dreadful moment when the prisoner himself must give the signal to the hangman that he is ready to proceed, and the lever pulled and the hatch dropping beneath him. After that, the dreams became even worse, for I envisaged a variety of situations, each worse than the previous, too awful to dwell upon here, but mostly involving a slow and ghastly strangulation, the rope having failed to break the poor man's neck, so that the executioner was required to jump up from underneath and attach himself to the legs of the condemned man in order to speed his end.

For a long time these dreams were so bad that I was afraid to fall asleep at nights, and in consequence of that, and I daresay of general malnutrition, I started to waste away, so that when I saw my reflection in a shopfront one day I scarcely recognised the gaunt stripling staring back at me. Shocked by this apparition I decided that, regardless of my apprehensions about the fate awaiting felons, and even despite my brief experience of incarceration at the magistrates' court, I had no other course but to expand my criminal activities if I were to survive.

Even as I came to this conclusion I imagined I could hear the gates of Hell creaking open to admit me.

It gives me no pleasure to recount what follows, as it has given me no pleasure to recount some of the passages already herein recorded, but I have resolved to be nothing but honest in these pages, so will press on, trusting to my readers' stores of Christian compassion and understanding. And I should say by way of mitigation that during this period of my life I made many attempts to find respectable employment, without success.

No sooner had I taken the dishonourable decision to do whatever it took to survive, regardless of right or wrong, than I fell in with one who seemed well equipped to assist me in my course. One night I was passing a small and dingy tavern close to the river's edge when a man came striding out and turned to the left, marching along confidently, pipe in mouth, until he was less than a yard away from stepping straight into the river. 'Hold hard, sir,' I shouted, and flung myself at him, managing to make such an obstacle of my puny body that I tripped him up and nearly catapulted him into the river from which I had been trying to save him. He was on his feet again in a moment, and I saw him to be a small stout man with a dark complexion, made darker by his anger at me. Dressed in a black suit and smart red waistcoat he seemed a cut above the average denizen of Hell.

'What are you about?' he shouted, and I realised that a small dagger had appeared as if by magic in his hand and he was preparing to defend himself against me.

'Please, sir,' I panted, frightened out of my wits at having another knife presented to me. 'You were about to fall into the river.'

He looked about him and saw the truth of my words. Then he laughed long and loud and put the knife away. 'Faith, there's a pretty thing,' he said. 'The rotgut I've poured down my throat in that place has made me blind. All right, boy, thank you, you saved me from a drenching at best and a drowning at worst.'

He said all this with perfect diction and apparent sobriety, but no sooner was the last word out of his mouth than he dropped where he stood, crumpling in a heap on the ground. I was used to seeing drunks insensible upon every street and in every lane in Hell, and there seemed no reason to be concerned about this one. The night air was cool, to be sure, but not so cold as to pose any threat to his survival. I made off down Stanley's Lane, but halfway along, stopped. I had realised with suddenness of thought that if I wanted to graduate to the next rung of the criminal ladder, I could take my opportunity now. The streets were deserted and as far as I could tell no one had seen my exchange with the well-dressed little man.

I retraced my steps, keeping a sharp lookout. Everything was quiet except for my heart, which was making a noise to rival Big Ben. The man had not moved. I knelt beside him and reached inside his coat pocket. I could feel a bulge. I insinuated two fingers as gently as possible and withdrew his purse, slipping it immediately inside my own jacket and then retreating. His other pockets could have been stuffed with valuables, but I was too frightened to investigate further. I hared off down Stanley's Lane and did not stop running until I was inside the sanctuary of St Martin's.

I waited until everyone was gone and the building locked for the night before I took out the purse. Then I lit a candle stub and prepared to count my ill-gotten gains. When I undid the string I almost stopped breathing. The bag was stuffed with pound notes. I pulled them out and slowly counted them. I could hardly believe the total. One hundred and fifty-three pounds, as well as a few silver coins. It was more money than I had ever seen in my life, and certainly more money than I had ever dreamed of possessing. I sat in a daze, the notes spread in front of me, wondering what I could do with a fortune so vast, but also feeling afeared of the man's reaction when he awoke and found he had been robbed of such a sum. Would he remember my face? If so, I would be his first suspect, and he was certain to come looking for me. I had exacted a heavy penalty for saving him from a ducking.

Next day I kept off the streets as much as possible. When I did have to go out and about I skulked along the darkest laneways and alleys. I half-expected the whole of Hell to be in a ferment over so big a theft, but as far as I could tell, nothing had changed.

It was virtually impossible for a boy such as me to pass a pound note. Nothing was more certain than that anyone to whom I offered it would call the Bow-Street Runners or else pocket the money and laugh at me when I asked for it back. I spent the coins easily enough, and quickly, on food for Quentin and me, but I did not touch the notes for four days, and I did not dare tell Quentin of my sudden prosperity.

Alone, and cogitating agitatedly as to my best course, I called to mind the name of a certain Mr Weekes. He had a reputation for trading in almost any commodity without asking uncomfortable questions. I knew the gentleman by sight, and so resolved to take my windfall to him.

Mr Weekes had an office, for want of a better word, atop a rickety old staircase which crawled up an old building jutting out over the river. The whole thing looked as though it could topple into the Thames at any moment. I made my way up there with much trepidation. Carrying one hundred and fifty-three pounds through the streets imposed an enormous weight on my mind, even though I had not seen the stout little man with the knife again.

Mr Weekes seemed pleased to welcome me into his establishment. 'Come in, my young friend, come in,' he cried. He was sunning himself on the windowsill, his legs hanging out of the window, and eating a pork pie, with a bottle of beer by his side. A black cat with a white spot on the very tip of its tail lay beside him, draped across the sill and accepting occasional titbits of pork from Mr Weekes's fingers.

He waved those same greasy fingers at me. He struck me as a young man, though I had never thought of him as such before. I remembered him as having a beard but now he was clean-shaven. His hat was pushed back on his head, and altogether he seemed remarkably nonchalant for a man who, according to rumour, might one day keep a similar appointment to that recently kept by Mr Ogwell. I stood nervously just inside the doorway, wondering how to broach the topic that had brought me there. But he no doubt had more experience in this line than did I, and with the same joviality with which he had welcomed me, he put down his pork pie, swung his legs around and jumped up. 'I see by your manner that you are here on important business,' he said.

I found this disconcerting, as people did not normally speak to me in such terms. Nevertheless, I took another couple of steps into the room and produced the canister in which I had concealed the money.

'I have something I want to sell,' I said.

Without answering, Mr Weekes bustled across the room and shut the door, sealing us off from the long-nosed gossiping world outside. Then he turned back to me and said: 'Well, you wish to sell something, you've come to the right place. I like to buy and sell. I trade, that's what I do. What is it you have?'

'Money,' I said.

He smiled, although his smile reminded me of the creatures in the menagerie in the Tower of London. 'It's a little early to speak of that, my young friend,' he said. 'You'll need to show me what you have in your canister first.'

'That's what I have,' I said. 'Money.'

He pushed his hat back further and scratched his head. 'Indeed you speak in riddles. You are selling money for money, is that what you are saying?'

I gave a little nervous nod. I knew there was no going back now.

Mr Weekes frowned and looked around, as if to make sure no one was looking in the windows. 'What exactly do you have there?' he asked. His tone had changed.

I had to remind myself to breathe, then took the lid off the canister and turned it upside-down, giving it a shake to discharge the contents. The banknotes fell with a soft thud onto the table. Mr Weekes gave a long soft whistle. 'Well, well, my young friend . . .' he said, as if to himself. He stepped up to the table and fingered the wad of money. 'How much is here?'

'One hundred and fifty-three pounds,' I said, almost proudly.

He whistled again, then began to count it. He counted it not once, not twice, but three times, backwards and forwards, before he looked at me again. 'How hot is it?' he asked.

'Hot?' I asked. I was so new to this game that I did not know what he meant; for a moment I thought he must be referring to the weather outside.

He shrugged, then laughed. 'You're a green one,' he muttered. 'Well, how much do you want for it?'

I had no idea how much to ask for. 'The notes are too big for me to take around,' I explained. 'I just want coins.'

He laughed again. 'You just want coins,' he repeated. 'Well well, if you stay in this game long enough, you hear everything. All right my young friend, you shall have coins.'

He picked up the notes, stuffed them into his pocket – with some difficulty – then disappeared through the doorway into another room. I could hear him rummaging about, and I heard a jingle that signified coins. He soon re-emerged, holding a cloth bag, which he held out to me. I took it and was surprised at its weight. I opened it and looked inside. I saw a mixture of silver and copper. I put in my hand and pulled out a few coins. They were all silver: three pennies, a sixpence and a half-crown. I dipped into the bag again, and this time pulled out copper: three farthings.

I looked at Mr Weekes. He looked steadily back at me. 'There you are, my young friend,' he said. 'You have coins. Now be off with you and mind you never breathe a word of doing business with Nathaniel Weekes.'

I nodded. I was happy enough to go. I was excited at the weight of the bag and the number of coins within it. Now I felt that I truly had a fortune. I was like a child who swaps a precious jewel for a lollipop. I scuttled to the door. As I left he called after me: 'Come and see me again, young friend, next time you have something to sell.'

Chapter 14

QUENTIN AND I LIVED for nearly a week on the proceeds of the coins. I doled them out parsimoniously enough, but it did not take him long to realise that I had an almost inexhaustible supply. Although he nagged me for explanations, I refused to tell him the source of my riches, afraid that he might talk too much around the streets of Hell.

We had, however, by no means depleted the contents of the bag when our situation changed most unexpectedly. We were wandering along the banks of the river one morning, speaking, I recall, of a dark-skinned man we had just glimpsed on a barge. People from Africa were becoming more common in London but they were still a novelty to us.

We were only a block from Mr Weekes's office, but he was not in my thoughts as we followed the path, passing into the shadows of a large tavern. The sign affixed to it described it as the River Inn, but it was known to all and sundry as Riley's, that being the name of its owner. Riley's was rarely closed, but it was either closed now or just very quiet, for there were no signs of human life in its vicinity. Suddenly, however, with a quick movement a man appeared to my left.

For a moment he seemed to be a shadow himself, but then he became detached from the shadows and I realised it was Mr Weekes. My lips started to form a greeting but before I could speak or utter a sound he was on me and his arm came around my neck. He forced me back against a tree, pinning me to it with considerable force. He was stronger than he looked.

'Now my young friend,' he said in a voice that could have been mistaken as pleasant, 'what do you take me for, hey?'

If it were not for the arm preventing me from breathing I could have again imagined he was asking me about the weather.

With his arm at my throat I could not speak, and I pointed to it to explain my muteness. He eased the pressure a little, but then as if to compensate slapped me across the side of the head, still smiling all the while.

'I'm sure I don't know what you mean, sir,' I said, gasping with the relief of the air eking its way into my lungs. 'I take you for a very smart and fine gentleman, sir.'

From the corner of my eye I could see Quentin, pale with fear, edging away, and I could not help thinking that it would be best for him if he were to abscond, and the sooner the better.

'Mean? Why, I'll tell you what I mean,' Mr Weekes said, establishing a policy of equilibrium by slapping me now on the other side of my head. 'I mean that you were in a fair way to have me on the gallows, my young friend, to join your late employer Mr Ogwell. Seems like you have something of an infectious disease. Let's call it gibbet fever, shall we? For a lad of your tender years you have a deadly way with you.' He went into quite a fever himself with those words, a fever of slapping, hitting me left and right half-a-dozen times.

'Begging your pardon, sir,' I said, not sure that my head would stay on my shoulders much longer with this treatment, 'I would never mean any harm to you, and I'm sure I never meant any to Mr Ogwell. I wish you would explain, sir.'

At the same time as I professed my innocence, I was aware that my theft of the money from the pocket of the unconscious drunk must have somehow rebounded onto Mr Weekes. Now he pinned my head back against the trunk of the tree and spoke very slowly and distinctly, but softly, right into my mouth: 'Every one of those notes, every single last one, is a forgery. Do you hear me? A forgery.'

A cold running feeling went through my insides, as though a tributary of the Thames had formed in my guts. I did not know much of the world, but I knew that forging banknotes was a sure path to the gallows. Royal pardons were few and far between for those caught with counterfeit currency. 'I hear you, sir,' I squeaked.

'You evidently have a poor opinion of my intelligence, young friend.' He struck me a savage blow to the stomach, driving the air out of me. Insensible to almost everything, I was aware only of Quentin running away at last, like a little mouse. I felt alone in the world. I did not know if I would survive the next few minutes, and I did not know that I cared, given the pain Mr Weekes had inflicted on me. I regretted very much embarking upon the path I had taken since losing my position with Mr Ogwell.

'Where did you get those banknotes?' Mr Weekes hissed. He made no pretence at smiling now. I did not answer because, deprived of air, I could not, but my silence apparently enraged him, and he slapped me vigorously again, backwards and forwards. My cheeks seemed to get bigger with each slap. My skin burned. Tears that I was not able to control ran out of my eyes. I could feel my teeth getting looser. When he stopped it was only to repeat the question: 'Where did you get those notes?'

'Let me speak, sir,' I tried to say, but I am not sure if the words came out in any intelligible form. I suspect they did not. Nevertheless, my attempts appeared to have some effect on him, because he stopped slapping me and snarled into my face: 'Where?'

'I stole them from a man who had fallen down drunk, quite a short man, outside the tavern on Oxley Street.' It took me a full minute to get all this out as I could only manage a couple of words at a time.

'Who was he?'

'I don't know, sir. I'd never seen him before and I've never seen him since. He . . . he looked like a foreign gentleman, but he spoke like an Englishman.'

'Short, was he? With a black beard, neatly trimmed? Red waistcoat? Smoked a pipe, did he?'

'Yes . . . yes, sir. Is he a friend of yours, sir? If so, I'm exceedingly sorry . . .'

'A friend!' He laughed, but without a trace of humour. 'You keep dangerous company, boy. Yes, it had to be him. Any less of an artist would never have taken me in. Well boy, you're in a fair way to end up on the gallows yourself. Now, where's the money I gave you? The bag of coins?'

'Why, most of it's spent, sir.' Only now was I starting to get my breath back. I tried to tighten my stomach muscles in case he hit me there again. 'But I can get you what's left, sir.'

'Oh, deuced generous he is. So, spent you say? Well, you can just unspend it. You deliver all of it to me by Sunday morning, or you won't have to wait for the Tyburn Tippett. I'll turn you off myself.'

I didn't dare ask what he meant by the Tyburn Tippett, but I guessed it was a nickname for the gallows.

'Fifty pounds you owe me,' he said, and before I could respond, he flung me across the little clearing into a mess of brambles and weeds.

I would not have guessed he had strength enough to do that, for, light though I was, he lifted me well clear of the ground and threw me quite a distance.

I lay in there scratched and sore and frightened, watching him stalk away. He had only gone a few yards when he suddenly turned on his heel and came back to me. 'Send your ugly little mate to my office with the money,' he said. 'I don't want you coming anywhere near me ever again.'

Off he went, and suddenly the black cat with the white-tipped tail sprang from a straggly bush outside Riley's and followed, like a vicious little sprite trailing behind him.

I waited until he had gone before crawling out of the prickly weeds. I did so gingerly, and with exclamations of pain, for it was impossible to avoid having my skin ripped in many places by the thorns. Then I lay on the bank for some time, unable to move, still struggling to breathe properly, though that may have been as much the effect of fear as a result of the blows he had rained upon me. Fifty pounds! I was sure he had paid me nothing like so much. He had probably just made up a figure. Unfortunately Quentin and I had never counted it, so we could hardly contradict him, even though I had not seen him count it either.

Fifty pounds or not, I was too afeared of him to contemplate paying him a penny less. But where was I to get such a sum? I guessed that I had between seven and eight pounds left in the bag of coins. It seemed that my decision to live so far outside the laws of God and the King was already bringing me to the brink of disaster. As I limped back towards the refuge of St Martin's, I could see no way to obtain the balance of money demanded by Mr Weekes, short of committing another felony. And who knew where that might lead me?

Chapter 15

THAT VERY NIGHT I had the chance to become acquainted with one who was apparently a felon of long standing. Quentin and I were in a small smoky tavern in Nicholas Street that went by the name of the Pie and Peas. We were in the smallest room, at the very back. I had been practising a policy of discretion since robbing the unconscious drunk man of his money, and so not for me the noisy front rooms, nor the raucous corridors and staircase, which were crowded with as rough a bunch of ruffians as one might expect to find anywhere in London that night.

Quentin and I huddled on the floor, as close as we could get to the fireplace. In the small room any decent fire would have radiated heat enough to blister the skin, but this was a feeble conflagration, based on a few meagre green sticks.

Barely a dozen people could fit in the room at once, and it was at capacity by nine of the clock. The only other person sitting on the floor, a little way to my left, on the other side of the fireplace, was a man who did not attract my attention for some time. His grey hair, tanned skin, grey beard and dirty dark black overcoat caused him to blend in with the shadows, the room being dimly lit anyway.

But after we had been there an hour or so he broke into such a fit of coughing that I felt compelled to notice him, if only to ask if he required assistance, which he indicated by a wave, between coughs, that he did not. When he seemed to have recovered his breath I asked him again if he was all right.

'For the moment,' he growled. 'The accursed air of England . . . it'd kill anyone.'

Such was my ignorance of the world that it had never occurred to me that there might be other places where the air felt different. I looked at him in some surprise and asked where one might go to experience a change of climate.

For the first time he looked full at me. 'You heard of a place called New South Wales?'

'Is that where they're going to send the convicts?'

'My oath it is. They've already started. Not only have men gone out there, and women too for that matter, but at least one of them's come back already.'

He laughed as though this was indeed a good joke, then looked at me again. 'Know where New South Wales is, lad?'

'I suppose it would be near South Wales somewhere?'

He laughed so hard at this that the coughing came back upon him. He pulled out a red kerchief and held it to his mouth. The fit lasted nigh on a minute, and when he took the kerchief away I noticed that, red as it had been before, it was now even redder, splattered with dark spots. He saw that I had observed the spots, and put the cloth away quickly, saying: 'Aye, lad, I'm not far from the Judgement Seat, and no mistake. That's why they gave me a ticket home.'

'A ticket home?' I asked, puzzled.

He leaned in closer. I recoiled a little, for he had a smell on him that I had not smelled before, but knew in my bones to be the precursor to the grave. He grinned at the distaste that must have shown on my face. 'I was in the First Fleet out there and the first one back,' he said. 'Yes, they did me for robbery on the King's highway, but by the time we got to New South Wales the surgeon said there were naught he could do for me, and so I got a governor's pardon, and a ride home. All the way back they had the sail ready, to sew me up and slip me over the side. But I cheated them. I saw the white cliffs of Dover, and I'm yet to see the red flames of Hell.'

To my relief he sat back again, but it was just for another coughing fit. It was some time before he spoke again. Finally he said: 'You talk about climate now. Oh aye, they've a climate out there that a man would dream about. All day long you can have your shirt off and the sun warms you, inside and out. And at night, no need to bother with blankets. Even when it's raining, you never feel cold.' He leaned back further, to get closer to the fire perhaps, but his voice was becoming fainter and he was harder to hear. 'It were grand out there,' he whispered. 'Those rascals they sent out . . . They didn't want to go, no sir, they didn't. It's not an easy trip, but when you make it . . . and when he gets his ticket-of-leave, a man could do anything. All the land he wants, as far as the eye can see. It would have been a fair place to die in. But I came back to see my wife and children, only to find she'd run off with old Blakey, the stablehand at Sir Matthew's . . . she didn't want to know me. And the little 'uns too. Funny, I did it all for them.'

'So where is New South Wales?' I asked. But his eyes had closed. He could have been entering his last sleep for all I knew. I didn't wait to find out. Even more people had squeezed into the room and it was now impossibly crowded, as well as smoky from the fire and the pipes. I motioned to Quentin and we hightailed it out of there.

Skulking along the side of the street, both of us with one eye out for Mr Weekes, I couldn't stop thinking about what the man had said. I was desperate to get the money I needed, to pay Weekes, but I knew I had virtually no chance of succeeding. All I could think was to stumble upon another drunk, one with genuine banknotes. The likelihood of that did not seem good. Most drunks who littered the streets of Hell could be relied upon to have empty pockets. Well-dressed men in suits and waistcoats might fall out of the sky occasionally, but they were few and far between.

We talked gloomily of our lives and our prospects. Quentin probably had no need to fear Mr Weekes, for he had done nothing to harm the gentleman, but for my part, I considered I was at great risk of being murdered. I seemed in a fair way to be tossed into the river for the second time, if I was not able to cough up the dosh for my tormentor.

It was too late to get into St Martin's at that time of night, so we headed for another of our familiar haunts. The cemetery of St Martin's was for some reason nowhere near the church, despite that it bore the church's name. I didn't mind it too much, as somewhere to sleep, but Quentin was always reluctant and would only go if he were with me. It was an unnerving sort of place, to be sure, even in the daytime, but one of the reasons I liked it was that it was generally safe from the hooligans and bash-artists and gangs of hobbledehoys that were always such a threat for youngsters like Quentin and me. They were scared witless of the place.

It's true, there was a fearful sort of man hung around the cemetery day and night, like it was his home, and I think it probably was. I didn't know his name but folks called him Mad Man Abraham. He had a long beard and a hat with holes in it. People said the holes were for his rats; he had pet rats, they said, and they lived in his hair. I didn't know about that, but it wouldn't have surprised me. I did know he talked to himself all the time, and he must have thought the cemetery was his kingdom, for every time he saw us boys near the place he came after us waving his arms like he was demented. He used a big hazel stick as a cane, and he'd shake that and call out threats about how he had our graves ready and waiting. So you wouldn't want to make his acquaintance in the cemetery in the middle of the night, and Quentin and I took pains to ensure that we kept out of his path. It wasn't too difficult if you knew his habits, for he tended to favour certain parts of the place and shun certain others.

Just outside the cemetery we met the Ferret, one of our friends, who was about the same age as me. I didn't know back then why he was called the Ferret, because although I knew there was a creature with that name, I'd never seen one. When I did meet one at last, and it sank its teeth into my hand, I understood why our friend in Hell deserved the sobriquet, for he would bite anyone, friend or foe.

The Ferret was looking for a place to sleep, same as us, so we skinned over the fence one at a time and crept to a hollow on the hillside. There we nestled down together, out of sight of Mad Man Abraham, or so we hoped.

We talked for a while, until Quentin dropped off to sleep. I didn't tell the Ferret of my difficulties with Mr Weekes, but I did tell him that I needed fifty pounds, and in a damn hurry. When the Ferret laughed it was something like the bark of a small dog, and he gave one of his short laughs at the sum I mentioned. 'Fifty pounds,' he said. 'You want the moon up there? I'll get you that before I'll get you fifty pounds.'

That summed up the situation pretty well. Once Quentin was asleep the Ferret and I didn't talk for some time. Quentin was lying half across my lap and I had my arms around him. It didn't seem right to disturb him. After a considerable while the Ferret said: 'Looking at the moon and them stars, it makes you think there might be something else somewhere.'

I'd never heard him talk like this and I asked him what he meant by it. 'Oh, nothing in particular,' he said. He sounded quite embarrassed. 'Just, you know, that there might be something better, even for such as us. That's the trouble with the damn stars and such. They make you so you're not satisfied.'

I told him then about the conversation in the tavern with the dying man, the conversation about New South Wales. 'Aye,' said the Ferret. 'They've sent a few thousand out there already. You know the Hulks?'

Oh yes, I knew the Hulks all right, down by Woolwich. Who didn't? And who didn't fear them? A hundred times worse than any prison, people said, and prison was a hundred times worse than Hell, and Hell was a thousand times worse than the life ordinary folks lived. Yes, the Hulks were to be avoided at any cost.

'Well,' said the Ferret, who knew everything. 'There's been a fuss made by the rich 'uns about the Hulks. Seems like the Government had to do something. There were that many crims dropping off the perch every day that even the rich 'uns said it weren't right and it had to stop. So they've been emptying the Hulks and sending them out to Botany Bay.'

'Botany Bay?' I asked.

'That's New South Wales. Over on the other side of the world it is. You know, transportation. They used to send them to America until those damn Yankees and Frenchies did the dirty on us. Can't send 'em there any more. That's why they were piling up in the Hulks. Now they've got New South Wales.'

He looked at me in the moonlight. I can see him now, his thin pointy little face, more like a fox than a ferret, his sharp eyes that never missed a thing. 'There's your answer. Get yourself sent to Botany Bay.'

'How do you mean?'

'Get yourself transported. If it's good as the man said . . . nothing but sunshine. What've you got here? Rain and cold and half-starved, and getting your throat cut by Weekes when you don't come up with the fifty quid.'

'How did you know it was Mr Weekes?' I asked, startled.

He gave a dark laugh, out of the darkness. 'I hear stuff. You got yourself a good one there. He'd cut your throat just for saying a bad word about his precious cat. He'll never let go of you, that one. Yeah, you got yourself a bad one all right.'

I pondered his words. 'How would I get transported?' I asked.

He gave his fox-bark-laugh again. 'Couldn't be easier. Just pick the right crime. Steal something worth less than five shillings, say. You don't want to go over five shillings or they'll put the black cap on for you. Not that they wouldn't commute it for young 'uns like us. Still, it wouldn't be a nice feeling to stand in the dock and listen to the judge say them words. But a couple of shillings worth, that should get you a free ticket to Botany Bay.' Then he started getting excited. 'Of course! You'll be in the clear with Weekes as well. You get arrested, he'll think you were trying to get the money for him. He won't bother going after you, not when you're inside. He'll think, Ah well, he were trying to do the right thing. And if you're in New South Wales, that's too far away even for him.'

Chapter 16

I N THE COLD LIGHT of dawn, when our plans and intentions are so often
exposed as impossible or unwise or ill-advised, I lay in the graveyard,
Quentin still draped across me, and contemplated the Ferret's counsel.
Partially sheltered though we were, I had not escaped the morning dew.
I was wet and cold, and the fog of London was seeping into my soul,
as it has a way of doing, yet the description of New South Wales by
the man in the Pie and Peas kept a small part of me warm. Although in
some ways the idea of transportation made me fearful, yet the alterna-
tive made me more fearful still. Being pursued by Mr Weekes through
the streets of London was a death sentence, and despite the miserable
circumstances of my life I was not yet ready to go to Judgement.

Trust the Ferret to come up with a scheme that was sharp and sly.
He had slipped away already, so I could have no further discussions
with him about his advice. When Quentin awoke we too hastened from
the graveyard, on our daily ceaseless search for food. Yet as we roamed
the streets I thought continuously of the delights of that place – what
had the Ferret called it? – Botany Bay? I imagined oranges and apples

dangling from trees, fresh-baked bread, fish being pulled from the rivers, all in endless abundance . . . a kind of Garden of Eden, somehow mixed with the scene near Bethsaida where Christ had fed the multitudes with seven loaves and two fishes.

I took little notice of Quentin that day. He as always was uncomplaining, although at times I did contemplate with pangs of guilt the effect on him of my possible desertion. It would leave him altogether alone. On the other hand, if I was killed by Mr Weekes, Quentin would be left alone too. Better for my sake that I be alive in New South Wales than dead in London; for Quentin, the outcome was the same either way.

Even so, I was scared to leave Hell. Scared out of my wits. Hell it may have been, but it was the only world I knew. To me it was more like Purgatory, and everything beyond it was Hell. But I got to the point of thinking I had no choice. My decision to steal that money . . . how it had rebounded on me! It had led inevitably, fatally, step by step, to my present position, and what was worse, I felt that I was in all probability nowhere near the end of the path and had no idea of the destination for which I was bound.

But I could not weaken myself further by dwelling on these fearful topics. Instead I set about thinking of a crime I could commit that would get me transported. I knew I had to be careful. I had already experienced the treatment meted out to those who strayed outside the law; I had put myself in that very position when Quentin and I had entered the house that was on fire, and again when I stole the counterfeit notes; I had been put in that position when accused of the heinous crime against Josephine Ogwell. I wanted a plan now that would not expose me to more than I could bear.

How ignorant, how naive, I was in those days! Truly, nothing can equal the ignorance of the child, for his extensive knowledge of some

topics is betrayed by his complete ignorance of others. The adult generally has at least a smattering of knowledge of most aspects of the world.
The child is like a creature who hibernates in winter; it may know the
world of spring and summer intimately, but should it wake in winter it
will find itself utterly confounded.

At any rate, the upshot of my musings was that later the same
day I found myself in Tallent Street, approaching the shop of Messrs
Sanderson and Trott, Purveyors of Fine Articles for the Gentry.
Mr Sanderson had not been sighted for many years and was most probably dead. Mr Trott on the other hand was very much alive and was well
known among the boys of Hell for his rigorous referral of anyone who
stole from him to the Bow-Street Runners. Yet I had never heard of him
taking the law into his own hands, and after my experiences at the hand
of the servant who flogged me, and with Mr Weekes, I had a distinct
preference for the slow-grinding processes of the law.

I entered the premises of Messrs Sanderson and Trott as surrepti-
tiously as possible, because I knew my way was likely to be barred by
any vigilant assistant who saw me. They were all busy with customers,
however, so I had no difficulty there. I went down the left-hand side of
the shop, which I judged to be the least busy. It was also the darkest. My
path took me to the hairbrush counter. I had reason to believe that these
hairbrushes were Mr Trott's pride and joy. They were always exhibited
in the window, and a large sign outside proclaimed that Sanderson and
Trott were the only London merchants to stock brushes made by the
French company Les Brosses Réputés.

I stood there gazing down at the display. The brushes were spread
across the counter in a sequence from the cheapest to the most expensive. I chose the middle one, as being four shillings and sixpence and
therefore within the range the Ferret had specified: too cheap to get me

a sentence of death, but too expensive for the courts to ignore. I looked around, trying to appear furtive, trying to look like a boy who was there for a felonious purpose. Then I picked up a brush and boldly put it in my pocket. It made quite a bulge and the handle stuck out at the top. Good enough, I thought, and began the long terrifying walk towards the door, a walk that I fully expected would lead me all the way to New South Wales.

No one shouted at me, no one came running across to intercept me. As I approached the door I thought that they must be waiting until I got outside, for some boys held the belief that you could not be arrested for theft until you had left a premises. I reached the door, pushed it open, and passed out into the street, where I found myself standing on the pavement without a voice raised against me.

I was completely disconcerted. It seemed that I had gained a hair-brush from France, of the finest quality but of no use to me whatsoever. I had no idea where I could sell such an item. I had never stolen anything other than food and money before, and certainly Mr Weekes was no longer in contention as a client for my ill-gotten goods. I walked on, and when I had gone a block or so I threw the brush into a gutter, under a culvert.

An hour later, after giving myself a severe talking-to, and thereby strengthening my resolve once more, I entered the premises of Mr Jonathan Usborne, Stationers to the Nobility, in South Street. There did not seem to be any nobles inside, just an old lady dressed in black, who had a Scottish accent so dense that it took me some moments to realise that she was speaking in my native tongue – more or less.

She was not of course talking to me but to a shop assistant, a middle-aged man who, I was disappointed to note, appeared to be the only person behind the counter. I went and stood just along from the old lady, inspecting the pens. When the assistant went out to the storeroom to fetch a quarter-pint bottle of ink, I boldly picked up a fountain pen worth four shillings and dropped it into my pocket. I then looked along at the lady. She had observed me all right. Her eyes widened and she opened her mouth, to call, I was sure, for the assistant. I steeled myself for the ordeal that awaited. The lady came close to me and touched me on the elbow. 'You poor wee lad,' she said, pronouncing 'poor' as 'purr' and 'lad' as 'lud'. 'I ken how it is with ye. I saw ye take the pen. I ken how hard it is fer ye wee bairns without a place to be resting yer head, nae doot. Be putting the pen back nae, and take this instead, and try not to give in to temptation. Be putting your trust in the Lord Jesus, for He is the Great Redeemer for our sins.'

She pressed a whole shilling into my hand. I was so ashamed that I blushed and blushed, and mumbled, 'Thank you, ma'am. I'm sorry, ma'am,' replaced the pen on the counter and left the shop as quickly as my feet could carry me.

Disheartened by my failures, I did not make my third attempt until early the next morning. This time I went to a grog shop right across the road from the Old Bailey. I thought I would save them the trouble of carting me any great distance to court. I took a bottle of gin, hid it inside my shirt in such a way that the neck was sticking out and made my departure. Not a cry could be heard as I left; not a voice was raised in protest. I stood out the front of the shop wondering if I should throw the bottle straight through their fancy window.

I disposed of the gin for fourpence to an old woman selling flowers on the corner, then wandered down Spensley Street to the Billingsgate fish markets. I loved this place. The smell was strong, too strong for some. I remembered coming here with the Ferret once, and him being sick when the smells overwhelmed him, and then being so embarrassed afterwards that he denied it had ever happened, threatening me with dire consequences should I ever hint at his weakness to anyone.

The smells didn't bother me overly. Not as much as the butchers outside the Tower of London. What I liked at Billingsgate was the beautiful fish laid out on their platters, in all their different shapes and sizes and colours. Already much of the day's supply had been sold, but there was still plenty enough left to interest a boy like me. I didn't know the names of most, but it was a marvellous thing to see the array of creatures that lived in God's ocean. You could understand God saying to Job about how great He was to create the wonders in the world when you saw how many varieties there were and how every type of fish differed from every other type. Some were as long as Quentin was tall, and lay there shimmering, their eyes so bright they could have still been alive. Others, the sardines for instance, were not much bigger than my middle finger, and their eyes merely black dots, but no doubt they could see out of them just the same. It was a marvellous sight to behold, and marvellous to think about. The other thing was how smooth they were. You could tell by looking at them that they would have sped through the water like a swallow through air. There was nothing to slow them down.

And the crabs! Still alive, tied up, but their legs quietly seething, keeping in practice mayhap. They were so monstrous looking, and what you might call ancient. And the claws! I shuddered to look at them. Quentin and I used to grab each other in fear at the sight of them and try to outdo each other in finding the biggest crab there. We'd speculate on how you'd get the bugger off if it sunk its claws into you. Just being stupid, the way boys can be, but you wouldn't have caught me going near one of them. Not within cooee, as they say in this country.

We'd go to see the lobsters too, but for some reason the men who sold them were a snarly bunch, foul-tempered the lot of them, as savage as the beasts they sold. They'd chase us off as soon as look at us. The only time we could get a real look was when they had lots of customers and were too busy to be bothered with the likes of us.

I wandered down in the direction of the lobsters, stopping to look at a couple of squid on the way. They were the most evil creatures I ever did see, although eels weren't much better. I didn't understand how squid could swim, but maybe they just skulked around on the ocean floor. I knew I wouldn't want one of them latching on to my arm. Mostly the squid appeared at the fish market during Lent. Christian folk could eat them then, because they have no blood, or so people say.

I was approximately halfway through the market when I heard a bit of commotion behind me. I stopped and looked around. You could see a surge through the crowd, like the waves a big boat makes when it's on its way down the Thames. The waves go rolling to the left and to the right, and if they're too big you'd best get out of the way. Suddenly the surge parted though, and there right in front of me was its cause: a boy a little younger than me, a desperate look on his face, going like the clappers, and somewhere behind him half-a-dozen people in pursuit. Then I heard the cry that was all too familiar in my part of London: 'Stop! Thief!'

At the same moment the boy flung something away from him. It landed almost at my feet, and looking down I saw it was a purse. He swerved to the right and, running like a whippet, went into the little lane opposite the sign for St Jude's Church. He ran three steps then dove into the pile of rubbish that's always there and burrowed down into it so that in an instant he was lost to sight.

I was dumbfounded but I didn't hesitate. Only a couple of people had seen what had happened, and if they were like the general run of Londoners there was a good chance they wouldn't involve themselves in other people's affairs. I bent down, grabbed the purse and hightailed it down the street, making myself the target of the chase. I ran through the lobster area, but not at full speed. I was anxious to be caught. The cry of 'Stop! Thief!' ran out again, and all of a sudden a big burly man with forearms bigger around than my waist stepped into my path. I couldn't help myself, couldn't stop in time. I cannoned into him. He was that solid I went sprawling backwards onto the ground, banging the back of my head.

He picked me up like I was a fish and held me at arm's length. The chasers arrived a moment later, panting, shouting, and crowding around me. A fat little man, puffing as though his lungs were fit to burst, plucked the purse out of my shaking hand and cuffed me across the head. To my surprise the man who had grabbed me, one of the bad-tempered lobster sellers, said: 'Don't ill-use the lad. He's in enough trouble already.'

The fat man just growled, stepped backwards and opened the purse to check the contents. I looked hard, trying to see how much money was in there. To my relief I could see only a few coins.

Just a couple of minutes later two Bow-Street Runners arrived. Immediately the owner of the purse became animated, waving his arms and shouting in indignation at the outrage I had perpetrated upon him. He spoke in bursts, leaving out all the unimportant words. 'Money for ribbons ... my daughter's birthday ... four shillings ... mongrels ... scourge on the streets ... they'd stick you with a knife as soon as pick your pocket ...' And then to me: 'Where's my watch, you little piece of filth?'

Watch? I hadn't seen a watch. Maybe the boy still had it, or maybe he'd thrown it away earlier in the chase and someone else had picked it up, or maybe it was lying in a gutter somewhere.

'I never touched your watch,' I said with as much fury as I could muster. I knew I needed to talk down the value of his losses, because four shillings and a watch added up to a picture of the gallows looming over me. He hit me again. I cowered away, but the lobster seller told him: 'Don't hit him again or I'll give you a thump that'll take you into next week.'

'That's right,' one of the Redbreasts said; then, to the fat gentleman: 'Now, sir, what's the value of your losses to this wretch?'

'Told you already . . . Four shillings in my purse . . . watch, gold, paid forty guineas . . . just last December.'

'Forty guineas,' the Runner said, and there were whistles from the crowd, and much respectful muttering at the thought of a watch worth such a sum.

'We'll take him along,' the other Runner said. 'You'll be coming with us, sir? Without you, there'll be no prosecution.'

'Of course, of course,' the man said, huffing and puffing with excitement. And so I was led away.

Chapter 17

THE IRONY OF THE situation was not lost on me. If I had somehow obtained the watch as well as the purse, and if I had run a little faster, I would have had a substantial deposit on the money I needed to repay Mr Weekes. Say I fenced the watch for fifteen pounds, that, combined with the coins still remaining from selling the counterfeit banknotes would have at least bought me time. I felt the grim satisfaction of knowing that my understanding of the mysterious workings of the Creator was being borne out by my experiences. The capricious way in which God had dealt with Job was being reflected in my life yet again.

In the magistrates' court I found myself facing the fat gentleman familiar from my previous visit, Sir Bennett Cousins. I had no difficulty remembering the character given him by the three arsonists with whom I had shared a cell. Their assessment seemed by way of being fair, if a trifle generous to the honourable gentleman. 'Everyone is guilty as far as he's concerned,' they had said.

His first words in my case were to the Bow-Street Runners: 'Well, what's this young reprobate done? He looks a bad 'un and no mistake.'

I had no answer to the charges, except to say that I had never seen or touched the watch. Sir Bennett Cousins wasted no time in committing me to trial, mentioning in passing that he trusted the Lord would spare him long enough to grant him the pleasure of seeing me hanging from the gibbet outside Newgate.

I awaited the next stage of the process with trepidation, not knowing to which prison I would be transferred after the magistrate's hearing. I made the grim discovery soon enough, and by the end of the day found myself entering through the gates of the infamous Newgate Prison.

I suppose it is public knowledge that those who can afford it can live moderately well in His Majesty's Prisons of the United Kingdom. Indeed, there are those who take themselves in and out of prison as though it were a convenient hotel: those blackguards, for example, who have their debts discharged by going into prison as bankrupts and emerging with a smile to begin a new round of swindles. For the rest of us however, all prisons are places of horror and degradation, and in this respect Newgate is outstanding.

The keeper did not waste his time asking me if I had any money for the master's side. He took one look at me and assigned me to the commons. He didn't even bother to ask for garnish, and as for taking my clothes in lieu, as he was entitled to do, I'm afraid he showed scant respect for my garb by ignoring the potential of that penalty too.

I do not know the current conditions at Newgate, except from hearsay, for I understand it has been much modified again since my residency came to its end. I can only say that far from being altered it should have been burned down and the ruins buried forever. Its very existence is a blight on the name of British justice, and I say that as a loyal subject of the Crown, and an Englishman.

The commons occupied thirteen rooms, and I was taken to the westernmost one, shackled by my kindly keeper, and left to my own devices. The room held, on the day I entered it, some thirty souls in different degrees of torment, from the madman walking around in strange patterns comprehensible only to himself, to the young curate awaiting trial for stabbing three inmates of the workhouse to death because he believed they were possessed by Satan; from the mother nursing a baby which looked shrunken and grey and prematurely aged, to the old deaf woman accused by her neighbour of having stolen two cloaks and a petticoat, and who sat against the wall sobbing piteously. If justice had a heart, that heart would be broken by the sight of that old lady, if it had not already been shattered by the imprisonment in the penitentiary of the innocent babe, and the inconsolable weeping of its mother who could find no milk to give the child, but who said justice has a heart? Ask Job if God's justice had a heart. Why should Man attempt to do any more than emulate his Maker and Master? Would it not be blasphemy for him to aspire to a higher standard than He who made us?

I hoped that I could scuttle into a corner and stay there until my trial, unnoticed and inconspicuous. No doubt many entered the commons at Newgate with a similar ambition. However, mixed in with the innocent and the pure of heart (who, it may surprise the public to know, can surely be found there) are the evil and corrupt, the wicked and intransigent. And there is a power possessed by such as them which is unknown to others. The wild animal dominates the tame. The wolf is stronger than the dog, the lion than the lamb. The savagery that runs in their veins seems to give them a special ferocity.

The commons was governed by a fearful man known to all and sundry as Lord Blood. He seemed to relish the name. As the discerning reader might well surmise, he was no lord according to the British nobility, and his family tree is unlikely to be found in Mr Amon's *The New Peerage*, but in his commanding manner and ruthless domination of his little estate in Newgate he was a lord indeed. He swaggered around as though the place had been in the title of his family since William the Conqueror. He had been arrested for armed robbery and manslaughter, and surely the gallows awaited him, but somehow he had been able to put off his dreaded appointment for a long time, for when I arrived in Newgate he had spent seven months there already and was not even brought to trial yet.

He noticed me within ten minutes of my arrival. He came towards me with a look that I can only call ravenous. He was dressed like a dandy, but like most of us in there was shackled. Unlike us others however he wore his shackles as though they were pieces of jewellery, and he moved as quickly as anyone in the place. I stood as he approached, for there was something so menacing about him that I did not dare remain huddled in my corner. He wasted no time with words but grabbed me under the armpits and lifted me so that our faces were at a level. His eyes were bloodshot and wild; even in my terror I wondered if he were some sort of looking glass, and I was seeing the reflection of the man I would become if I stayed in this place long enough. He smelled of beer, which I soon became aware was easily purchased by prisoners from passers-by, through the grilles in the wall. Leering at me, he said: 'You're a juicy piece of meat now. How would you like to be gutted and bled and baked over that fire over there?'

'I . . . I wouldn't like it at all, sir,' I stammered.

'Well if I gets hungry enough, that's what I do, see?'

'Then I very much hope you won't get hungry, sir,' was all I could think to say. As he continued to scrutinise me, without speaking again,

I thought that he must expect something more, so I added: 'I . . . don't have any food to give you, sir . . . but if I get some, I'll certainly share it with you . . .'

It was the wrong thing to say, for he flung me across the room, where I collided with a gangling sort of young man who had his back to me. 'Watch what you're about,' he growled, pushing me from him with a curse. I landed on the hearth in front of the fire; indeed, I had to jerk myself quickly in the opposite direction to avoid rolling into the coals. I began to perceive that I was in danger of being used as some sort of ball. I crawled away from the fireplace, dazed and sore, looking for refuge in the shadows, as injured animals do.

Then Lord Blood was on me again. He crouched over me and pulled me by my hair up to a sitting position. 'You can expect me tonight,' he said, his wild eyes staring at me. 'I always taste the new meat in here. You understand?'

'Yes, sir,' I said, although I was not sure that I did.

'Then be ready,' he said, slamming me with all his strength into the wall.

Luckily I was already close to the wall, so the damage was not as considerable as it might have been. Nonetheless my head, already sore from my fall in Billingsgate markets, now hurt even more, and the alcohol fumes he had breathed all over me made me nauseous. I lay there, feeling sick and frightened, and wishing that I had not embarked upon so perilous a path. It seemed that I had exchanged Mr Weekes for Lord Blood, and the bargain did not strike me as a particularly good one.

This suspicion was confirmed within just a couple of hours. As darkness crept through Newgate, stealing across the floor and up the walls, leaving nothing but the hellish glow of the coals to throw any light upon the miserable scene, I tried again to find a corner to nestle into, but was quickly made aware that at night-time corners were highly valued, and their occupants did not welcome company. So I found a spot against a wall and made myself as small as possible. All too soon, however, I heard the light rattle of shackles as Lord Blood sought me out.

In my brief life I had been exposed to a variety of vice, of course, but I understood little. I was like a stranger who moves through a large house in the middle of the night. All he sees of the contents of the house is whatever falls within the radius of his torch. He may see this armchair, and that coffee table, and in the flickering light he may get a glimpse of a vase and a coal scuttle, but he does not see the portraits on the wall or the candelabra or the sofa, and thus he has no knowledge of their existence. And consider, if this man is a savage from some primitive country where men know not houses or furnishings, what will he make of the contents of such a place? How will he comprehend their uses?

I still dwelled in that place of primitive innocence, so that although I had seen certain goings-on here, and other goings-on there, much more than was right for a boy my age, nonetheless the images I had were fragmented and incomplete, and my understanding was completely undeveloped.

However I understood pretty much what Lord Blood wanted from me; indeed, had I not when he first approached me I would have done so within a short time, for he was not ambiguous about his requirements. I did not understand the urgency that possessed him, but that was not a matter to which I paid particular attention. As he uncovered himself and made his demands, I looked to my right and then to my left in the hope of finding someone who might come to my aid, but quickly realised the futility of such a search. In the dim light it was clear that my neighbours were looking in every direction but towards me.

As he pressed himself upon me, nausea arose within me, but I complied as best I could. However, I was only shortly engaged with him when revulsion overtook me so completely that my stomach convulsed and I emptied its meagre contents down his front. This, I am pleased to say, had the effect of immediately quelling his ardour, but it also earned me a fearful beating while he berated me in rage for befouling his fine clothes.

As I lay in the darkness, sore and bleeding, I came to an awareness of my folly in imagining that I might be better off here than in Hell. Truly had I left a cesspool for a cesspit. There would be no sanctuary in the commons of Newgate. I fell asleep against the wall, to the occasional thin wails of the baby I had observed upon first entering the place, and awoke in the morning to find that it was dead.

Chapter 18

I T IS A GREAT CONVENIENCE of the judicial system that Newgate Prison and the Old Bailey, the latter known by the name Justice Hall, though it does not always merit such a title, are neighbours. They exist side by side, and we can assume that they are on the friendliest of terms, for there is frequent intercourse between them, and they each seek to serve the other.

At some stage an official of the Old Bailey informed me that the grand jury had approved a true bill in my case, which apparently signified that my trial was imminent. I intended to plead guilty and throw myself on the mercy of the court, as it seemed unutterably foolish to contemplate any other course. I clung to the hope that I would avoid the gallows and be transported. I held true to a vision of the colony of New South Wales as a kind of paradise that would restore me to a life of peace and content-ment, such as I fondly imagined I might have experienced in my infancy.

During my time in Newgate I received only one piece of helpful advice, which came from a man with the unusual name of Carmichael Lance. He had all the appearance of a refined and scholarly gentleman, but he was rather a puzzle to me, because his presence in the commons indicated that he had no money. He had been convicted of forgery and sentenced to death, and so should have been in the condemned cells. However, crime in London was thriving to such a degree that the condemned cells were filled to overflowing, and the health of the residents was considered to be jeopardised by the unsanitary conditions. Naturally the authorities did not wish to endanger the lives of those about to be executed, and so in the interests of their own welfare, Carmichael and various others slated for the gallows were quartered with us.

I met Carmichael when for no accountable reason he offered me a share of a haunch bone of beef someone had brought in for him. I was exceedingly grateful, for most of the meals were deplorable and I had become very hungry; in fact I was dizzy and light-headed from lack of food. Every shred of that beef was delectable to me; I fancy I can still taste it now.

The next day Carmichael told me about his crime, to which he seemed indifferent. He was quite sanguine about his prospects, having petitioned the Bank of England for a discount on his sentence. He assured me that such petitions were frequently successful, and sure enough, three days after our conversation he was notified that the bank had agreed to commute his sentence from death to transportation for fourteen years, which he regarded as a good bargain.

When I told him that I was going to plead guilty he shook his head vigorously. 'No, no, no, my boy, that would be most ill-advised.'

'But why? I was caught with the purse in my hand, and although I have no knowledge of the watch, the judge won't believe that.'

'It has nothing whatsoever to do with whether you're innocent or guilty,' he replied firmly. He looked away from me, shaking his head, and spoke as if to an imaginary person located halfway up the wall. 'What a foolish boy it is.' He looked back at me with twinkling eyes. 'As if innocence or guilt has anything to do with justice. That may do for the provinces, lad, but not here. My dear Barnaby, you will find that at the Old Bailey even the judges encourage the most incorrigible felons to plead not guilty. The point is, cases need to go to the jury. When the trial is by jury the judge can listen to all the evidence, and the verdict, before he decides the sentence. Most judges don't want to put on the black cap if they can help it. It spoils their appetite for their victuals. Your judge will look for reasons to keep you away from the gallows, and if the jury can help him in that noble task, then so much the better for everyone.' I think he saw the shadow which passed over my face when he mentioned the word 'gallows', because he quickly added: 'I really think you can rest easy about a death sentence. The Great British Public has rather exhausted its fondness for executing children. The most likely outcome is that the jury will commit pious perjury, and the judge will be mightily relieved if they do.'

'Pious perjury?' I asked. 'What's that?'

'My dear Barnaby, what is an innocent like you doing in this den of iniquity? Do you know nothing of the workings of the judicial system? Pious perjury is the result of juries being as chary of capital punishment for minor offenders as are judges. Not infrequently a jury chokes on the idea that their verdict will mean death for a prisoner. And so they return a verdict which makes it impossible for the judge to order the gallows. In your case, they may well convict you of stealing an amount which is less than five shillings in value. This watch for example . . . how much does the man say it's worth?'

'Forty guineas.'

Carmichael raised his eyebrows. 'That much? Well, it would be easier for the jury if it were five guineas. But nonetheless, if they take a shine to you they will almost certainly do their best to find a way out of your difficulties.'

'But how can I get them to take a shine to me?' I asked.

Carmichael laughed. 'The more you try, the less likely you are to succeed. Be polite and respectful, but put the idea of pleasing them out of your head.' He laughed again. 'Mind you, I invariably treat juries with contempt, and judges too, and look where it's got me. I adopted a far more courteous tone in my petition to the bank. I was positively obsequious.'

He was the only adult in Newgate who was kind to me, and I was sorely disappointed when he was taken away the day following his remission. It seemed that a fleet was about to set sail for Botany Bay, and he had been assigned a place on one of the ships. He was well pleased by the news. 'I've bypassed the Hulks,' he told me. 'A very good thing to do. Too many men leave the Hulks feet first, and that's an uncomfortable prospect for one like myself, who by and large finds life an enjoyable business.'

Two days later I took my place in the Old Bailey dock. I went in with my heart in my boots. I was still but a slightly built lad, and the courtroom seemed almost infinitely vast to me. An immense gulf separated me from the judge, and although there were many chairs and tables between us, for clerks and lawyers I believe, few were occupied. The jury was to my right, seated in three rows, four men in each row. Beyond them, and stretching around behind me, were a dozen or so spectators. I despised them for their idleness, and their inquisitiveness, and wished they would be off about their business.

As I waited for the judge to enter, a series of loud coughs caught my attention. It sounded like a juvenile who was thus afflicted, but after a while the coughs became so irritating that I turned around. How great was my amazement when I saw none other than Quentin and the Ferret sitting proudly in the public gallery. They had not been there when I'd first looked. As soon as they caught my eye they grinned triumphantly, waved, and made gestures of optimism.

I have no idea how they found out the date of my trial, but I was greatly heartened by their presence. I motioned for them to go around to the gallery behind the jury, so that I could see them throughout the proceedings. Much did it cheer me during the ordeal of the hearing to be able to look at their familiar faces.

The judge entered. I was relieved to see that it was not Sir Bennett Cousins. In contrast, this was quite a small man, peering over the bench with sharp eyes and bobbing his head like a sparrow on a tree branch looking for an insect crawling through the grass below.

The trial began. When asked for a plea I whispered, 'Not guilty,' and was told sternly to repeat it so that all could hear. The owner of the purse and watch, a Mr Mullins, prosecuted the case against me, and in the same terse manner he had used at Billingsgate gave a short description of the theft and my subsequent arrest. He then called several bystanders as witnesses. It did not seem to occur to anyone to question my identity as the thief. I suppose to most members of the public one young ruffian dressed in rags looked much the same as another. I wondered fleetingly how the boy who actually took the items would feel if he could see me now. It had been his lucky day when he ran past me in the fish market.

I was invited to question the witnesses, but could not think of anything to put to them. When Mr Mullins finished presenting his case, the judge asked me if I wished to speak. Trying hard to raise my voice in the intimidating atmosphere, I said: 'If you please sir, I did take the money, but not the watch.'

It sounded feeble even to my ears, and I was greatly surprised when the judge seemed to write my words down and sit looking at them for some time. Then I suddenly thought of something else. Hesitantly I added: 'Sir, I did say to Mr Mullins when I was caught that I hadn't taken his watch. After all, if I did take it, I would still have had it, like I had the money.'

The judge turned to Mr Mullins and asked him: 'Did the prisoner tell you at the time of his arrest that he had not taken the watch?'

Mr Mullins looked sulky. 'Not sure . . . No memory of that,' he said.

I was annoyed, because I was sure he was lying.

The judge then surprised me even further when he recalled each of the witnesses and asked them if they had seen me with the watch. None had. Mr Mullins was looking increasingly indignant, and finally he rose to his feet and said to the judge: 'Sir, forty guinea watch . . . extraordinary coincidence . . . I lose watch just as boy purloins purse? Surely, sir . . .'

'Sit down, sir,' responded the judge, quite sharply. 'You have put your case, the jury has heard it, and they can make up their own minds.' I had the feeling that the judge had not 'taken a shine' to Mr Mullins. He looked now at the jury. 'It is time for me to sum up,' he said. 'You have heard the evidence regarding the purse. You have heard the words "I did take the money" from the prisoner's own lips. You may think it significant that he did not dispute the evidence of the witnesses that he stole the purse and its contents. You may well think that you need not waste much time arriving at your verdict on the charge as it relates to that.

'However, the situation regarding the watch is somewhat more difficult. Is it conceivable that the watch went missing from some other cause than theft by the prisoner at the bar? After all, things go missing all the time, from a variety of causes. It is not unknown for example,' and here he looked sternly at Mr Mullins, 'for a complainant to take advantage of a crime in order to make a claim on an insurance company for property that is in fact still in his possession.'

As Mr Mullins clambered to his feet, red-faced with indignation, the judge waved him back down and went on hastily. 'Of course there is no question of such an eventuality in this case and I mean no reflection on the honourable gentleman prosecuting the prisoner. Courts are indebted to members of the public who perform their civic duty in these cases, and thus help rein in the excessive degree of crime in this city. I merely make the point that there can be many explanations for complaints of missing property. Members of the jury, you have heard no specific evidence relating to the watch, other than Mr Mullins's statement that it is lost. You must ask yourself whether this is enough to justify a conviction upon this charge, bearing in mind that, given the value of the items in dispute, a verdict of guilty would require from me nothing less than the maximum sentence allowed by the law, that being a capital one. Nevertheless, if you feel that a verdict of guilty is justified, you must say so, without regard to the tender years of the defendant in the dock, and the consequences which may befall him. Now, if you have no further questions for me, I invite you to consider your verdict. You may retire if you feel it necessary, and if you wish to do so. Should that be the case, the usher will escort you to the room designated for the purpose.'

With that, we all rose, so that the judge could make his exit, a thing he was evidently incapable of doing whilst we remained seated. After he had gone, the jury filed out. It seemed that they did indeed need time to agree on my fate. I looked across at the Ferret and Quentin. They were gazing at me with rapt attention. Perhaps the seriousness of the situation, that they might be about to hear a sentence of death imposed upon their friend, had just dawned on them. Nevertheless, I felt heartened by the judge's summing-up. Naive as I was, and ignorant of the law, it seemed to me, after my conversation with Carmichael, that the judge was going as far as he could in inviting the jury to take the path of 'pious perjury'.

I was right, and Carmichael was right. After about fifteen minutes the jury returned, followed shortly afterwards by the judge. The foreman stood and announced the verdict. I was guilty of stealing the purse and its contents. The jury valued the contents of the purse at four shillings. Although there had been no evidence as to the value of the purse itself, the jury assessed it as being worth sixpence. Total: four shillings and sixpence. I was not guilty of stealing the watch. For the sake of sixpence the possibility of a death sentence was averted. I wondered briefly at a justice system which would take a life for a five shilling crime, but not for a crime valued at four shillings and eleven pence. It seemed that in the British legal system, a single penny could make the difference between life and death.

There was little time for such reflection, however. The judge had turned to face me and was addressing me. 'Prisoner at the bar,' he said. 'You have been found guilty, quite rightly, of a serious violation upon an innocent member of the public. The people of London are entitled to go about their business without having their pockets picked at every opportunity by idle ruffians such as I find you to be. There has been a notable increase in this type of offence lately, and it is timely to make an example of dissolute young persons such as yourself who come before the court. I am going to remove you from this kingdom, so that the citizens of London can be kept safe from your depredations. You are young; I abjure you most earnestly to reflect upon your misbegotten ways, and to resolve to tread the path of righteousness from this day forward. Given your youth, there is still time for you to repent and begin a new life. I will ensure that you have an ample period in which to do so. I hereby sentence you to seven years transportation to the colony of New South Wales.'

It was what I had wanted. Why, then, did I suddenly feel dizzy, and reel where I stood? Why did the faces of Quentin and the Ferret seem suddenly blurred and distant? Why did I have to clutch at the handrail of the dock to prevent myself falling? And why did my hands, reaching for the handrail, fail to achieve their objective, so that the next thing I knew was that I was lying on the floor of the dock whilst a man unknown to me sponged my face with a wet cloth?

I suppose that the enormity, the reality, of transportation had suddenly dawned upon me. As the result of a short conversation with an incoherent dying man late one night in a tavern, I had committed myself to an irrevocable course of action that would take me away from everything I had known to a completely alien land, and change my life forever.

Chapter 19

A LL I ACTUALLY KNEW of New South Wales could be summed up on the back of a postage stamp. The man at the tavern had spoken of the climate and of the vast tracts of land. I remembered hearing of strange hopping animals, and Captain Cook discovering the place but then being murdered by cannibals. And that was the full extent of my understanding.

When I was returned to Newgate I opened my ears more widely when I heard anyone talk of transportation, but it seemed that not many people knew more than I. As the man in the tavern had said, no one wanted to be sent there. They were all afeared of savages and cannibals and wild animals. The only things I found out were that Captain Cook had actually been murdered a long way from Botany Bay, and that the Indians in New South Wales wore no clothes and had killing weapons the like of which no one had ever seen before. This last fact made me feel even more agitated about the turn my life was about to take, and I believe I made myself quite ill with anxiety.

However, before I could even get to New South Wales and ascertain for myself if the stories were true, I had first to survive Newgate.

Between the food and the water, both of which were foul, and the keepers and the other prisoners, both of which groups were savage enough to compete with the headhunters of the Pacific, I knew I would be lucky to make it out of the place alive. If I was not made ill by anxiety, I was certainly made ill by the conditions. The food was often rotten, and even when it was not, there was never enough of it. For breakfast, we were supposed to get one pint of oatmeal gruel and six ounces of bread a day. For dinner, on Sundays and Thursdays, one pint of soup and eight ounces of bread. On Tuesdays and Saturdays, three ounces of cooked meat without bone, eight ounces of bread, and half a pound of potatoes. On the remaining three days, eight ounces of bread, and a full pound of potatoes. Supper was the same as breakfast: oatmeal gruel and bread.

The old lags, of whom there were many in Newgate, knew these weights and measures exactly, and seemed to know within a fraction of an ounce when there was any shortfall, and most loudly and bitterly did they complain at any depredations to their rations. Their cries of protest and their incessant grizzling appeared to achieve no amelioration of our conditions, but perhaps they made the keepers hesitate before plundering us of our entitlements.

Even when we received full measure I went to bed hungry, but that was no surprise, as I spent the days hungry as well. No one as kind as Carmichael, who had shared his haunch bone of beef with me, had happened along again. Occasionally if a prisoner was sick, he might give me some of his rations, and I am ashamed to say that there were times when I wished a man suffering ill health would suffer more, so that his appetite might desert him. But I myself was sick many times, and forced to give my food away in consequence of being unable to swallow.

At an early point during my stay in the commons I became aware that Lord Blood was mortally afraid of catching prison fever, so I began to feign the symptoms of illness whenever there seemed danger of his paying too much attention to me. Since that first night he had, however, been somewhat less enamoured of me than might otherwise have been the case.

There were two other circumstances which aided me in avoiding him. For one thing, during the day we were free to go pretty much anywhere within the prison, even among those on the master's side; hence it was easier to keep away from Lord Blood. Secondly, a boy about my age, but prettier than I, and dainty in his ways, was admitted to the same westernmost room, and this boy, who went by the name of Joshua, became an object of greater interest than I to His Lordship. There were times when I could hear them at night, and I lay shuddering in the darkness listening to Joshua's cries but unable to do anything to assist him.

Not long after Carmichael left, I experienced a night in Newgate which was made memorable by an unexpected resolution to the fearful reign of Lord Blood. Early in the evening, shortly after darkness fell, I heard him at Joshua again. Then he finished, and I heard him move away, to his habitual place near the fire. I believe I dozed after that, perhaps for some hours. Sometimes, when things were very quiet, I could hear the doleful sound of a distant church bell tolling the passing hours, and on this occasion I heard it strike midnight. Not very many minutes later I saw a small shadow pass in front of the fire, and then heard a grunting cry from Lord Blood. I had heard such sounds from him before, when in the throes of his nefarious night-time activities, so I blocked my ears and tried not to listen.

I was woken in the morning by the clamour of agitated voices from the fireplace end of the room. As I awoke, four keepers burst in through the door. The crowded room parted for them, and they made their way to Lord Blood's palliasse. Then I saw the proof that his name had been well chosen indeed. A thick river of blood, running through the middle of the cell much as the Thames runs through London, represented the brutal end to His Lordship's life. I had never seen so much blood; indeed I had no comprehension that so much blood could be contained within one human body. No wonder the body, recumbent upon the palliasse, was as white as marble.

As I drew nearer, compelled by the awful sight, I could see the handle of a knife protruding from his chest, with His Lordship's hand resting upon it. It appeared then that he had killed himself. What strength of mind must it take to drive a dagger so fiercely into one's own heart? I shrank away, appalled, and went back to my own resting place. I could not pretend to be sorry that Lord Blood's reign had ended, but the terrible sight made me, in my weakened condition, frightened and shaky.

I lay for a while on the ground, in my accustomed place, watching the keepers come and go, seeing them stop for frequent whispered consultations. I saw them constantly looking around the room, and I heard the word 'murder' mentioned more than once. From time to time they called various prisoners to speak to them, but I could see that they met with nothing but stubborn silences. Newgate was a place where anyone who wished to survive was well advised to practise discretion when speaking to the turnkeys.

We had not yet been allowed out for our morning ablutions, due no doubt to the unusual circumstance, and I was feeling thirsty and restless. I had been keeping an eye on Joshua, because I was curious to see his reaction to the death of his tormentor. He had not moved in all that time, but he was watching the scene through hooded eyes. I began to become aware that there was something unusual about the way he was sitting. His right arm was tucked inside his tattered shirt, as though he were hiding something.

It occurred to me suddenly that his hand might need to be washed.

I went over to him, as casually as I could. He watched my approach warily. I sat down beside him, but did not speak for some minutes. When I had ascertained that no one appeared to be taking any notice of us, I said to him: 'You know, if I bring the piss bucket over here, you could wash your hand in that.'

He started with sudden fear. His eyes widened but he did not say anything. I added: 'That is, if your hand needs washing.'

Many moments passed. Then he gave one tiny nod, and that was enough for me. I went and got the bucket, heavy as it was, and lugged it across to him. He watched me every inch of the way, his wide eyes terrified. It wasn't unknown for one prisoner to fetch the bucket to another who was bedridden, as an act of kindness. In all honesty, though, I have to add that it was more common for prisoners who were bedridden to foul themselves.

I positioned the bucket between Joshua and the wall, so that he could turn his back on the rest of the room. He plunged his hand in, as quickly as possible, but not so quickly that I could not see the dried blood all over it. 'The other hand too,' I whispered. 'You'll have to scrub.'

He did as I said, though with an expression of repugnance. He may have looked frail, but he had some spirit, firstly to do what he had done in the middle of the night, and secondly to immerse his hands in the foul-smelling liquid. Soon enough he was able to withdraw them, and I saw with relief that the evidence linking him with Lord Blood was almost gone.

'Give me your fingers,' I said, and he obliged. His hand felt soft and delicate. I did not know his background, but it was surely different to mine. With my own fingernails I picked around his nails, removing the traces of dried blood that still lingered in the crevices.

As a result of this transaction Joshua formed an attachment to me, and during the remainder of my time in Newgate we were inseparable. He was being prosecuted on a charge of passing counterfeit notes. I felt cold when he told me this, as I well knew it was a crime for which I too could have been charged, and which generally attracted a capital sentence. He struck me as a most unlikely criminal, and this was confirmed when he told me that his father, who was a gentleman, had commissioned him to take the notes to various merchants, buy small items and bring back the change. Taken into custody by the Bow-Street Runners, Joshua was escorted back to his father's home, but in the street, a hundred yards from the house, they passed his father, who was hurrying away, evidently having seen the Redbreasts approaching. He accorded no sign of recognition to his son, and his son, taking the hint, returned no recognition to the father. Thus was the father enabled to escape and thus the son ended up in Newgate Prison.

I thought this was infamous conduct indeed, and I expressed myself in no uncertain terms to Joshua about it. But he defended his father and had faith that eventually all would be made well. I was by no means so sanguine about his prospects, but knowing so little of family life I dropped my objections to his father's conduct, thinking that this kind of behaviour was perhaps the way of the world.

We never discussed Joshua's assassination of Lord Blood, but I let him know in numerous small ways that I approved of his action, despite the high risk it had involved. There was much talk about the unlikelihood of it having been a suicide, but it was no doubt convenient for the prison authorities to characterise it as such, and so the matter was soon dropped. Within a couple of days the name of Lord Blood was no longer mentioned and it was as though his existence had already been forgotten. *Tempus fugit!* How brief is the life of man, and yet the marks Lord Blood had left upon Joshua and me were not easily erased.

Chapter 20

LATE ONE AFTERNOON AN apparition appeared before me; a figure so unlikely that I thought I must have begun the process of going mad and was having delusions. A person was standing by the well in the central courtyard, looking about him. I glanced up with little interest from my cold hard resting place against a brick wall. Visitors to Newgate were frequent during the day; at times it seemed as busy as a London street. Many were disreputable indeed, and were there for reasons that did not bear close examination. I spent much time averting my eyes.

On this occasion I can scarce describe my astonishment when my eyes lit upon the Revd Mr Haddock, the big young clergyman from St Martin's, standing there with his familiar black bag. He was gazing around as though in wonder at the depraved surroundings in which he found himself.

I stood, hoping that this was no manifestation of madness. Revd Mr Haddock's eyes lit upon me, and he at once gave every indication of pleasure and satisfaction. He came straight to me, arms outstretched, and took both my hands in his. I stared up at him, having to accept that he was real, but having no idea what his appearance in this place could portend.

'Well my young friend,' he said in a voice that was very familiar to me. 'We meet officially at last.'

I found myself unable to speak. He smiled and continued: 'I believe your name is Barnaby?'

I nodded. 'How do you know that?' I asked.

He smiled again. 'Sometimes we see more than you imagine.'

I did not know what else to say to him. I still had no idea why he would be in such a dreadful place. A keeper approached, with a chair, which the reverend gentleman accepted. Obviously his clerical collar commanded respect, even in Newgate.

My visitor sat down and crossed his legs. 'I suppose you are wondering why I am here,' he said.

'Yes,' I croaked.

'I found your young friend with the birthmark, Quentin, in a distressed state in the church yesterday morning. He informed me of your whereabouts. And told me of your fate.'

He reached out and took my hands. 'Transportation,' he said quietly.

'Yes,' I said again.

He nodded. 'Our Lord said, "Come unto me all ye that labour and are heavy-laden, and I will give thee rest." You have been heavily laden these short years of your life. I have been praying for you for some time . . .'

'You have?' I said in astonishment.

He nodded. 'And will continue to do so.'

'I didn't think you knew anything about me,' I said. 'I didn't think you knew of my existence.'

It was his turn to look surprised. 'Why did you think I put food out for you all that time? When I could, that is.'

It took me a moment to process his words. 'Do you mean you left that food deliberately? For me?'

'Of course.'

'Thank you,' I said shyly. I was somewhat disconcerted. I had been so sure that I was moving about the church like a little mouse, skilfully avoiding detection. Now it appeared that I had not been so clever after all.

Revd Mr Haddock reached into his bag. He took out a parcel and handed it to me. I unwrapped it, and felt faint when I saw the contents. The only time I had ever held such a quantity of food in my life was when the woman in the house with the fire gave me the half-chicken and the bread and biscuits. Revd Mr Haddock had brought me a slab of cheese that must have weighed a pound, a full loaf of bread, half-a-dozen baked potatoes, a meat pie, a slab of bacon, several carrots and a handful of beans. I was speechless. I could not imagine how one person could eat such a quantity, unless he took a week about it.

I had formed the impression over the years that Revd Mr Haddock was not possessed of independent means, so I was sure he must have expended a considerable proportion of his stipend on these provisions.

'Thank you, sir,' I said warmly.

'I will wait here while you eat,' he said. 'I am not unaware of the indignities perpetrated in these places. Indeed, I only have to look around to see what manner of people are here. I can well imagine that the food might attract unwelcome attention were I to leave you alone with it.'

I was grateful for his understanding. 'Sir, would you be offended if I fetched a friend to share it?' I asked. 'There is too much here for one person; indeed it is a feast for a dozen. And there is a boy about my age who is very thin and needy.'

He nodded. 'Of course. I will wait here while you get him.' He smiled grimly. 'I will stand guard on the food.'

And thus it was that Joshua and I shared the finest and most welcome meal of my life to that date. Truly is it said that hunger makes the best sauce. I formed the impression that Joshua was more accustomed to good food than I, but judging from his ejaculations of delight he had not eaten well for a considerable time. As we ate, Revd Mr Haddock preached to us of the love and forbearance of the Lord, and the hope of paradise that He offers to all who turn to Him, or, as the disciple puts it, 'that whosoever believeth in Him should not perish, but have eternal life'. In a gentle voice Revd Mr Haddock quoth to us the words of St John: 'He that doeth truth cometh to the light, that his deeds may be made manifest, that they are wrought in God.'

After he had gone I resolved to do all I could to be truthful, to lead a better life, and to repent me of my sins, in the hope of life everlasting, and that resolve has never left me, despite my many lapses since.

Looking back on my first twelve years I could not say that I had often experienced kindness, but perhaps I had sometimes been its beneficiary without realising it, as had evidently been the case when I was sheltering in St Martin's and supping on the food left by the young clergyman. The reverend gentleman's visit to Newgate represented, however, the apogee of kindness in my life thus far.

Equally I could say luck had not often been on my side, yet just a week after Revd Mr Haddock's visit I was favoured by Lady Luck too, when I was informed that, like Carmichael before me, I would bypass the Hulks and go straight to one of His Majesty's ships which was on the point of departure for New South Wales.

I received the news with some relief, because despite the luxury of the meal brought us by the Revd Mr Haddock I was so wasted away and debilitated by conditions in Newgate that I doubted I should last much longer. The reverend gentleman was quite right in his forecast of the probable fate of the food once he left the prison, for more than half of what remained from our feast was taken from me by violence, threats, stealth and deceitful inducements.

Given the deterioration in my health, and mindful of the terrible stories about the Hulks, and the death rates of the convicts aboard them, I was well aware that my chances of survival would not have been enhanced by any time spent in those floating coffins.

I parted from Joshua with much sadness. It seemed that my life was punctuated by separations. I had lost my parents at an early age, it seemed likely that I would never see Quentin in this world again, and now I had to say farewell to Joshua. He clung to me with much affection, and there were tears between us, but soon enough I was torn away and marched to the tumbrel which was to take me to Portsmouth Royal Harbour.

My only previous experience on water was in the boat belonging to Silas Piggott, as he and Thomas and I rowed up and down the Thames. I had never seen a harbour as fine as Portsmouth. It fair took my breath away, to look out over so much water, and the pretty houses of the town. We rolled in to the harbour area through a fine-looking gateway, under a wrought-iron arch, and on past the ropehouse and the great storehouses where the Navy kept everything from candles to anchors. We got a commentary as we went along, from one of our number who had grown up in Portsmouth, and though he was in all likelihood doomed never to see the place again, he boasted about its splendours as though he had built most of it himself.

He showed us where they had hung a man called Jack the Painter, not so long ago, in 1777. There was considerable interest among our number at this information. I had never heard of Jack the Painter, but I was alone in that regard. It seemed that he had been on the side of the Yankees in their infamous war against us, and he had led a campaign to burn down naval buildings, including the Portsmouth ropehouse. Our guide showed us where they had hung him, just inside the big gateway. They did it off a ship's mast that they put up especially for the occasion. Sixty feet high, the highest gallows ever erected in England! Twenty thousand people were on hand to watch him swing.

'My word, they did him proud then,' said one old lag upon receipt of this intelligence.

'Yes indeed, that's what I call a send-off,' said another.

'It'd be worth getting hung, for a crowd like that,' cackled the oldest among us.

I include this exchange in case the reader should be in any doubt as to the character of the old reprobates who were on their way out of the country. I am sorry to say they were as hardened a lot of villains as could be found in the length and breadth of England.

We came to the harbour, with an array of vessels the like of which I had never seen before. Our party fell silent as we passed the Hulks, for they had Hulks in Portsmouth too, and most of our number had come straight from the ones in London. Their talk of their experiences was bitter indeed, and I again gave thanks that I had not been consigned to one of these floating houses of misery.

The vessel to which we were assigned for our voyage to the other side of the world was the *Admiral Barrington*. They put down a ramp so we could walk straight off the back of the tumbrel. We would have had some difficulty otherwise, for every man jack of us was shackled with an iron collar and an iron chain run through a ring in each collar, which fastened us all together.

We were lined up along the wharf so that those who wanted to piss, which was pretty much everyone, could do so, straight into the water. 'That's a good way to say goodbye to this cursed country,' said the man next to me as he did up his flies.

Then up another ramp we went, and on board. A few sailors lounged on the deck, watching us, making derisory comments, as a file of soldiers belonging to a regiment called the New South Wales Corps supervised the loading. The soldiers, unlike their maritime counterparts, looked extremely vigilant; according to some of my fellow convicts there had been mutinies, successful and unsuccessful, on transport ships in the past, so they were alert for the slightest sign of trouble.

Three men stood at the top of the ramp to check us off as we boarded. Our neck collars were replaced by leg shackles, which I found heavy and uncomfortable. I had to adjust my gait to accommodate them, but if truth be told, I preferred them to the neck collars.

We passed along the deck, where we were issued with supplies for the trip. We each received two sets of clothing, on which were written a number, which in my case was 227, a number which I will never forget to my dying day, as it was to represent my identity in the months to come. One set of clothing was further labelled with the letter A and the other with the letter B, to signify which set was to be worn in alternating weeks. We were to begin with the set marked A. The clothing consisted of two blue jackets, two pairs of trousers, two shirts, two pairs of stockings, and a cap. Those who already had clothes that were in a decent state of repair were allowed to keep them, but I was not in such a fortunate position. We also received a pair of shoes, a blanket, a pillow, a large round mess tin, and a tin knife, fork and spoon, as well as a biscuit for lunch.

The soldiers subsequently assembled us in an area on the main deck, where after a short interval the captain of the *Admiral Barrington* appeared, to address us. He cut a fine figure in his uniform and I immediately formed a boyish wish to be like him, to be able to dress in such finery and guide the ship through storms and shoals and pirate attacks, and to have every man on board jump to attention as I passed. Not a realistic ambition, I fear, for one who had proved himself to be nothing but a delinquent and reprobate. Still, even the worst of us have dreams of goodness and glory, both temporal and spiritual, and I was no exception.

Master Robert Marsh had another advantage over me: he was evidently a gentleman; he spoke in a most refined manner, saying that he had no desire other than to get us to Botany Bay in the shortest time and in the most humane manner possible. He said that if we conducted ourselves with decency and decorum we should reap the benefits; for one thing he would strike the irons off those who demonstrated that they merited it, and as soon as possible. A murmur of approval ran through our group at these words. He also told us that divine service would be read every Sunday, an announcement that I must say was met with general indifference, especially compared to the news about the irons.

'But know you this,' Master Marsh went on to say, raising his voice, 'I give you my word that any man who stirs up trouble or makes himself disagreeable will be flogged at the yardarm here, or worse if it be deserved. Be in no doubt about the discipline on this vessel; my officers and I run matters on board the *Admiral Barrington* with precision and exactitude.'

He then yielded his position to a certain Peter Gossam, whom Master Marsh introduced to us as the surgeon superintendent appointed for the voyage. Surgeon Gossam spoke briefly and to the point, telling us to keep ourselves and our quarters clean, to have no truck with vice, and to refrain from gambling. He said that after we had been at sea three weeks we would be administered an ounce of lime juice and an ounce of sugar daily, for the prevention of scurvy, as well as three quarts of water daily, and three gills of good Spanish red wine a week. He said the rations were adequate and of decent quality, and that there would be a daily sick parade for those who required his services. 'I will take good care of any who fall ill,' he promised. 'But I will have no patience with malingerers. I believe that at the conclusion of this voyage you will be able to say that you have little to complain of.'

'You just watch us,' muttered the man to my left.

Then we were sent below decks. There was, I think, a sense of anxious anticipation, as every man, upon reaching the bottom of the ladder, strained to peer into the darkness to see the accommodation he would be occupying for the next uncountable months. I was of course no exception, but I could see little at first, after the bright light of the sun beating down on Portsmouth Harbour. I had to grope my way along a narrow thoroughfare whilst a soldier yelled at me to 'get a bloody move on'.

The place felt absolutely stifling. It was hot and airless, and smelled of rancid urine, of feet and armpits, of farts and faeces, to name but a few of the odours my delicate senses could distinguish. After Newgate I was somewhat more inured to such a stench than I might have been previously, but I still struggled with the revulsion that manifested itself in my stomach. I am almost ashamed to say that within a couple of days I no longer noticed the smell below decks, except when we had been up above, in the open, experiencing fresh air, and subsequently had to return to the accommodation kindly provided for us by His Majesty.

We, the newest and last group of convicts to be boarded for the trip, were allocated the rear of the vessel, the stern, which was at least illuminated by three candles, enabling me to see our quarters reasonably clearly.

A soldier looked at the number 227 on the clothes I had been issued, then pushed me towards a hammock with the corresponding number painted on it. 'And if you foul it you'll sleep in your filth for the rest of the voyage,' he added.

I should perhaps pause for a moment to say something of these soldiers of the New South Wales Corps. The old lags on board the ship, many of whom had known no other life than one of crime, seemed to know more about courts, sentencing, prisons, transportation and the like than the Home Secretary, the Attorney General, and the Lord Chief Justice combined. According to them, the Corps which now had charge of us was formed by a man named Major Grose, who held to the principle that the best candidates for the positions of supervising convicts were convicts themselves. Acting on that principle he collected as dissolute a mob of riffraff as could be found outside the walls of Newgate. As well as ex-convicts they included soldiers from other regiments who had committed felonies or misdemeanours sufficient to have them imprisoned in the Navy Hulk, and soldiers who had been ordered to India and would take any assignment in preference to that dreaded fever-hole.

Of course I had none of this information as we boarded the *Admiral Barrington*, but it was apparent from the start that the manner adopted by the soldiers was at odds with that exemplified by Master Marsh and Surgeon Gossam.

That was of no great concern to me during my first hours on board. There was too much to look at, to learn, to try to understand. I placed my few meagre possessions, so recently issued, under the hammock, as everyone else seemed to be doing, then – not without some difficulty – climbed into its embrace. It swayed a little but I found it quite comfortable. Within a few days I was leaping in and out of it with as much agility as the monkeys in the Tower of London menagerie.

Once in it, I looked around. This was the first bed in my life that I could truly call my own. We each had eighteen inches width for our hammocks. They were so close to each other that a grown man could reach across each of my neighbours and touch the man beyond him. Even with my short arms I could almost achieve this feat.

My first thought, as my eyes gradually accustomed themselves to the dim light, was to see if there were any boys my own age, but I was sadly disappointed. I could see three or four young hobbledehoys, but on past experience I considered them more likely to be a nuisance to me than anything else. This was a shipload of men. Men, and one boy.

I did not have the courage to speak to the fellow on my right, a big, bearded, intimidating man named Holt, who had said little during the trip on the tumbrel from London. He sucked on a small black pipe most of the time, even though it contained no baccy. Occasionally he glanced at me with a malevolent expression, much as a man will look at a rancid sausage before he hurls it into the gutter.

Looking at Holt, I felt that he was a desperate man indeed, and I resolved to keep well out of his way, if such a thing were possible in the confined space we occupied.

On my left was an older fellow, whose name I did not know then but later found out was one which was very strange to my ears, that of Pierre De Lafontaine. From his conversation on the tumbrel I believed that he had been sentenced to transportation for forging and uttering a promissory note, an offence unknown to me, but which seemed to have something to do with a counterfeit letter he had used to obtain release from imprisonment for debt.

Our quarters could fairly be called spartan. I had been pleased to see a stove and funnel between decks as I descended the ladder, and not far from my hammock were two swing stoves, with buckets of charcoal in hoops fastened to the wall. Hung up on walls were three posters, one of which listed the duties of the convicts who were to be appointed 'captains of the deck', 'captains of the mess', and so forth; another of which listed the procedures for divine service on Sundays, as well as the cleaning of the deck, the cutting up and cooking of meat rations, the washing of clothes and bedding and our own selves; and the third of which listed every imaginable offence that could be committed on board, with the penalties that could be expected in consequence of any breach of them. Flogging seemed to be the punishment most frequently adopted, and having a mortal fear of such a fate, I resolved upon reading the list of offences to do my utmost to avoid every last one of them.

Many conversations with transported convicts over the years have taught me that one thing is common to all, no matter when they arrived in the colony nor what ship brought them nor who was the captain or surgeon of the vessel. Some experienced kind and considerate treatment, some experienced treatment harsh and brutal, some had a calm passage and some a stormy, some shared the ship with women convicts so that their voyage was one of licentiousness and depravity . . . but even these last shared in the universal tale that the monotony of the voyage was almost unendurable.

I began to feel this even on that first afternoon. To begin with, everything was new and fascinating to me: I found the soft rocking of the boat as she lay at anchor strangely comforting, I liked the creaking of the timbers, I relished the sensation of having my very own bed. Already I was becoming accustomed to the stench. But the conversations of my companions, although amusing at times, were repeating the themes I had heard on the tumbrel between London and Portsmouth, not to mention in the commons of Newgate. There was no room to run, as Quentin and I had often done through the streets of London.

Once I had inspected our living quarters and read as much of the posters as I could understand, there was little else to look at. And there was certainly nothing to do. It was hard to form any sense of purpose, because our existence was essentially purposeless. Our only function was to be transported. Those three words, 'to be transported', suggest a passivity which accurately reflected our condition. We were as parcels, like those transported by the Royal Mail between London and other destinations, and just as nothing is expected of a parcel but to lie there without causing any trouble, so too was nothing useful expected of us.

Parcels had the advantage on us, though, in that they were not flogged for the slightest misdemeanour.

Chapter 21

THE STINK OF OUR living quarters was soon explained when we learned that most of the convicts had been on board for some weeks and had been confined to their quarters for all that time, apart from rare and brief visits above deck for exercise, during which they were shackled together to prevent attempts at escape. I felt intensely sorry for them when I learned of the duration of their detention, for to deprive men of fresh air and sunlight for so long is cruel indeed.

I was fortunate, because with our embarkation the *Admiral Barrington* had completed her loading for New South Wales and could get underway at the earliest opportunity. This event came so expeditiously that at dawn the next day I was awoken by a tremendous noise which appeared to come from just behind my head, but which I soon realised was from outside and was in fact the rattling of the chain as the anchor was raised.

'Now we're for it,' said a voice from out of the darkness. I imagined, however, that the men who had been languishing so long below deck were relieved that something was happening at last, even though the raising of the anchor signified the commencement of a journey into an unknown redolent with awful possibilities.

Soon the more pronounced creaking of the timbers, the shouts of the sailors that I could hear dimly from the deck above, and the sensations of movement signified that we were indeed underway, and going at a steady clip. After a couple of hours the soft and soothing rocking I had experienced during the afternoon and night were replaced by a more pronounced roll of the boat as, no doubt, we reached more open waters. Up until this time I had been obstructed from seeing through a porthole by the crowd of men assembled at each one, but as time went on they started to drift away, and I at last had my opportunity. There was however little enough to see. The holes had been shuttered over until we got underway, apparently to stop people on the wharf passing contraband to us convicts, but at some stage a small circle of wood had been removed, enabling a view and at the same time allowing a glimmer of natural light into our miserable surroundings.

I gazed through the thick glass at the ocean, a spectacle I had never seen before. I was gradually struck by both its variety and its monotony. The endless grey-green water, flecked with white, swirled away from the hull of the ship. After a while I imagined I could see patterns in the repetitive swirl. Did God determine the shape and hue of each of those movements of water? Was each carefully crafted, individually sculpted? Did each conform to the Creator's plan for the universe? After all, Elihu did say to Job, 'By the breath of God frost is given: and the breadth of the waters is straitened. Also by watering He wearieth the thick cloud: He scattereth His bright cloud: and it is turned round about by His counsels: that they may do whatsoever He commandeth them upon the face of the world in the earth.'

Later, as I came to know the New South Wales forest, I felt it had many of the qualities of the ocean. Even the colours seemed similar. A great expanse of water, a great continent of land. Standing in the forest, pondering the angle of a eucalypt leaf to its twig, the pattern of spots and lines on the leaf, the colour of its spine and the degree of its deviation from the vertical, I asked myself if, in its ever-changing colours and pattern and shape, its growth and decline for the duration of its life, it was a miniature masterpiece showing the touch of the divine hand, or merely a manifestation of chance, the outcome of all the random factors which affect the development of each form of life.

Gazing through the porthole, at my tender age, I could not of course have formulated such thoughts. But I did in my childlike way wonder at the tapestry I was observing, and at what a busy God it must be to create a vastness such as this, with its manifold threads. And for most of its expanse, these sights went unseen by any mortal. Was there meaning, then, in the shape of a ripple in the water that was gone in an instant and was observed by none but its Creator?

I became aware of a man standing behind me waiting for a turn at the porthole, and I stepped back to allow him access. Somehow, despite growing up in the slums of London, I had acquired some semblance of manners, or perhaps it was more that I was fearful of the other members of this cast of ruffians and villains. The man, whom I appreciated had not thrust me out of the way in the rough manner that I had experienced often enough from both men and women in my life, stepped forward. As the light from outside fell on his face I cried out in amazement.

'Carmichael!'

'Why, my young friend Barnaby.'

It was indeed Carmichael Lance, the prisoner who had helped me in Newgate by advising me to plead not guilty, and who had shared his food with me. I had never been more delighted to see anyone in my life, and he seemed pleased enough to see me too.

'So, I trust you looked His Honour straight in the eye and told him you were as innocent as a newborn?' he asked.

'Yes, I did,' I said proudly. 'And I think the jury took a shine to me.'

He laughed. 'Well, you appear to have avoided the gallows, or you wouldn't be in this den of iniquity. I imagine the jury saw you as "one who has gone astray like a lost lamb". What did you get?'

'Seven years transportation,' I said.

'Ah well, who knows what will happen at the end of this voyage? Assuming we survive the savage seas. And let us assume that we will survive, otherwise we shall make ourselves miserable. We are miserable sinners enough; let us not be miserable sailors.' He looked around and then drew a little closer to me. 'Now, my young friend, have you had time to make the acquaintance of any of your fellow prisoners?'

'Not really. Just the ones I shared the tumbrel with, coming from London. Some were in Newgate with me, but not in my quarters.'

'So it sounds as though, like me, you avoided the Hulks. That was well done, though I must admit that I did not anticipate being cooped up here for so long before we sailed. But you have avoided that fate too. Well, you were good enough to listen to my advice last time we met, young Barnaby, so I am going to presume to give you a further piece of it.'

'Yes indeed, sir,' I said.

'Choose your friends wisely,' he said. 'Be wary of those who are most ardent to make your acquaintance. God knows I am no tabernacle, but the deeds of some of these men are enough to make Heaven weep.' He paused. 'Think of this as your Slough of Despond mayhap, and that will give you the strength to persevere, to see beyond. At the end of the voyage we may find a destination with something extraordinary for those whose hearts remain true.'

'My Slough of Despondent, sir?'

He laughed. 'I thank you for bestowing the epithet of "sir" upon me, but I fear it is out of place in these circumstances. Slough of Despond, not Despondent. Yes. Many will bog down on this voyage, Barnaby. Some will emerge from the bog and others will perish in it. But I believe we are heading towards a light which shines for us.'

His eyes burned as he said those last words. He seemed a very different man at that moment from the one I had met in Newgate Prison. I said: 'The other men speak very differently about it, sir . . . I mean, Carmichael.'

'They are not people of imagination or vision, my young friend. They are not educated people.'

He put his eyes to the porthole and gazed through it as though he could see somewhat further than I or perhaps anyone else had done. I returned to my hammock, where the men were talking to each other in a way to which I had already become accustomed, not only on the tumbrel, but also in Newgate. As I was to find out, the established patterns of these conversations did not much alter during most of the journey from Portsmouth to Botany Bay. They consisted firstly of highly coloured and detailed recountings of the crimes for which they had been convicted, secondly of highly detailed (but frequently unconvincing, even to my immature ears) recountings of crimes for which they had not been caught, and thirdly of vulgar and salacious accounts of their adventures with women. These last were also frequently unconvincing.

I had been astonished – and remained so – at their boastful attitudes towards the conduct which for many of them had brought them to the very shadow of the gallows. Reformers would have been bitterly disappointed at the absence of repentance among these hardened offenders. There were those who were genuinely contrite, and who had fixed their minds upon nobler goals, but they were in a small minority.

Only occasionally would the conversation turn to the gentler topic of past lives, perhaps lived more wholesomely, more optimistically: and then tales were told of farms or villages or schooling. In short, tales of childhood. The names of fathers and mothers, sweethearts and wives, children, brothers and sisters, would be invoked, often wistfully, and with contrition and regret. I found myself more attracted to these stories than the others.

I should add that a fourth topic had become more and more common as we approached the harbour of Portsmouth, and it was to consume an increasingly large proportion of the men's attention as we made our insignificant way across the ocean. It was speculation on the conditions that we could expect to find in the new colony. That particular afternoon many were engaged in propounding their theories or sharing the stories they had heard. Pierre De Lafontaine, who like most forgers I have met had the gift of the gab, was describing a wondrously large wild man, a 'monstrous giant', who had been brought back to our native shores just recently from Botany Bay. Pierre De Lafontaine had an accent that was strange to my ears. The men called him Frenchie, for he was a native of France, but he spoke with great energy, his face alive and his eyes alight. 'Twelve foot tall was zis man, and all covered wiz fur, he could have been a bear but for his face, that was all 'uman, the most frightenin' sight. He could have picked up four of us and smashed us against the nearest tree, he was so 'uge, he was 'orrible.'

Looking around at the other men I could see their faces. Despite the bravado they affected at every opportunity, it was obvious that they were terrified by Pierre's description.

'Where did you see him?' one of them asked in a low growl, almost like a bear himself.

'Oh, I did not see 'im myself, you understand, but he 'as been shown up and down the country, I am surprised none of you 'as seen 'im. My friend saw 'im, he said it was the most wondrous sight, but very frightenin'. He 'ad teeth like the tusks of an elephant. Oh yes, my ami said so many people were fainting that they 'ad to drop a curtain in front of the giant to 'ide 'im from the people again.'

'I've heard that the Indians have captured half the prisoners what went out there,' said another man, a lugubrious-looking fellow with eyes like a basset hound. He was possibly big enough to take on the giant of whom Pierre had spoken. He could only fit into his hammock by lying with his knees folded. 'Took them and ate them, so they say.'

'Aye, the bloodthirsty bastards, they got into one of the barracks at Botany Bay and slit the throat of every second man as they lay asleep in their beds, and snuck away, and not a man knew until the morning,' said a fellow named Chris Norfolk, who seemed an excitable type. He was always prowling around and talking to anyone who would listen, about any subject under the sun. When he could not find an audience he talked to himself, as though it were all one and the same to him.

'What would they do that for?' I asked, wide-eyed. It was my first contribution to the exchange.

'For the simple pleasure of it,' Chris Norfolk responded. He sat up, which, with our limited experience of hammocks was still a precarious undertaking. 'You have to understand, they want blood in the same way that we desire our victuals. They are savages, the same as wild animals. Don't think of them the way you think of us civilised folk. Have you seen what a fox does in a henhouse? It bites the head off every bird, not because it wants to eat every one, indeed it cannot, but because it likes to spread havoc and destruction. No, these folk know nothing of civilisation.'

He lay back down again and, to my surprise, opened his flies, pulled out his member and began to work on it with much energy. As the voyage proceeded, I was to learn that this was his invariable response to any happening or conversation that excited his interest. I found myself drawn to watch, out of the corner of my eye, with a kind of unwilling interest, but shortly found the sight too confusing and overwhelming for my immature senses, and turned away.

The tales continued. 'The forest is alive with snakes, so they say,' said another man who, judging by his long thin frame might have had serpentine qualities himself. 'And every one of them venomous. One bite and there is no help for a man. He writhes in agony for a few minutes then dies with bloodcurdling screams and the blood rushing out of every orifice.'

The stories, combined with the motion of the boat, the fetid atmosphere and the spectacle presented by Chris Norfolk energetically manipulating himself just a few yards from me, were not conducive to my peace of mind. I closed my eyes, trying to prevent nausea rising from my stomach. I reminded myself of the one comfort I had: my recollection of the man in the tavern who had been to New South Wales and come back again. I may have been the only person among our number who had actually conversed with a returned convict. I did not mention the fact to anyone, because I did not want to draw any more attention to myself, but I remembered vividly that the man had not spoken of bloodthirsty savages or hair-covered giants or vicious serpents, but of a beautiful warm climate where a man could walk around all day with his shirt off, and where a golden future awaited him. He had made it sound like paradise.

However, I was soon to learn from Carmichael Lance that the Slough of Despond and many other obstacles beside await the person who would reach paradise.

Chapter 22

A S DARKNESS CREPT AROUND US so too a man crept to my bedside and importuned me in crude and vile language. I repulsed him, but he was not the last, and I lay awake in a nervous sweat hoping that I would survive the night. I particularly feared the man Holt, whose first name I still did not know, and who lay just inches from me in the hammock on my right.

After Newgate I was hardly a stranger to the chaotic darkness that engulfs a prison at night-time. My first night on the *Admiral Barrington*, while we were still at anchor, had been uneventful. Somehow however, the slipping of the vessel's chains and her departure from British shores coincided with, or more likely released, an ugly fervour, an animalistic passion, in many of my neighbours.

I do not believe that such behaviour is restricted to the criminal classes. I have seen enough and heard enough to know that a group of men living together are inevitably coarsened and brutalised over time, and when I have had a choice I have avoided such situations, for fear of the moral turpitude likely to be found therein. But of course I did not have a choice in the close quarters of the *Admiral Barrington*. Lying in my hammock, awake and in fear, I bethought me that perhaps I should adopt the practice of some women and girls and boys in Newgate and seek out a protector who would reserve me for himself, and in that way limit the assaults upon my virtue. Yet truly is it said that hope springs eternal in the human bosom, and somehow I could not bring myself to such a cold-blooded action as to renounce all hope and place myself willingly in the clutches of such a creature.

If I have not offended my readers' sensibilities enough by these reflections, I may do so now by stating that I was also aware, from what I had observed, that the brutes who possess women and children in these ways are not averse to sharing their possessions, for personal gain or to enhance their prestige and power. So the protection they may initially appear to offer is frequently illusory. I say no more.

In the blackest darkness of the night I had to fight off one man; a fight I would inevitably have lost, except that the descent into chaos initiated by our struggle spread itself quickly to the surrounding hammocks and provoked a storm of protest from my neighbours, so that eventually my attacker had no option but to slink away. It was too dark to see who he was.

When dawn came it found me tired and unwell. The pitching of the ship did not bother me as much as it did many – I soon learned, to my relief, that I was not particularly prone to seasickness – but the events of the preceding hours, combined with the sight and sound and smell of others retching caused my stomach to rise up in revolt on a number of occasions. In order to quell the feelings I learned to stare fixedly at the ceiling and command my body to be at peace, a procedure that seemed to work moderately well.

Our rations consisted of three quarters of a pound of biscuit per day, which I generally saved for the evening meal. For dinner, if the weather permitted, we were served plum duff or pea soup or, occasionally, if a pig had been killed, pork pudding.

For breakfast on this, as on every subsequent day at sea, we had a pot of gruel, which was made more palatable by the addition of sugar or butter, at least until the supplies of these commodities ran low.

After breakfast on this second day came a sudden hustle and bustle, with a wave of noise rolling through our quarters, which I soon found was initiated by Surgeon Gossam and a squad of soldiers he brought with him to give extra weight to his commands. To the disgust of the old lags, Surgeon Gossam was fixated on the idea that cleanliness would contribute to the good health of all on board, so to that end various members of our company were deputed to take the slops buckets up on deck and clean them out, whilst others were allocated the tasks of sweeping and mopping and scrubbing the walls and floors.

I wished fervently to be chosen to go up to the deck, for any reason, however humble, so that I could smell the fresh air and see the vista of ocean and coastline, but I was not honoured with such a summons. Instead I was added to a gang that was cleaning the living quarters.

The soldiers bustled about; in this early stage of the voyage they were much given to blustering and threatening. It was as though they feared that if they did not do enough shouting on the first day of our cleaning duties we would all be incorrigibly delinquent in our tasks by the second. There may have been reasonable grounds for this apprehension. Some of the men worked with more zeal than others, but although disappointed not to be allowed upstairs, I was still relieved to have something to do and set about my task willingly enough. I was on my hands and knees scrubbing when I saw Carmichael Lance at some distance further down the cabin, engaged in the same task, so I contrived to slip in beside him with my bucket and brush, and we scrubbed together.

We were not supposed to talk when on these duties, but it was easy enough to maintain a conversation when the soldiers were occupied elsewhere. He asked me about the preceding night, and I confessed with some reluctance and embarrassment that it had not been restful, for the reasons I have enumerated above.

This morning he seemed to be the Carmichael Lance of old, rather than the visionary of the day before. He was urbane, witty and cynical, but at the same time as concerned for my welfare as he had been at Newgate.

'My dear young friend, you cannot have lived the life you have described to me and be entirely innocent,' he whispered as the soldier guarding us wandered away. He glanced sideways at my face. I don't know what he saw there, but whatever it was made him mutter, 'Well, perhaps it is possible after all.'

When we next had the opportunity to talk, out of the hearing of the guard, he resumed the subject. 'I may have been too euphemistic in the warnings I gave you earlier,' he whispered. 'I will speak to you now more plainly. You can expect this vessel to be a veritable bed of vice. You will need to be on your guard. I will give you what help I can, but do not relax your vigilance for a moment. As you have already experienced, because of your age men will seek to bully you and take advantage of you.' He paused, then added: 'Men are attracted to innocence, but only so they can defile it.' I did not really know what he meant by that.

We worked on in silence for some time. As we were finishing the last section of floor he said to me: 'Perhaps there is something I can do.'

I clung to those words during the night that followed, which was much the same as the first. I understood little of men's lustful feelings, but I had some awareness that they increased over time were they not relieved, and I feared for my future should that prove to be the case.

I did not get a glimpse of Carmichael the next day. The night was even uglier, but not for any reason connected to me. At about four bells, after we had been locked down, a fight broke out in the darkness to my left. I heard angry voices, getting louder and louder, then a yelp of pain. The noise became an uproar, the air thick with insults and curses, and then a younger voice suddenly cried: 'Help, help, there's murder being done. Fetch a lamp!'

By now Surgeon Gossam had appointed several of our number as so-called captains of the deck, with various responsibilities pertaining to food, cleanliness and good order. Even while the cabin still resonated with the cries of murder, another man, carrying a lantern, went past my berth. I recognised him as one of these captains.

I believe everyone had been thoroughly awakened at this point, and there were shouts of 'Shove it,' 'Belay that row,' 'Shut your traps,' from all over the deck. I did not dare leave my hammock, but it was evident from the confusion of noise and movement further down the way that many had. I heard the captain of the deck shout: 'Bowers, fetch the surgeon,' and I saw a man I believed to be Bowers, another of these captains of the deck, go past, also with a lantern, heading for the ladder. Shortly afterwards I heard him hammering on the hatch and bellowing for the surgeon.

It was a long time before Surgeon Gossam appeared. He presumably did so in some trepidation, for he had an escort of six soldiers. I had a little sympathy with him. To descend into a nest of convicts, in the middle of the night, knowing that there was trouble but knowing little of what it might be, must take some courage.

They brought more lanterns and by their light I could see a rivulet of blood slowly trickling along the floor, rushing a little every time the ship tipped at the stern. I heard the surgeon exclaim: 'This is a bad business,' then a little later I saw four soldiers carrying a man past. I saw his sweating pale face and heard his groans. They were followed by the other two soldiers, escorting a man who had his hands bound behind his back. I wondered how they would get him up the ladder, with his feet shackled as well.

At least this terrible incident had a sobering effect on those of us left behind. There was a stillness and silence below decks, such as I had not experienced on the previous nights. I felt safe enough to go to sleep, reflecting as I did so that the medical care in this floating prison seemed very different to the standards I had experienced in Newgate. Surgeon Gossam appeared to care for his charges, to be anxious to keep them alive, to want orderly and clean conditions. The contrast with Newgate, and indeed the life I had known in Hell, was striking. It gave me another glimmer of hope, another reason to suppose that I should not yet despair about my future.

Chapter 23

As early as the following day I had further cause for optimism when Carmichael Lance quietly informed me, as we scrubbed pots in the galley, that he had fixed it for me to take the hammock next to his. I don't know how he managed this, but a sallow-faced man with skin pockmarked by old smallpox scars brought his meagre possessions to my hammock and I took my meagre possessions to his, and so the exchange was effected.

I also didn't know why Carmichael took such an interest in me, but as we lay in our hammocks that evening he told me a little about himself. For the sake of privacy we had to speak quietly, as anything above a whisper was heard by half-a-dozen men in surrounding berths. Carmichael came from a place called Bickleigh Vale, a rural hamlet a couple of hundred miles north of London. The son of a clergyman, he was born in the middle of a wild storm which blew the roof off the rectory. 'My father took it as an omen,' he said. 'I was the firstborn, but he believed me to be an ill-fated child. He proved a good prophet, I fear. Yet I strove to do all that he expected of me and to live piously. With the greatest respect to his memory, though, I fear it is not unreasonable for me to say that he was difficult to please. He had a harshness to his nature, and I saw my mother suffer at times from his lack of sympathy.

'When I was eight years old, by which time I had two younger sisters, my father sent me away to a school at Abbotsley.' Carmichael paused for a moment, as though recollecting troubled memories. 'You believe,' he continued, 'that Newgate and this ship lack a certain, shall we say, comfort, or gentleness. Well, I can only say that compared to Mr Pine's establishment at Abbotsley, Newgate and the *Admiral Barrington* are the epitome of luxury. Truly, only those who have been there can conceive the hell that is an English school for young gentlemen.'

He sighed. 'I was allowed home but once a year, and on those occasions my poor mother wept so much to see me that I could not break her heart by telling her of the privations at Mr Pine's Academy. I did not wish to add to her sufferings. But those sufferings were destined not to last a deal longer. One evening she accompanied me in our little pony trap to the coaching station, from whence I was to return to school. A fearful storm was raging and my father had forbidden my mother to go. But he was called out to see a dying parishioner – for all his faults he was a Godly man, and unlike some of those in holy orders would not neglect his duty, even on such a night. My mother for once disobeyed his instructions and travelled with me to the town. On the journey back, they came to the bridge across the River Wyburn but in the rain and darkness were unable to see that a span had been washed away. The pony and trap plunged into the torrent. The driver swam to safety but was not able to rescue my mother.

'And so the prophecies made at my birth were fulfilled. I received the news at my school some days later. My father then wrote to Mr Pine requesting that I remain at school during future vacations. I was not permitted to see his letter, but I understood that he expressed a view that I bore some responsibility for my mother's death. I myself was never to receive any direct communications from him on that or any other topic again.'

'That's a sad story,' I whispered.

I'm not sure if he heard me. He added: 'I had in mind to follow my father and take holy orders, but alas, my university career was short and inglorious. After just a few months I was rusticated. The demon drink, I'm afraid. From then on, my trajectory has been steadily downhill.' His eyes opened wide suddenly, and he looked at me again with the fervent eyes I had seen by the porthole two days earlier. 'Botany Bay . . .' he whispered. 'The Pacific Ocean washes gently into the harbour. No storms there. I believe it is meant to be. The very name "Pacific Ocean" gives me comfort and hope.'

I didn't know quite what he meant by that. We lay in silence for a while. I became aware that the insidious progress of darkness through the mid-deck section had begun once more. I felt a trickle of fear in my insides. I had put my faith in Carmichael to keep me safe, but I had never thought about the manner in which I expected him to do this. He was a lean man, quite tall, but with none of the bulk and obvious strength of my previous neighbour, Holt. Nothing about Carmichael gave the impression that he would be any use pitted in a fight with one of the more brutish occupants of our quarters. And I did not want him dragged away by our keepers for stabbing a man, as I had seen happen to the man the night before.

Some hours passed without incident, however, and I began to feel more complacent. I was drifting into sleep when I became aware of a movement, a shadow, a presence looming at the foot of my hammock. He had moved so stealthily and I had been so little awake that I had not noticed his approach. A moment later a callused hand made its way under my blanket and felt its way up my right leg. 'Carmichael,' I croaked urgently, hoping against hope that he would be awake and would be able to miraculously find some way to rescue me from my assailant.

I had underestimated Carmichael. And I had yet to learn that a defender need not use the weapons of the attacker; indeed, to use the attacker's weapons is oftentimes to give him the advantage. Fisticuffs would never have been to Carmichael's benefit. Words were his rapier, and he wielded them well.

'SODOMITE!' he suddenly bellowed, sitting up in his hammock as though possessed of a tremendous burst of energy. 'BEGONE SODO-MITE! Leave the child alone, or God's curse be upon you. BEGONE I SAY.'

I was astounded, but the brute at the end of my hammock was even more so. He snatched his hand away from my leg and stepped backwards. As other men began stirring and calling out, some telling Carmichael to cease his disturbance, others asking the cause of it, and at least two, whom I found out later had been recruited by Carmichael for this very purpose, shouting with equal force, 'AWAY WITH YOU, SODOMITE', the shadow fled back into the shadows from whence he had come.

I sank into the shelter of my hammock, frightened, embarrassed and relieved in equal measure. After a time I whispered, 'Thank you Carmichael,' to which he replied, 'Think nothing of it, my young friend. I doubt that you'll be troubled again, for some time at least.'

He seemed perfectly composed, as if this were an everyday occur-rence. I was filled with admiration for his ingenuity and courage. I thanked him again the next morning, but he made it clear that he was not interested in any further conversation upon the subject.

That morning was the dawn of the Sabbath, and for the first time the whole body of men was let up onto the deck, for divine service. With what inexpressible feelings of excitement and delight did I ascend the ladder! I, who had spent most of my life in the open air, despite it being the diseased and fetid air of Hell, had already come to think of such an opportunity as an almost unattainable luxury. And the smell of the sea air was like nothing I had experienced. I was as one who has never allowed strong drink to cross his lips but has just consumed an entire bottle of gin. The most powerful sensations engulfed me as I climbed out of the hatchway. I was almost deaf to the bullying shouts of the soldiers as they marshalled us on the main deck. Instead my eyes strove to take in the arena in which I found myself. I had never seen the horizon before. I had never enjoyed an unencumbered view of the ocean, only the pitiful perspective offered by the porthole below decks. Now I understood the boasts of the Creator to Job. The Divinity that had shaped this awful panorama had every right to heap scorn upon the man, so insignificant, no matter how many sons and daughters and camels and sheep and goats and servants he had. All of these possessions, so esteemed by Job's compatriots, were tiny elements in the unimaginable vastness of a universe shaped for a purpose beyond our mortal understanding.

The church of St Martin's had been a grand structure, and in my childlike way I had developed some dim awareness that the fine and noble words of the Prayer Book were worthy of such an edifice. Now I stood in the greatest cathedral I had ever known and listened to the words of divine service as read by the captain of the *Admiral Barrington*, Master Marsh. And even in these surroundings I felt that the words were not unworthy of the occasion.

He began with the scripture reading from Ezekiel: 'When the wicked man turneth away from his wickedness that he hath committed, and doeth that which is lawful and right, he shall save his soul alive,' and followed with the familiar prayers and confessions: 'Dearly beloved brethren, the scripture moveth us, in sundry places, to acknowledge and confess our manifold sins and . . .

'Almighty and most merciful Father, we have erred and strayed from thy ways like lost sheep. We have followed too much the devices and desires of our own hearts. We have left undone those things which we ought to have done; and we have done those things which we ought not to have done.'

And when Master Marsh pronounced the absolution, which he did most feelingly, I was glad that I was on my knees for those words, which I heard for the first time under the all-encompassing heavens stretching from one horizon to the other. 'He pardoneth and absolveth all them that truly repent and unfeignedly believe His holy Gospel.'

I dismissed from my mind my doubts about the treatment meted out to Job and felt truly joyful in the Lord.

The next morning the ship was hove to, and we were brought up into the open air again. The significance of the hour was lost on me, but not upon those among our number who had nautical experience: they knew well enough that eleven o'clock in the morning is the time when punishment is meted out on His Majesty's ships, and we were ushered upstairs at about twenty minutes short of eleven. The sight of a yellow flag at the masthead of the *Admiral Barrington* gave further concern to those who were privy to the ways of the sea, and upon seeing it their faces assumed a grave demeanour indeed.

Their expressions were well justified. It soon eventuated that we were there not only to observe a punishment but also to take part in another religious observance, of a very different kind to the service of the day before. I would cheerfully have remained below decks rather than be a witness to it. We were dressed at close quarters, and a roll call taken, after which Master Marsh appeared before us again. The prisoner whom I had last seen being led away in the night-time, handcuffed and shackled after the fight between the two men, was at this point dragged forward from the brig in which he had been confined. It appeared that his name was Thomas Ffolkes, and a tribunal had been convened upon the vessel to consider his conduct. The master now read the findings of the tribunal. The injured man had died and been buried at sea that very dawn. The tribunal's finding was that he had died as the result of being stabbed in the chest by Thomas Ffolkes. The defendant's plea of self-defence had been rejected; he had been found guilty, and the sentence was that he should be hanged at the yardarm.

The captain told us in the sternest tones that we were compelled to be witnesses to the execution, as a lesson to us that the laws of His Majesty the King were to be observed at all times and in all places, including on board ship. The wretched man was then asked whether he had anything he wished to say. He raised his eyes towards us and began: 'Comrades, I beg of you . . .' His voice faltered and he did not seem able to continue. He looked helplessly at Master Marsh, who did not meet his eyes but instead nodded to the bo'sun, whereupon that officer stepped forward. He invited the prisoner to quick march to a scaffold that had been erected upon a platform projecting from the ship's side, directly beneath the fore yardarm. Ffolkes seemed unable to move. He took one dragging step in the direction indicated, then stood swaying, as though he might fall at any moment. The officer failed to persuade him to go any further, and in the end he resorted to calling upon a couple of soldiers, who half-dragged, half-walked the reluctant man to his awful destination.

Once he had reached the platform, another command was given, and six sailors stepped forward, taking up a rope which had been laid upon the deck, and which led to the scaffold.

I began to see now how the thing was to be done.

Thomas Ffolkes, who still seemed barely able to stand, had the rope reeved around his neck, a blue cap placed upon his head, then a pocket handkerchief put into his hand. A large shot was carried, not without difficulty, to him, and tied to his legs. The whole scene was one of horror to me, and I became aware, from the sound of stifled sobs around me, that I was not alone in my feelings.

It appeared that the handkerchief was given to Ffolkes so that he might drop it when he was ready for the punishment to be carried out. Once he had been prepared for his fate a long silence ensued. Ffolkes seemed as unwilling to play his part in this aspect of the ceremony as he had been in all the proceedings to date. We waited, with every eye fixed upon the small white cloth which the condemned man gripped convulsively.

Then, slowly, his fingers began to open. A terrible silence reigned on board the ship. Not a man moved. The only sound that could be heard was the gentle susurration of the small waves slapping against the timbers of the vessel. For a moment, the handkerchief appeared to be stuck to Ffolkes's hand, no doubt by sweat. But then, in an instant, as lightly as a bird's feather, it dropped to the deck. I believe that a cry issued from the doomed man, but before I could be sure, my ears were deafened by a mighty blast.

Directly below the scaffold, right beneath the feet of the prisoner, the bow gun had been fired. The sound of it caused such a shock to my system that I believe I screamed, and certainly I clapped my hands to my ears. A cloud of white smoke enveloped Thomas Ffolkes, and at the same moment the men who had taken up the rope charged as fast as they could away from him, with the effect that he was run up the yardarm.

I closed my eyes at this sight, but quickly became aware, from the horrified murmurs of my shipmates, that things were not going according to plan. For some minutes, whilst I kept my eyes grimly shut, the mutterings continued, but were gradually succeeded by a sense of relief, until I heard a man behind me say, 'There, I think he's gone,' to which another man responded, 'Aye, the bloody butchers, may God have more mercy on his soul than they did.'

I was surrounded by anger that was palpable. It was not until we were below decks again, and permitted to talk openly, that I learned of the scene which I had resolutely avoided observing. Apparently the knot around the neck of the condemned man had somehow worked its way under his chin, so that his neck did not break, but he was instead slowly strangled.

At least, some of the men observed, Master Marsh showed decency in not letting the corpse hang for hours, as was so often the custom in those barbaric days. When there had been no movement of the body for several minutes he ordered it to be lowered to the deck again. I observed this, for by then I had my eyes open again. The surgeon examined the body and pronounced life to be extinct.

At this point, a canvas bag was brought forward, and the same half-dozen sailors who had run Ffolkes up the yardarm lifted his body and placed him in it. Another of their number began stitching the bag closed, which he did with despatch and not inconsiderable skill. Upon the completion of this task, all eyes turned to Master Marsh once again. He had taken up the Book of Common Prayer, from which he had read with such effect the day before, and now he began the Funeral Service for Those Who Die at Sea, culminating in the words: 'We therefore commit his body to the deep, to be turned into corruption, looking for the resurrection of the body, when the Sea shall give up her dead, and the life of the world to come, through our Lord Jesus Christ.'

A couple of sailors brought out a plank and ran one end of this over the side of the ship. Ffolkes's body, wrapped in its canvas shroud, was placed on the plank. It seemed heavy, because, I believe, they had at some stage, unobserved by me, added metal to its contents, to help it sink. Despite this, I was pleased to see that the sailors treated it gently and with respect. They pushed the plank further out, until the body was positioned well clear of the side of the ship, upon which, at a signal from the captain, they lifted their end. After a moment the body slid from the plank and disappeared from view. I did not hear its entry into the water.

I believe that on some vessels, malfeasors executed by order of the captain were not even afforded the privilege of a prayer being uttered over them before they were dumped in the ocean. I suppose by those standards Master Marsh should be considered more humane than some of his compatriots. Nonetheless, I found it difficult to reconcile my feelings of awe and reverence during the service of Morning Prayer the day before on the Sabbath, with my horror and revulsion at the cold-blooded manner in which a man had been cruelly executed and then consigned so rapidly to the deep. The same book had been used for both services. Yet in one service Master Marsh had read the words, 'Come unto Me all ye that labour and are heavy laden, and I will give you rest,' then barely twenty-fours hours later he read, 'We give Thee hearty thanks, for that it hath pleased Thee to deliver this our brother out of the miseries of this sinful world.'

I was not aware of a man amongst our number who looked to be in accord with these latter sentiments. Judging from the expressions on the faces of the soldiers and crew, it seemed likely that they too did not feel inclined to offer hearty thanks for the despatch of poor Ffolkes. I suppose a theologian, who is much wiser than I, would explain that the man had been freed of his heavy burden by being given eternal rest, but speaking for myself alone, I did not feel pleasure at the deliverance of my brother from the miseries of this sinful world. I shivered and shook with shock for many hours after this, and for weeks could not get the image of his poor befouled body out of my mind.

Chapter 24

THE WEEKS THAT NOW passed were placid compared to the first days of our voyage but were marked for me by a great change in my education, thanks to my friend Carmichael Lance. This period began, however, with an act of great significance for most of our number. Following upon the execution of Thomas Ffolkes, we had supposed that severe restrictions would be put upon us, partly because of the fear that Ffolkes's action might be taken by the captain as proof that we were a violent gang of ruffians who would be forever fighting and assaulting each other, but also because of fear by the ship's officers that the botched hanging might lead to anger and unrest among the prisoners.

Yet to our considerable surprise, Master Marsh adopted a different course. The morning following the hanging we were brought back on deck, for the third consecutive day, but this time in small groups, whereupon the irons were struck off most of us by members of the ship's company. The feelings of felicity conveyed by this simple act are impossible to describe, but when I was given permission by the good-hearted sailors who performed the deed upon me to walk freely from one side of the boat to the other, I felt that I floated rather than walked, and indeed broke into a dance of delight, to the amusement of the watching crew members.

Only an annulment of my sentence could have given me a greater sense of liberty, and as there seemed little prospect of that, I was happy to settle for the sense of lightness conveyed by being able to exercise my limbs freely once more.

Coincidentally, a liberty of mind was to be mine also, brought about by the steps taken by Carmichael Lance to improve my education. As I lay listlessly in my hammock one afternoon, I observed him to be reading a small book. Lifting myself onto an elbow I gazed at him for some time before enquiring: 'What is that, Carmichael? A very small Bible? Or the Book of Common Prayer?'

Without looking up he replied: 'Neither, Barnaby.'

'Neither?' I was perplexed. I had not been aware of the existence of other books. 'Then what is it?'

He put it down and looked at me. 'There are other books than the Bible and the Book of Common Prayer, my young friend.'

'There are?'

He shook his head and smiled a little. As I got older I was becoming increasingly embarrassed by my ignorance of the world, and Carmichael, though it was never his intention, often made me feel especially embarrassed.

'I have made enquiries among all the likely candidates on board this ship,' he said, 'and this is the only book I have been able to procure. I am well satisfied to have it. For a while I was faced with the awful fear that I would be bookless for the entire voyage. And that would have been insufferable.'

'Why do you like books?' I asked.

He paused, then answered slowly: 'Books are little treasuries of thoughts and wisdom and beauty. Not all books are all of those things, but the seeker after truth can often find illumination in the pages of a book.'

'Is there illumination in that book?' I asked.

He held it with its spine towards him and studied it carefully. 'Many would say so,' he said. 'And yes, I think it can be fairly described as a book that sheds light.'

'But what do the words say?'

'You can read, can you not?'

'Yes. Not as well as I'd like. I can read, but I want to get better.'

He regarded me thoughtfully. 'So, the little vagrant would like to better himself?' he said.

It seemed a cruel observation, but I don't think he meant it as such. I was already well aware that he came from a privileged class to which one of my background could never aspire. He treated me with great kindness, but he would have been raised to treat his horse and his dog with the same degree of benevolence. Now he handed me the book. I took it almost reverently. It was the first book I had ever handled. I had been too afraid to touch the Bibles in St Martin's.

I looked at the spine and read the difficult words out loud. '*Pilgrim's Progress*, John Bunyan. What does that mean?'

'*Pilgrim's Progress* is the name of the book, and its author is John Bunyan.'

'But what does that mean?'

'The author? The author is the person who wrote the book.'

It had never occurred to me to question how a book was produced. I asked: 'But how can a person write a book?'

He sighed. 'My dear young friend, I see I need to start at the beginning.'

He went on to explain that there were hundreds of thousands of books in the world, and some of them were true accounts of events in history or the lives of famous people, such as Plutarch's *Parallel Lives* or Marco Polo's accounts of his travels in China, whilst others were made up, such as the stories of Mr Daniel Defoe and Mr Henry Fielding. 'Have you never heard stories such as Cinderella or the Sleeping Beauty?' he asked.

'No, I don't believe so.'

He then had to explain to me the nature of fiction and fairytales and myths, which I found intriguing, though rather mystifying. He went on to tell me some of the tales of M. Perrault, including the two afore-mentioned, and Little Red Riding Hood. I am a little afraid of exposing myself to the ridicule of my readers when I say that I listened to these stories with the utmost seriousness and took them quite literally. I found it difficult to separate fiction from fact and was greatly concerned at the predicaments encountered by the characters. I was particularly horrified at the perfidious behaviour of Cinderella's sisters and much relieved that the Prince was not deceived by them. I thought him an admirable fellow.

I was perfectly ready to believe in a talking wolf and a godmother who could turn a pumpkin into a coach.

Carmichael was most patient with me. At some point during our conversation he formed the resolution that he would take me in hand and become my tutor. The first step in this process was to improve my ability to read, and with a text readily to hand, namely *Pilgrim's Progress*, we commenced the endeavour that same afternoon.

I am afraid that my woeful ignorance of every subject except scavenging and thieving appalled Carmichael, but he stuck to his task with a kind of grim determination. Perhaps he had learned more from his father about dedication to the task of helping one's poorer brethren than he realised. And I slowly became aware, as the voyage progressed, that whilst others around me were becoming increasingly bored by the monotony of shipboard life, both Carmichael and I, engrossed in my studies, for the most part held boredom at bay.

In one respect at least Carmichael could not fault me. I became a rapacious reader, thanks to Mr Bunyan and my tutor. I was enamoured of the story of Christian and his progress, reading of his vicissitudes with alarm and his victories over temptations with joy and relief. I doubt that Mr Bunyan, for all the honours and praise heaped upon his worthy tale, has ever had a reader more deeply involved with his book than was I.

When Christian reached the Slough of Despond I became very excited, for I recognised at last the reference to this quagmire made by Carmichael as we stood at the porthole in the hour of our reunion. I think it was at this point I started to realise that a story can have something more than a literal truth. I still believed Christian to be as real as anyone I had met, as real as the convicts with whom I shared my miserable days and nights. I was appalled that his wife and children could not see the danger they were in and would not accompany him in his flight from the City of Destruction, and I shook my head with exasperation at the folly of Pliable in turning back. I felt the pleasure of Christian when the burden was removed from his back as he reached the Sepulchre, and I wondered at the weakness of Formalist and Hypocrisy in choosing the easy paths of Danger and Destruction instead of struggling up the hill called Difficulty.

Yet I also understood that the story was written as a guide to assist those such as myself who had wandered far from the path. Looking around me it was easy to identify Sloth, in the figure of the old man over there in the hammock against the wall, and Timorous and Mistrust down the end of the room, and I certainly saw plenty of examples of Formalist and Hypocrisy, who believed that they could take a shortcut by climbing over the wall. 'Know you not that it is written, that he that cometh not in by the door but climbeth up some other way, the same is a thief and a robber?' I was surrounded by thieves and robbers; I was such a one myself; but more than that, almost all the company of convicts on board the *Admiral Barrington* were people who believed in shortcuts. Not for them the Hill Difficulty. They scorned it, believing that they could get all they wanted with no arduous endeavour, and so they went blithely towards Danger and Destruction, never realising the folly of their ways.

Thus I read my first novel with the greatest avidity. I read the second part as well, but I confess I did not like the story of Christiana and her four sons quite as much as I liked the story of Christian himself. And when I had finished the whole thing, nothing would do but that I had to read it again, marking as I did so with some satisfaction that I was more fluent, and recognised the difficult words more easily, than had been the case upon my first reading. This seemed to bring considerable satisfaction to Carmichael as well, who was thus rewarded for his goodness.

I believe it is thanks to these two unorthodox teachers, Mr Bunyan and Carmichael, that I became a great lover of literature and language, and hold the position I have today – and have even been emboldened to write this simple account of my own beginnings.

Chapter 25

LITTLE DID I REALISE as we continued our journey south that we had been unusually fortunate with the weather. I thought that the conditions we had experienced were customary for an ocean-going vessel. Although I had acquired a notion that sea travel could be treacherous, no one had explained to me, thus far in my young life, the extent of the perils.

For the first few days quite a number of men had suffered seasickness, as I have mentioned, and the sights, sounds and smells of this had contributed to the general unpleasantness in our quarters. Gradually, however, my fellow passengers became accustomed to the motion of the vessel, and this particular discomfort ceased to be a concern for most men.

At times the few convicts with maritime experience would speak of the exceptionally placid nature of our voyage thus far. I took little notice. And when, more than three weeks out from Portsmouth, the tossing of the boat became somewhat more severe, I still did not feel any great alarm.

By then all the trusted prisoners, of whom I was one and Carmichael another, were permitted to exercise upon the deck twice daily. This was a privilege much appreciated, and the highlight of every day for me, exceeding even the pleasure of reading *Pilgrim's Progress*. The fresh air was like the sweetest food I had ever tasted, but there were also many remarkable sights, inducing in me the greatest excitement. I may seem like something of a simpleton if I say that amongst the most marvellous to me was that mundane presence in the night sky, the moon. To see her from the dank gutters of London, glimpsed through sooty smoke and fog, was generally nothing remarkable, but to observe her rising over the ocean, illuminating the clouds and the foam and crests of the waves, was a sight that never failed to inspire me with awe.

The stars seemed to sink into the ocean as we proceeded further south, and the day came when we could no longer see the North Star; she had dropped out of our lives, perhaps forever, an occasion that caused some maudlin reflections from some among our number but which, I must say, had little effect on me. The Southern Cross had already replaced her, and as night followed night, she gradually edged her way higher in the sky, as she was to eventually edge her way into my affections. I have to say that I have grown more attached to her than I ever was to the North Star.

I was also impressed by the number of creatures we saw, having previously supposed the ocean to be a sort of aquatic desert, bereft of life. But birdlife was numerous, and although I could identify few specimens from my own limited experience, there were plenty around me, including the friendlier of the sailors, who could tell me their names. These included albatrosses, which had enormous wings three to four yards from tip to tip; boobies, which much resembled ducks; and later in the voyage, cape pigeons, which were somewhat larger than the common pigeon to which

I was accustomed in London. The sailors caught these birds, keeping the feathers so they could sell them when they got to port, to be used in ladies' hats. The manner of catching them was most ingenious. The men threw out lines of thread with corks on the end, whereupon the birds' curiosity got the better of them. They could not resist inspecting the corks, after which their legs became entangled in the thread and the sailors simply had to pull in the lines to complete the capture.

The albatrosses were notable not only for their size but also for their ability to fly great distances with rare rests upon the water. They were caught by more conventional methods: the sailors, and soldiers too, threw hooks baited with lumps of pork or beef over the stern of the vessel, letting the lines trail in the water. For some reason they were more successful in rougher weather, and there were days when they caught a dozen or so.

We saw stormy petrels, seahawks and those strange creatures which seem to be neither fish nor bird, the flying fish, which at times appeared in their thousands, occasioning the greatest excitement in me at least. They appeared to beat their tail on the surface of the water in order to gain height, but once airborne could travel for hundreds of feet. Some of the sailors swore that they had seen them fly for so long that they passed out of sight. Even allowing for the notorious tendency of seamen to exaggerate, I was inclined to believe their stories, for I saw them travel extraordinary distances.

Boobies appeared to hang around the bow of our boat at times, waiting for the flying fish to take to the air in order to get out of the vessel's way, upon which the boobies would attempt to seize the fish. I thought this an ingenious tactic on the part of these dumb creatures.

One fine morning I was scrubbing the deck when I became aware that Surgeon Gossam was not far from me, leaning forward over the deck rail, gripping it as he stared at something in the distance. It was as much as my life was worth to go and see what had caught his attention, so I kept scrubbing, but I was curious and kept an eye on him. After a few minutes he glanced at me, then said suddenly: 'What's your name, boy? Fletch, isn't it?'

'Yes, sir,' I replied.

'Well, come and look at this, Fletch. It's a sight you won't have seen before, I wager.'

Nervous at the notion of leaving my duty, I nonetheless had no option but to obey him. I edged over to the rail and stared out to sea, trying to find the source of his interest. But the water was calm, the sky clear, and I could see nothing worth remarking.

'There goes one of them now,' Surgeon Gossam said excitedly. 'You're a lucky boy. I wish I had my son here.'

'But what is it, sir?' I asked.

'What, are you blind?' he said crossly. 'Can't you see them? Whales. A goodly pod, I'd say. Watch for the spouts.'

'The spouts, sir?'

'The spouts!' He was an even-tempered man, but evidently I was testing his patience. 'The spouts. It's how they breathe. They have a hole in the top of their heads, and they blow air and water out of it when they come to the surface. Some of them can spout fifty feet or more. See, there's another one.'

I just caught a glimpse of a faint spray of water far in the distance. I nodded hard, trying to feign enthusiasm. 'Yes, sir, I see it.'

He looked at me with disgust. 'You had better go back to your scrubbing, Fletch.'

I found the dolphins and the porpoises far more interesting and attractive. The dolphins in particular came close to the ship, in large numbers, and at times appeared to be escorting us on our way. I have never seen creatures illustrate the nature of freedom more attractively than dolphins, and the contrast between the easy and graceful way in which they moved through their medium of water, and the painful and circumscribed way in which we lived our lives on land, profoundly affected me.

We frequently saw sharks as well. They were sometimes caught by the throwing of a running bowline into the sea. The shark would attempt to swim through the loop, upon which the knot would be tightened and the shark hauled on board, to be boiled and fried. Sometimes we were the beneficiaries of a part of the meat. Although reluctant to try it at first, I found it quite tolerable.

However, a shark was the inadvertent cause of my incurring the hostility of one of the members of the New South Wales Corps. Corporal Arnold was the keenest of the soldier-fishermen and when off duty could usually be found on deck, tending to several lines at the same time. A short, pudgy man with eyes set close together, he had a nose so red that it was difficult to look at anything else when he was speaking to me. He frequently supervised my detachment when we were scrubbing and cleaning, whether below decks or above deck, but he was disliked by, I think, all of us. He seemed to take pleasure in finding fault with every task we completed, making us redo the work over and again, accompanied by abusive language and, when he thought no one was looking, cuffs and kicks.

Pierre De Lafontaine called him a coward, but not to his face. 'When we get to New South Wales,' he said, 'I will challenge 'im. We will see what kind of man 'e is then.'

Naive as I was, even I thought it unlikely that Corporal Arnold would agree to fight a duel with a French convict.

The incident when I first attracted the corporal's wrath began with my seeing one of his fishing lines suddenly drawn down. Judging by the pressure it looked as though a sizeable fish had been hooked. Corporal Arnold and I saw it at about the same time. As he began hauling the line in I edged ever closer, attracted by the excitement of the event but still pretending to clean the deck. The struggle was a long one. Perhaps ten minutes passed before I saw the shape of the fish below the surface. I abandoned all pretence at scrubbing and called to Chris Norfolk, who was closest to me. He came over to have a look.

'A sawshark,' he said. 'You don't normally find them close to the surface.' Chris Norfolk had all sorts of knowledge, which he shared only occasionally. He was silent about his past. As far as I could tell no one knew anything of his history, but when not engaging in his unattractive habit of self-abuse he was not a bad fellow.

Several minutes more went by before Corporal Arnold was successful in dragging the shark up the side of the boat. I took a few steps forward and to the right, hoping to be able to help land the creature and thus be of some use, but in doing so I inadvertently kicked the corporal's bucket of bait. This, with the rocking of the boat, which was quite severe on this occasion, threw me off balance and I fell against the corporal, who as a result was knocked over. He let go of the line, grabbed for it again, but Chris, who was rushing in to help, tripped over him too, and by this means the line was lost; not just the line but of course the shark also.

The corporal was infuriated, and turned on me, smacking me fiercely about the face and shoulders until my head rang and I cried out with pain. I tried to protect myself but I knew there was little I could do without getting in more trouble, so I covered my head and accepted the blows, though at the same time backing away to try to evade them.

It was lucky for me that Surgeon Gossam was going past at the time, and I heard him call out: 'Corporal, what are you about? Desist, sir, before I report you to your officer.'

The corporal did desist, but with the greatest reluctance, saying sulkily to Surgeon Gossam: 'He ought to be given the cat, sir, for what he just did to me. I was merely saving the captain the trouble.'

'Well then, report him. But we'll have no rough justice on this ship. I believe you know the captain's views on the subject.'

Corporal Arnold had no more to say. He merely scowled and turned back towards me. 'Get below,' he snarled. 'And you too,' he said to Chris Norfolk.

I scuttled away. Chris followed, at a slightly more dignified pace.

This incident was to have ramifications for me that I could not have dreamed of as I clambered down the ladder to the dark underworld. I did not think much more about Corporal Arnold. After all, I was used to being in trouble, and many an adult had lifted his hand against me in the past. I was not aware of the vengeful nature of the bulbous-nosed corporal. His life was to intersect with mine again before long.

I had been developing quite a keen interest in the creatures of the sky and ocean and picking up fragments of information about them, principally from Chris Norfolk and Pierre De Lafontaine. The wild creatures were of course best observed in calm weather, such as we had enjoyed until, as I say, some three weeks into our voyage, when the wind picked up and the waves became more choppy. Thunderous grey clouds began to amass in the sky, and I could see flickers of lightning dancing among them. I heard the distant mumbling of thunder and started to feel apprehensive.

As the wind got higher, the crew were called upon to reef the main-sail. No fewer than fifteen men swarmed over the main yard, reefing it with the greatest industry and energy. One poor fellow, though, had his hand shockingly injured; he hung on to a rope that was loosened, but his hand was then trapped in a belaying pin; his knuckles were torn off and his fingers terribly cut. It seems that among sailors, however, any weakness is seen as intolerable. Cuts and bruises and heavy knocks are ignored, and even this fellow, with his hand mutilated and his face white with shock and loss of blood, appeared of stoical disposition as he hurried past me on his way to the surgeon.

The wind built up further and the temperature dropped rapidly. The ship began to roll more and more, and we were ordered to make haste down the ladders to our quarters. It was as well we did. Already a quantity of water had poured through the hatchway, and as I descended the ladder a vast rush of it engulfed me, almost knocking me from my perch. My legs lost their footing, and my right hand lost its grip, but somehow my left hand managed to cling to a rung with enough tenacity for me to recover my position once the bulk of the water had passed.

I staggered to my hammock. All around me were anxious questions from those who had not been on deck, whilst others were clearly suffering the first spasms of seasickness. My teeth were chattering too much for me to join in the conversation; I wrapped myself in my blanket and lay in my hammock shivering as the ship tossed frantically from side to side. Further down the cabin I could see Chris Norfolk's nervousness manifesting itself in his customary response. I turned my eyes from the sight.

Thus began a storm which raged for three days and had us at all times in mortal fear. Time and again the sea swept over the bulwarks, defeating the cook's attempts to light a fire, with the result that no cooking could be done and we had nothing but dry biscuit to eat. Our portholes were sealed over to prevent their being broken, and the hatches kept shut to prevent the ingress of water, which meant that apart from a couple of lanterns, we lived in perpetual darkness. Yet we could feel that at times we were teetering on the crests of high waves, and at other times, with a fearful rush, we were plunged into the abyss, much like the deep pit that Vain-Confidence fell into in Mr Bunyan's book. In fact I could not help recalling the words of the pilgrim Christian to Simple, Sloth and Presumption that they were like 'them that sleep on the top of the mast, for the Dead Sea is under you, a gulf that has no bottom'. On a number of occasions, as our little vessel seemed to plummet towards the depths of the sea, I feared that we had found the bottomless gulf and were about to be crushed by the dark ocean.

Judging by the cries and imprecations and prayers and predictions of disaster around me, I was not alone in my fears, as many times my compatriots gave themselves up for lost. So many of these men, like myself, had cheated the gallows, and thus it could be said that every day since had been a day spared from eternity, but that thought did not seem to occur to anyone other than myself, and I have to say it gave me small comfort. Wisely, considering my tender years, I refrained from pointing out the irony of the situation to the tormented souls around me.

The Frenchman, Pierre De Lafontaine, who up until then had been one of the calmer, more philosophical members of our company, roamed constantly from one end of the cabin to the other, weaving his way among the many obstacles, hugging himself and gabbling in his native tongue, with occasional bursts of English. He looked to be going mad with terror. I believe he did not sleep for the three days. At times, when the ship appeared to be almost lying on its side, he grabbed me, asking urgently: 'Are we sinking, Barnaby? Is zis the end?' I found this frightening. I had no answer of course, but although the same fears possessed me I tried to reassure him.

Surgeon Gossam visited three or four times a day, despite being badly affected by seasickness himself. I greatly admired his dedication to his profession. Of course there was little he could do to ease the chaos and distress which prevailed in every corner. He did administer coca wine to the worst cases, but to the rest had nothing to offer but ginger, which seemed to effect some benefit for a short time. He reassured us constantly, telling us of the skills of Master Marsh and the sturdiness and seaworthiness of the *Admiral Barrington*, and I found this comforting whilst he was among us, but as soon as he went away the fears returned.

Carmichael was as badly affected as anyone. Though he did not give way to the panic that reigned amidships, he was physically in a bad way, retching and vomiting for hour after hour. His stomach was soon emptied of its contents and hence little came out of his mouth. I was not spared, indeed no one was, but I was well enough to tender to Carmichael and a few others by bringing them water when possible and encouraging them to eat the dry biscuit, of which there was an abundance due to the fact that so many were unable to partake of food.

Surgeon Gossam dosed Carmichael quite a few times with coca wine, which enabled him to sleep more placidly. Carmichael developed a taste for it and was in the habit of asking Surgeon Gossam for more at every opportunity; the surgeon, however, was reluctant to dispense it too liberally, explaining that his stocks were limited.

In one of his few lucid moments, Carmichael quoted me a cure for seasickness from a Dr Samuel Johnson, which was 'to find a good big oak tree and wrap your arms around it'. I appreciated the gentleman's drollery, but resolved not to seek medical advice from Dr Samuel Johnson.

Our situation was not helped by the foul atmosphere that soon developed in our darkened quarters. Though never salubrious, except for a few hours each morning after the hold had been scrubbed out, conditions became grim indeed. The slops buckets were fastened to the walls, but the wild swings of the ship, coupled with the fact that the buckets were not emptied in the usual way, ensured that the floor, already awash with a soup of seawater and vomit, now had sewage added to the mixture. The smell became so rancid that the cook and steward, on their occasional visits with water and biscuits, wore on their faces cloths upon which they splashed scent of some kind. Even so, they were able to endure only a couple of minutes in our company before they had to flee.

Halfway through the days of storm, groping my way past the hammock I had first occupied upon boarding the *Admiral Barrington*, I became aware of a pathetic cry emanating from somewhere close by. 'Mother, Mother,' came the weak voice. 'Mother, help me, I'm sick, Mother.'

Wondering to hear such a forlorn cry amid this band of desperados, I cautiously approached its source. Much to my astonishment my search took me to the hammock of none other than Holt, the man of whom I had been so afraid when we first boarded the ship. He lay curled like a baby, in a lather of sweat, whimpering and sobbing. I fetched him a pannikin of water, which, rancid though our water was becoming by that stage, seemed to do him some good. 'Thank you, thank you,' he murmured. 'God bless you.' To my embarrassment he seized my free hand and kissed it several times before releasing it again. I crept away, feeling that as long as I lived I would never understand the ways of men. I would have to leave that to the Creator.

I returned to him regularly after that incident, tending to him as best I could, which I have to confess did not amount to much. But he seemed gradually to improve, and the fever passed. The time came when he waved me away as I approached, indicating that he no longer required my help. I had the feeling he was embarrassed at the frailty he had displayed earlier, but to tell the truth I doubt he would have remembered the words he spoke in his delirium.

When the storm at last abated, and the hatches were opened, and we staggered up the ladders into the open air, covering our eyes from the bright light, three among our number lay motionless. Their eyes were forever closed, their torments ended, and they were shortly committed to the mercies of the very ocean that had ended their lives.

Chapter 26

I N MY IGNORANCE I had no idea of our route, but the day came when we crossed the equator, and we were permitted on deck to take part in the ceremonies attendant thereupon. This was, I believe, forty days after leaving the Old Country, which was considered quite good time.

At noon of the day in question a booming voice was heard, which seemed to emanate from the ocean itself. 'Ahoy there! Ahoy!'

A sailor positioned adjacent to the poop deck replied: 'Ahoy!'

'What ship is that?' came the voice again.

'The *Admiral Barrington*,' the sailor replied.

'The *Admiral Barrington*? I don't recollect her passing this way before – I shall come on board and examine her.'

At that point an old man with a huge beard clambered on board the boat by means of a rope ladder which had been slung over the side. He was introduced to us as no less a personage than Neptune himself, though he seemed to bear a strange resemblance to one of the sailors who was known to all as a jovial fellow. With him was his wife, a particularly unattractive figure, also bearded, and of surprising muscularity, and two other attendants of similar appearance. They appeared to be wearing wigs made of some sort of spun yarn and were further disfigured with red ochre and robes. They were placed on a gun carriage, upon which they were conveyed aft, where they addressed themselves to the captain, claiming that he was carrying a number of Neptune's subjects who must be handed over at once. Master Marsh confessed that such people were indeed aboard, and all those who had not previously Crossed the Line were then summoned.

I took my place among the crowd and because of my age was the first neophyte called forward. Neptune addressed me in gruff tones, asking about my health. When I said that it was tolerably good, he requested to examine my throat. I opened my mouth and he immediately stuffed a lump of something in it, which he bade me swallow. It tasted of treacle and soap and I don't know what else, and was very foul. He then handed me a mug of water, so I could wash down his 'medicine'. I took it gratefully, but found it to be salt water. As I choked on this, he passed me on to his wife, who offered to shave me with a razor made from an iron hoop. I was reluctant but did not want to seem a 'bad sport', so nodded my assent. He had lathered up a prodigious amount of foam, which he now proceeded to paint on my face, making sure that a goodly amount went into my mouth. He then pretended to shave me, before passing me to a group of sailors who threw me into a sail full of water that they had collected and rolled me around in it for a time.

All of this would have been tolerable enough had not Corporal Arnold joined in. The sailors had just lowered a corner of the sail, to allow me to crawl out, when I noticed a different coloured uniform among the group. Suddenly Corporal Arnold's arm shot out and grabbed me around the neck. Laughing brutally, he pushed me back under the water without giving me time to take a proper breath.

I choked, got a mouthful of water, panicked, and thrashed around, trying to break his grip or get my face clear, or both. His grip only tightened and he forced me down further. My head started to feel thick and heavy and seemed to fill with a kind of cloud. I continued to flail but could feel that my arms and legs were losing strength. I did not want to open my mouth again, knowing that to inhale more water would be fatal for me, but soon my need for air was so desperate that I could keep my mouth closed no longer. I opened my mouth. Water rushed in and I felt a terrible pain run through my whole body. And then I was pulled out of the water again, coughing and choking and gasping and spitting.

Corporal Arnold dropped me on the deck, where I landed hard indeed, then kicked me in the ribs for good measure, all the time laughing heartily. I lay there, sobbing and vomiting salt water. I could hear my lungs heaving and wheezing as I tried to get air into them. 'Come on, get up you little scamp,' Corporal Arnold shouted. 'Leave the playacting to King Neptune.'

I staggered onto my hands and knees and, still gasping for breath, with long lines of spittle trailing from my mouth, crawled back to my companions. Carmichael helped me wash the foul taste out of my mouth with fresh water. Our tanks had been replenished with rainwater during the great storm and the drinking water was now quite sweet, so eventually I was recovered enough to watch the rest of the ceremony.

And in this merry way I was inducted into the select company of those who have Crossed the Line.

The goings-on that day afforded great amusement to many of the spectators, but watching the treatment meted out to others, I noticed that a number of sailors and soldiers took the opportunity to settle scores, real or imagined, with various of the convicts to whom they owed grievances. I am sorry to say that neither Master Marsh nor the bo'sun intervened, no matter how rough the horseplay. The captain's only contribution was to order half a pint of wine to be served to each of us at the conclusion of the ceremony, which at least assisted to restore my body to a better state.

Some of the old salts aboard had been talking about us making landfall at the Cape of Good Hope, and so it proved. Before this, however, we replenished our fresh water again at the Isle of Ascension where, we were told by a sailor, a man named William Dampier had been marooned, with his crew, in 1701. 'Some call him an explorer, others call him a buccaneer,' the sailor said, adding darkly: 'His boat was devoured by worms.'

Upon enquiry I learned that this was a common problem for wooden boats, with shipworms, known to sailors as the termites of the sea and growing up to a yard in length, eating their way through the hulls, with fatal consequences for the vessels.

Dampier's life on Ascension would have been lonely; it was a tiny island indeed, arid in appearance, but topped by a great peak which reminded me again, if somewhat more literally, of the Hill Difficulty which threatens to defeat Christian in *Pilgrim's Progress*. Given that the island was named Ascension, I thought it apt that Mr Bunyan quoted Christian as saying of this hill:

> *The Hill, though high, I covet to ascend,*
> *The difficulty will not me offend;*
> *For I perceive the way to life lies here:*
> *Come, pluck up, Heart, let's neither faint nor fear . . .*

From then on, when difficulties in my life seemed to conspire against me, I pictured Green Mountain on Ascension and imagined myself scaling its heights in the same way that Christian achieved the summit of Hill Difficulty.

We had a fair run, so far as I could judge, from Ascension to the Cape of Good Hope, which we sighted at the very moment I was rereading *Pilgrim's Progress* and had come to the scene where Hopeful joins Christian on his journey. At first sight, the Cape of Good Hope seemed likely to meet the expectations raised by its name. The imposing mountain range in the background, reputedly above three thousand feet in height, was impressive indeed, though somewhat dark and threatening. The town looked clean and well tended, despite the frequent clouds of dust raised by the strong winds blowing from the tableland. We dropped anchor in Table Bay, where we saw a great range of ships; not as many as in Portsmouth Harbour, but a wider variety, and sailing under all manner of flags. We were close enough to read the signs on the shops, but also close enough to see a row of gallows, which should have been a familiar enough sight to me but which still struck terror and sickness into my heart. As well, however, I could see on the shore a row of wheels. My fellow felons were quick enough to tell me their use, delighting as they did in all matters pertaining to crime and punishment, the more grotesque the better. It seemed that the function of the wheels was to facilitate the execution of a condemned man by tying him in outstretched fashion to one of them and then smashing each of his limbs in turn with a heavy wooden bar or an iron hammer, followed by the smashing of his spine, after which the wheel was placed upright, against a vertical stake, and the man left to die a prolonged death. It was said, with relish by the more violent and vicious among us, that birds would sometimes feed from the man's body as he waited helplessly for release from his earthly cares. In Cape Town I believe this pleasant practice was embellished by the cutting off of the right hand of the felon, which was then nailed to the side of the wheel.

The sharper-eyed among us swore that they could see several bodies attached to the wheels, and indeed, when I could bring myself to look, I discerned shapes which may have been human, a sight which distressed me greatly. When I spoke to Carmichael Lance about it, he made no comment for a long time, but stood on the deck gazing at the top of the mountain. Eventually, without looking at me, he said: 'I wonder why it is, my young friend, that men put so much time and thought into devising ever more horrible ways to torture and kill each other.' When I did not answer, he added: 'You would think that they might find other matters to contemplate.'

We were not permitted to go ashore while the ship lay at anchor, but watched hungrily as the sailors and soldiers took their turns at shore leave. Judging from their condition as they returned, they made the most of their opportunities. A rumour spread that a number of sailors had to be bailed from the local prison for fighting, at a cost to the captain of five dollars per head.

To make things worse for us, we were ironed again, as the captain feared that escape attempts might be made, with such a tempting vista spread before us. It was a terrible inconvenience to be reduced to the slow shuffle of the convict again, but also it weighed upon my spirits to be reminded so bitterly of my loss of freedom.

We did at least benefit from a welcome improvement in our rations. Those who had money were able to purchase bread, grapes, fish, sausages, tobacco, pears and apples at very fair prices from bumboats that visited the ship. But all of us had the advantage of supplies of fresh mutton and beef, fruit and vegetables, and of course water, and a great relief this was, and a great boon to our health.

Nonetheless it was galling to stay in our cramped and confined quarters and to see such a beautiful and spacious land within a stone's throw, knowing all the while that we would not be permitted to set foot upon it. The greatest pleasures we were able to derive from Cape Town was the calmness of our anchorage, after the weeks of rocking and swaying, and the opportunity to scrub out our quarters and indeed the whole ship. After my years of living in an area of London where people swarmed like maggots in cheese, and where I had known nothing but squalor and filth, I had become somewhat enamoured of cleanliness. It may have been partly the influence of Carmichael Lance, who managed to stay scrupulously neat even in the debilitating circumstances in which we found ourselves. He was as precise in his arrangement of his possessions and the maintenance of his toilet as he was in his use of language.

So we scrubbed and scrubbed, as other members of the ship's company disported themselves ashore. From time to time, both at Cape Town and during the voyage, those convicts who helped the crew or performed other services adjudged worthy of merit were rewarded with an issue of a glass of rum. We were so rewarded at least a dozen times during our stay in Table Bay, so the master and the bo'sun must have thought we were doing a fair job. The rum was of some benefit to me, as although I did not drink it, not being enamoured of the taste, I was able to trade it with my fellows for grapes and bread and apples. Verily I think this diet suited me better than the rum suited my shipmates, for I was in particularly good health during this time and started to acquire more vigour than had recently been the case.

Chapter 27

WE DEPARTED CAPE TOWN after eight days, short four sailors and two soldiers who had deserted during our stay. I was saddened to note that Corporal Arnold was not among them. Master Marsh had, according to shipboard gossip, made strenuous efforts to recover the missing men, but without success.

We also lost one of our own, an ex-soldier named Seamus O'Mahoney, who had been transported for life on a charge of mutiny. He had, by repute, received a thousand lashes as part of his sentence, though I do not understand how anyone could survive such a terrible punishment. The cause of his death was not known to me, but he was taken ashore by the soldiers and buried on land.

Despite this sad passing, I would have to say that crew and convicts alike were in fairly good spirits. We had a journey of six thousand five hundred miles ahead of us, but the respite in Cape Town had refreshed all on board. A number of the more trusted convicts who had been to sea previously, or were strong and capable, were recruited to replace the deserters. A day out of Cape Town we had our irons removed again, and the bo'sun informed us that we would be permitted up on deck more frequently for the remainder of the voyage. This proved to be the case, although the motivation for it was not entirely philanthropic, as a good deal of old tarry ropes and cordage had been taken on board at Cape Town and we were put to work unravelling it into fibre. I was informed that this was the trade known as 'picking oakum', though I was the only one on board who appeared ignorant of its nature, it being a popular occupation assigned to prisoners in His Majesty's gaols. The tarred fibre was apparently used for caulking the timber in ships.

The men were expected to pick two pounds per day, but because of my age I was let off lightly, having to produce only one pound per day. I was reliably informed that when we got to New South Wales the oakum could be sold for at least five guineas a hundredweight, so a tidy profit appeared likely to be made by someone as a result of our efforts.

Somehow, both above and below decks, we had arrived at the mutual understanding that is necessary if any society is to survive, and our unlikely company, ranging from a naive child such as myself, to the most desperate and brutish villains, was a society of sorts. At times we made accommodations for each other, usually in simple ways, like lending a tin knife to a man who had lost his, or picking extra oakum for a man who was not going to reach his daily quota, or helping a fellow up if he fell on deck. On one occasion I saw a sailor who would have been washed overboard as he came down from reefing the topsail, save that a prisoner grabbed him by the trousers and pulled him back.

I had never lived communally before, so everything was new to me. I observed how, as the trip went on, the quieter members of our company were generally left alone, the humourists drew people to them as a lantern attracts moths, the oafs were largely ignored and the men of integrity won respect. A man who could tell a good yarn was also highly regarded, and on many a night silence would settle through the cabin as one of the favourite storytellers regaled his neighbours with a new tale.

Carmichael had said to me: 'There's nothing worse than a man who is talked out after a couple of days.'

'What do you mean?' I had asked, a question I frequently found myself addressing to Carmichael.

'I mean,' he had said, 'that some men run out of stories, of conversation, in no time at all. Either so little has happened to them or, more likely, they are incapable of understanding or retaining what has happened to them, and so they soon find themselves with nothing to say. Such a man makes a terrible companion.'

Fearful of losing Carmichael's friendship, I resolved to try to retain the stories of my life.

There was plenty of singing, by both sailors and convicts, though we mostly heard the sailors' songs whilst they were on deck and at work. They used songs in order to achieve the rhythm they needed for the job they were doing; for example, when they were at the topsail halliards and they needed to pull together, they sang:

Hurrah, my boys, we're homeward bound,
Hurrah, my boys, hurrah . . .

The convicts' songs tended to be either bawdy or comical or maudlin. But the political prisoners had a leaning towards songs that were critical of conditions in Great Britain, or, as many of them were Irish, their own country:

I'm a four loom weaver, as many a one knows.
I've naught to eat and I've worn out my clothes.

My clogs are both broken, and stockings I've none.
They'd hardly give me tuppence for all I'm getting on
Old Billy at Bent, he kept telling me long
We might have better times if I'd not but hold my tongue.
Well, I've held my tongue till I've near lost my breath
And I feel in my heart that I'll soon starve to death . . .

My favourite, which never failed to draw a tear from my eye, was
'Barbara Allen':

All in the merry month of May,
When green buds they were swelling,
Young Willie Grove on his death-bed lay,
For love of Barbara Allen.

He sent his servant to her door
To the town where he was dwelling,
'Haste ye come, to my master's call,
If your name be Barbara Allen.'

So slowly, slowly got she up,
And slowly she drew nigh him,
And all she said when there she came:
'Young man, I think you're dying.'

He turned his face unto the wall
And death was drawing nigh him.
'Goodbye, goodbye to dear friends all,
Be kind to Barbara Allen.'

When he was dead and laid in grave,
She heard the death bell knelling.
And every note, did seem to say
'Oh, cruel Barbara Allen.'

'Oh mother, mother, make my bed
Make it soft and narrow
Sweet William died, for love of me,
And I shall die of sorrow.'

They buried her in the old churchyard
Sweet William's grave was nigh hers,
And from his grave grew a red, red rose
From hers a cruel briar.

I found it deeply affecting, but Carmichael pooh-poohed it as maudlin. He preferred the old hymns of his childhood, such as 'When I Survey the Wondrous Cross', 'A Mighty Fortress Is Our God', and 'Amazing Grace'.

Amazing grace, how sweet the sound,
That saves a wretch like me.
I once was lost, but now I'm found,
Was blind, but now I see.

There were occasions when a largish number of the convicts, moved by a rare fit of piety, sang hymns, but mostly they were the province of a sanctimonious group of older men who called themselves devout Christians, and who met every day at one end of our quarters for prayers and singing. Carmichael never joined them, and indeed seemed to despise them, but I often saw his lips moving in time with their songs, and occasionally heard the words emanating quietly from his mouth.

It may seem from my account of the voyage that our lives were truly miserable, but in fact there were many moments of levity. I have observed elsewhere in my life that nothing can restore harmony in a group so quickly as laughter. At times the laughter on the *Admiral Barrington* would be at the expense of one of our own number, but truth to tell the derision was often well merited, being aimed at a man who for good reasons had failed to make a positive impression upon his fellows. Among these were the braggarts, especially those who had boasted of careers as wicked desperados, but who were later exposed as frauds. It seems odd that convicts would have such contempt for liars, when so many of them had made lying their lifetime occupation, but they were merciless towards those who exaggerated their misdeeds. A man named Marmaduke Wyatt had waxed grandiloquently on the tumbrel from London about his exploits. To hear him talk was to believe that you were in the company of the arch-fiend of the British Isles. He claimed to have robbed the Duke of Cumberland on the King's highway somewhere near Canterbury, to have murdered a coachman who tried to disarm him, to have picked the pocket of a justice of the high court. As a credulous child I had listened spellbound to these stories and had thought Mr Wyatt a formidable fellow indeed. It was only after he had been on board a few days that the truth emerged: he had been sentenced to transportation for two crimes, one somewhat similar to that committed by the late Mr Ogwell, and the other, the theft of a lace shawl from a baby in a perambulator in Hyde Park.

Once this information came to light Mr Wyatt was treated with derision by all and sundry and became the object of many a practical joke.

He was proud enough to have his own night bottle in which to pass water, but as he used it one evening he was disconcerted to find that its bottom had been pierced in several places and he was wetting his boots with his stream. On another occasion the slops buckets were placed in a circle around his hammock, so that when he got up in the morning he stepped straight into one of them.

Some of the jokes were undoubtedly cruel. Mr Wyatt constantly found items of clothing, especially his cap, missing. One night the men caught a live rat and hid it under his blanket, so that it jumped out at him when he climbed into his hammock. Particularly disgusting was the use of his boots one night for functions intended to be performed in a slops bucket. Corporal Arnold told him to throw them overboard, but knowing that he would never be issued another pair, Mr Wyatt somehow found a way to clean them out; after a fashion, at least. From then on he slept with his boots in his bed, clutched tightly to his chest.

Not all jokes, however, were at anyone's expense. A man named Angus Buchan made himself a great reputation by presenting occasional concerts, using the most unusual musical instrument I ever did hear or see. Mr Buchan had perfected the art of performing well-known popular songs by the manner in which he broke wind. His rendition of 'Rule Britannia' was always a great favourite, and men would laugh until tears ran down their faces at the spectacle of him peering around at his audience with a droll expression whilst emitting his peculiar tunes.

I have written about King Neptune's arrival on the boat for the ceremony of Crossing the Line, but some weeks before that, a month out from Portsmouth, we had been allowed on deck while the sailors 'burned the dead horse'. This inexplicable ceremony, which I confess I found rather more enjoyable than Neptune's visitation, was somehow related to the fact that the sailors were given a month's pay in advance, before beginning any long voyage, but because they almost invariably spent the money whilst still in port, they were fond of saying that they had worked the first month 'for nothing'.

When this month expired, they made a horse out of the various materials they found to hand, such as sailcloth, and some tarry material which they stuffed into a barrel to make the body. A sailor dressed himself as a jockey, and he and the horse took their places upon a gun carriage and were hauled around the deck by the sailors as they sang various shanties. They pulled up on the poop deck, from which an auctioneer called for bids for the noble steed, after listing its various qualities. The officers, and the paying passengers, of whom there were but a few, pooled their funds to make a bid that the auctioneer found acceptable. This money was distributed among the sailors, and the horse was then dragged under the yardarm, whence he was hoisted. When he had reached the highest point possible, he was ignited, and we had the grand spectacle of blue flames burning in the moonlight until they went out, at which point the old horse leapt from the yardarm into the sea, with a little help from his attendants, and accompanied by the cheers of the spectators.

The captain subsequently spliced the main brace and handed out rum to all, including the convicts, but the sailors continued to drink and celebrate long after we had been confined to our quarters once again. No one seemed to have the least idea of the origins of this peculiar ceremony, but it afforded amusement to all.

In keeping with the natural instincts of men, many opportunities were found for races and competitions. One fine day the crew held a race from the lowest rat line to the top of the foremast; the winner was a big Irishman, in the remarkable time of two minutes and eleven seconds. The more active convicts held races around our cramped quarters from time to time, but these were more in the nature of obstacle events than true races, as some of the men did everything possible to obstruct the competitors, putting out a leg to trip them, throwing mugs and pillows, and even bodily tackling them from behind. The captains of the deck sometimes tried to put a halt to these raucous proceedings but were invariably howled down for their attempts.

Needless to say, and despite Surgeon Gossam's injunctions when we first came on board, prisoners played games with dice and cards, and gambled on anything and everything. One young fellow had nothing to eat for three days because he bet his rations on the roll of the dice. Another lost his boots when he bet them on a race that had been organised between two cockroaches. Opposite me, early in the voyage, two men had bet on the number of fleas they could find and kill in a given time. They appointed me their umpire, and I had to count to one hundred slowly, by the end of which time one man was able to display forty-one bodies to his rival's thirty-three.

Although vermin constantly irritated us, this at least was nothing new to me, as they had irritated me all my life. The care given by Surgeon Gossam on the *Admiral Barrington* was, however, superior to anything I had experienced previously. He strongly believed that most of the eruptions to which we were prone were owing to improper food and the neglect of cleanliness. When we came on board, I think it fair to say that most of us were swarming with vermin and were covered with the scab, itch and other maladies. The most stubborn of all the eruptions I suffered was scabbed head. Surgeon Gossam's remedy was to have my head shaved once a week, and then washed daily with soap suds and anointed with liniment. This proved very effective.

I suffered also from threadworm and had probably done so all my life. For this, Surgeon Gossam prescribed a potion which he informed me was a mixture of apple cider vinegar, horseradish and glycerine.

It tasted potent indeed, and was most unpleasant, but seemed to achieve some amelioration of my condition.

Fleas and lice, cockroaches and rats, infested our quarters in large numbers, and when our party arrived from Newgate, covered in vermin, we made the situation worse. However, the constant insistence by Surgeon Gossam on hygiene and cleanliness, the daily scrubbings, the frequent baths and the regular meals, monotonous though they were, slowly brought about a noticeable improvement in the health of most men aboard. For a time after Cape Town the situation deteriorated, but Surgeon Gossam did not relent in the assiduity of his application, and the parasites were once again forced into slow retreat.

For a number of our company, from the more remote parts of Britain such as Scotland and Ireland, notions of cleanliness were primitive indeed. Some men thought nothing of using their mess tins as privies when they passed a bowel motion. Quite frequently they were caught squatting wherever they found convenient, which was just as likely to be under the hammock of one of their neighbours. They avoided baths at all costs, which was understandable during cold weather, but on warm days I found it pleasant to jump into the tub on the deck, especially as, by virtue of my age, I was indulged by being one of the first invited to take advantage of the facility. I concede that it would not have been such an attractive prospect to be the last in the tub, as by then the water was the consistency of sludge.

I have set out in this chapter of my memoirs to make it clear that the voyage to Botany Bay was not, on the *Admiral Barrington*, the horrific experience that many on other vessels have described. Mine is not always a popular point of view, as there is, in my opinion, a certain class of convict who likes to exaggerate his trials and tribulations, and make great capital out of recounting his sufferings, in order to excite public sympathy and to incite hatred against the authorities. Many a time have I seen one of my fellows from the *Admiral Barrington* sitting in a tavern or a coffee shop earnestly reciting the tortures he endured, particularly when his audience is a member of the female sex on whom he evidently wishes to make an impression. When I see the lady leaning forward, her hand upon the sufferer's knee as she expresses her sympathy with brimming eyes and consoling touch, I am tempted to say to her as I pass, 'You know the greatest deprivation this old humbug endured was to spill his wine one night in a storm,' but I am not one to queer another fellow's pitch, as the saying goes, so I keep my counsel. And I am of course aware of the severe privations suffered on some ships. For example I have friends who came out on the *Hillsborough*, which docked in Sydney Harbour in July 1799, and which recorded ninety-five deaths from the three hundred convicts who had embarked in England. I believe they lost fifty in Cape Town alone, and the captain threw several of the bodies unceremoniously overboard, because the authorities on shore were becoming alarmed at the number of deaths and he wished the corpses to drift out to sea. However, his attempt at concealment did not work when they washed up on the beach the next day.

Yes, the prisoners on the *Hillsborough* have stories of neglect and ill treatment that would make a man envy an African on a slave ship as having the better passage, and which make me grateful I was spared that particular voyage, under an odious captain and a reckless surgeon.

The fact that we had nothing like such a dreadful toll must, I believe, be attributed to Surgeon Gossam, whose dedication was exceptional, and who would go to the captain if necessary to advocate on our behalf. And I pay tribute to Master Marsh, who had nothing of the sadist about him, unlike some captains, but who ran a fair ship and was greatly respected by crew and convicts alike.

Chapter 28

ALL OF THE FOREGOING is not to understate of course the general sense of dismay at the state in which we were kept, as well as fear and despair for the unknown dangers that awaited us in New South Wales. And it is not to deny that there were many unpleasant incidents. Not a day passed without arguments and fights, some of which, such as the stabbing I described earlier, had fatal consequences. Not a day passed that those noble representatives of His Majesty's Forces, the members of the New South Wales Corps, did not come swaggering through our quarters, knocking aside anyone within their reach, knocking down anyone who showed insufficient respect and kicking mess tins and mugs out of their way. Chief among these was Corporal Arnold.

Carmichael said to me one day, as we were reading *Pilgrim's Progress* again: 'What do you think, Barnaby, are the greatest passions to be found in the bosoms of Man?'

After some thought, I ventured to suggest that love and hate might fit the bill.

He nodded. 'Yes, I suggest that most of the population would give the same response. And I will grant you love. But hate – what is that? It is a word that is used too freely.'

I tried to look as though I was following what he said, although I had difficulty with much of his conversation, especially when he was in a reflective state of mind, as appeared to be the case on this occasion.

'No,' he continued, 'I would say fear, anger and greed are at least equal with love, if they do not surpass it. I include greed for power and social station in that. And I would rank lethargy almost as highly.'

I did not even know what lethargy was, but Carmichael continued without noticing. I felt that sometimes when he was purportedly talking to me he was really talking to himself, trying to make sense of the nature of the world and of the human beings who dwelled in it. 'Your friend Corporal Arnold,' he said, 'I would put him down as one who is driven by fear and anger above all else. And that makes him dangerous.'

'But of what would he be fearful? And why would he be angry?' I asked.

'I think,' said Carmichael, taking his time, 'that he may well be fearful that he cannot assert enough authority over people like us. Such men as he are deathly afraid that if they cannot effectively wield the power that has been placed in their hands they may be overwhelmed by the rabble.' He looked around him, at the men gambling, arguing, sleeping, singing, walking up and down or around and around in desperate response to our confinement. He looked at Chris Norfolk, idly engaged in his usual occupation. Carmichael sighed. 'Yes, the rabble,' he said again. 'In my youth, a number of my schoolmasters at Mr Pine's establishment were of similar disposition. And as for anger, I suspect that your friend has some inkling that he is right to hold the fears that he does. He is failing, he has failed, he will always fail. Nothing makes a man more angry than constant failure. No doubt Corporal Arnold believes he should be a general, instead of which he will be fortunate if he is still a corporal at the end of this trip. In fact he will be lucky if he survives this trip.'

As soon as he said the last sentence his eyes flickered around to see if anyone had heard, but Carmichael always talked quietly, and no one was particularly close to us at the time.

'What do you mean?' I hissed, sitting up excitedly.

'I should not have said that,' Carmichael said. 'You will oblige me by forgetting those words.'

We stared at each other. I did not want to leave it at that, but I knew Carmichael would not speak again of the matter if he did not wish to. I tried again anyhow. 'What do you mean?' I repeated.

He shook his head. Then he seemed to reconsider. He said flatly: 'Do you know there have been five floggings since this voyage began, and four of them have been as a result of complaints laid by Corporal Arnold?'

It was my turn to shake my head. 'It is unwise for an isolated man to make enemies,' Carmichael said. 'He is not popular with the other members of the Corps, and he is hated by some of our shipmates below decks here.' He leaned forward and spoke with great intensity. 'I tell you this for a reason, Barnaby Fletch. Keep well clear of Corporal Arnold when you can. If anything happens to him, you do not want to be in the vicinity.'

He sat back and resumed his customary appearance of indifference. I felt rather as I had done when Corporal Arnold held me by the neck and nearly drowned me in the sail filled with water. I found it difficult to get air, I felt pain through my body and a tingling in my extremities.

Unfortunately, however, I was not always able to follow Carmichael's advice to stay clear of Corporal Arnold. One morning between Cape Town and Botany Bay we were on deck when a massive hailstorm broke over us. Within minutes the deck was covered to the depth of several inches by hailstones, some of which were the size of limes. Before the soldiers could get us down the hatch a hail fight had erupted and missiles were flying in every direction. Several of the less popular crew members and soldiers were heavily bombarded, to which they did not take kindly, but there was nothing they could do to prevent the assault. I participated with enthusiasm, but met my comeuppance when I threw a hailstone as hard as I could at Corporal Arnold and hit him in the left eye. Unfortunately for me, he saw that I was the perpetrator. Snarling, his face suffused with rage, he came at me like a mad bull, but he could not get traction on the slippery deck with his military boots. Suddenly his feet went from under him and he crashed heavily onto the deck, on his front. 'Get down below quickly,' Carmichael whispered to me, and I did not hesitate to obey, as the soldiers were now succeeding in marshalling my fellow prisoners.

My skin felt like ice, but when the coldness faded I found I had plenty of stinging red marks of my own. Still I feared for my fate when I next crossed paths with Corporal Arnold.

I did not see him again that day, but the following day I was one of those designated to take the slops buckets up on deck at first light and tip them over the rails into the ocean. It was, needless to say, of the utmost importance on these occasions to ascertain the direction in which the wind was blowing, and so we stood on deck for a few moments working out the best place to stand in order to deposit the contents of the buckets.

Just as we moved off again, towards the starboard rail, a stocky figure loomed out of the mist and, leading with his elbow, deliberately crashed into me, knocking me sideways onto the deck and, perforce, causing the ordure to spill. The figure moved away as quickly as it had arrived, but I recognised Corporal Arnold easily enough.

My first concern was with the mess. Nothing would offend a sailor more than to see such an unsightly stain on the deck. The only protection I had from the wrath of the crew was the mist, which might give me a few moments grace before a sailor stumbled upon the filth.

I had something else to protect me, though, something I had not counted upon: my fellow convicts. There were five other members of the group appointed to empty the buckets, but I knew none of them well, although Holt, my erstwhile neighbour, was one of them. For a few long moments they were as paralysed as I, staring in horror at the mess. Then Holt suddenly said, in his low, barking voice: 'All right, look lively, men, you know where the mops are.'

I had rarely seen a convict move quickly or work hard since our vessel had left Portsmouth Harbour, but suddenly they sprang as one for the lockers in which the mops and scrubbing brushes and buckets were kept. We got in each other's way trying to get the equipment out. Holt and one other began drawing up buckets of salt water from the sea, to wash down the decks. The rest of us mopped and mopped. The task seemed endless, but the mist remained our friend. A sailor went past, and scowled when he saw the slops on the deck, but the sight of us working so frantically might have placated him, because he said nothing and went on his way. Two more sailors loomed up. They looked, frowned, and one of them said: 'You'd better get every last drop of that shit out of the timber, and quick smart too.'

'Aye aye sir,' Holt said, and I think his deferential attitude impressed them, because they too went on their way.

We were almost done, rinsing the mops yet again, trying to remove the detritus caught in their strands, when two sergeants of the New

South Wales Corps appeared, with a third man, whom I realised, to my apprehension, was Corporal Arnold. 'Here you are, gentlemen,' he said, in his usual bluff, loud voice as he approached. 'Just as I told you. The pigs have fouled the trough. Or at least the little piglet has.'

I thought suddenly of Job, plagued without mercy or justice, subjected to endless cruel sufferings. All he could do was endure, and hope that one day a meaning or purpose to his privations might be revealed. For now, I could discern no greater power at work in my own destiny. We convicts stood there grimly, staring at the three men. I recognised the two sergeants of course. No doubt Corporal Arnold had chosen them carefully. They were known to all the prisoners as bullies and thugs.

Powerlessness was our daily experience, and the sensation of it was once again being strongly impressed upon us.

Yet all three of the soldiers, as they looked around, seemed a trifle disconcerted. One of them said to Corporal Arnold, in a low voice: 'There's not much here to go on.' The other said in a sarcastic tone: 'You woke us up for this?'

'I'm telling you, I saw him do it,' Arnold answered fiercely. 'He just laughed and emptied the buckets right across the deck.'

I felt weak at the knees in the face of such a calumny. I could scarcely believe that a man would lie in such a cold-blooded manner. Although I had been exposed to a great deal of wickedness and depravity in my short life, I felt that this, in its cold-bloodedness, represented a new nadir.

Trying to formulate an answer, I could only stammer, but as my lips struggled to form the first syllable, Holt spoke. 'You filthy cur,' he growled at Arnold. 'We all saw what happened. You ain't worth swinging for, you ain't.'

The corporal, red-faced, made as if to answer, but before he could say a word, Holt took a swing at him. If the punch had connected properly I do not doubt that Corporal Arnold would have been stretched unconscious on the deck. However, he avoided its full impact and caught only a glancing blow to the cheek and ear. It did knock him off balance; he went down on his haunches, shaking his head and putting a hand to the side of his mouth, as if his teeth had been loosened.

He did not have to do anything more. The sergeants leapt upon Holt and, assisted by Arnold as he recovered, pinioned him and wrestled him to the deck. It took all of their strength to do it. They knelt on him, panting and cursing, then one of them called for help. Sailors came and took over the task of holding my protector down, while the sergeants went for leg irons. We completed our task of emptying the slops buckets under the strictest supervision and were then escorted below.

At some stage during the furore the mist had cleared, suddenly and completely. I had not noticed it at the time, but in the full bright light of the morning I saw Holt being dragged away by the sergeants, with Corporal Arnold following, still holding his jaw as though trying to keep it in one piece.

Chapter 29

I HAD BY THIS TIME acquired sufficient understanding of the world to be reasonably sure that Holt had deliberately sacrificed himself for me. In the uproar created by his attack upon Corporal Arnold I had been overlooked, and my alleged sin forgotten.

Trembling with the shock of what I had seen, and my fear for Holt's fate, I told Carmichael the story. He nodded. 'I'm sure you're right. He is a good man, Michael Holt. A simple man, but a good one. He would have done it with full awareness of the consequences.'

'What will happen to him?' I asked.

'The captain will hold an inquiry. You may be called to give evidence. But at the end of it, Michael will be punished. The captain is no fool, and he will not take long to work out the rights of the matter, but it is the way of the world that men like him believe discipline is more important than justice, and they cannot see that the two are always compatible.'

Once again I was not sure of his meaning, but he was right about an inquiry being called, and right also about my having to give evidence.

About three hours later, and for the third time in my brief life, I found myself facing a tribunal constituted to rule upon a matter of law. This was held in the crew's mess room, a place I had, needless to say, never frequented before. Master Marsh sat at the head of the table, with Captain Phillips of the New South Wales Corps at his right-hand side, and slightly behind him. Holt, shackled, had been placed at the other end of the table. The corporal and the two sergeants were seated along the side of the table, facing me.

I have to confess I found this arrangement most confronting. Consider, a boy of thirteen facing three grown men, all of them in uniform, all of whom he knows to be aggressive and unpleasant, and knowing that if he speaks the truth it will be thoroughly and violently resented by all three soldiers . . . I broke out in a fit of trembling, and to try to calm myself turned my eyes to Michael Holt.

For a man who had cried out to his mother in the most piteous tones during the big storm, Holt looked remarkably composed. He sat with his eyes fixed upon the ship's captain. He could have been carved from rock, so motionless was his form. Yet when I looked at him, his eyes flickered across to me and he gazed at me as steadily as he had surveyed Master Marsh. I had the sense that the two men at opposite ends of the table mirrored each other, and that no one else in the room mattered very much. I drew comfort from Holt's strength.

Master Marsh ascertained from me my name and my age, then asked: 'Do you know the difference between truth and lies, Barnaby?'

I was somewhat affronted by the question, but also disconcerted by his use of my Christian name. From persons in authority I was more accustomed to 'Fletch' or 'Prisoner 227'.

'Yes, sir, of course,' I said.

'What happens to people who tell lies, Barnaby?'

'Why, sir, I believe they go to eternal damnation.'

He held up his notebook. 'And if I say to you that this object is a piece of cheese, would you call that the truth or a lie?'

'Sir, I would not believe you capable of telling a lie, so I would say, begging your pardon, that you had made an error.'

He smiled, rather grimly. I thought the questions were patronising, but they helped settle me down, because they were so easy to answer. He turned to Captain Phillips. 'I find the witness capable of distinguishing between truth and lies, and therefore acceptable to this hearing,' he said. I realised then that his questions had been a response to some objection expressed by Captain Phillips before I came into the room.

Captain Phillips did not answer, merely nodded, somewhat sulkily I thought. The master resumed his interrogation of me. 'Now, at around five bells this morning, you were on the foredeck of this vessel, with a group of other prisoners, including this man here,' he nodded at Holt, 'engaged upon the task of emptying the slops buckets over the rail?'

'Yes, sir,' I said.

'And the contents of several buckets were spilled upon the deck?'

'Yes, sir, the two buckets I was holding, sir,' I said. Feeling the trembling begin again, and without looking at the three soldiers opposite me, I launched into a statement that I knew would spell huge trouble for me from Corporal Arnold. 'The corporal here came . . .'

Captain Phillips cut me off quickly. 'How the muck came to be spilled upon the deck is immaterial,' he said.

Master Marsh considered this for a moment. 'Aye, sir, I agree,' he said.

I did not know whether to feel concerned for Michael Holt, because I felt that he had a better chance of getting off if the evidence about Corporal Arnold was admitted, or relieved that I would not have to confront the wrath of the corporal as soon as he had an opportunity to gain revenge upon me.

Master Marsh addressed me again. 'You and the prisoners set about cleaning the deck? And then the three soldiers approached you?'

'Yes, sir.'

'What happened next?'

'Corporal Arnold accused me of deliberately upending the buckets.' I paused, confused. The two officers had just agreed that I was not to speak about how the buckets were spilled, but I could not see how I could answer Master Marsh's question without revealing Corporal Arnold's involvement. I decided that I had to go, like Christian, to a place where I greatly feared to go.

I took a deep breath and said, as steadily as I could, 'But the corporal was lying. He had deliberately knocked me over . . .'

Before I could continue, Corporal Arnold was on his feet. 'Sir! I protest! Am I to sit here and have my reputation impugned by this mere . . . this convicted thief and liar?'

Master Marsh looked at him steadily. 'Sir, you will sit down. We are here to take evidence. It is my job, and that of Captain Phillips, to determine truth and falsehoods.'

Corporal Arnold looked like he had been hit by another hailstone, a huge one, and this time full in the face. He went red, blinked several times, and flopped down heavily in his chair. Then he seemed to gather himself and leaned forward, deliberately and cold-bloodedly glaring at me across the table with narrowed eyes.

'Corporal, you will sit back in your chair,' Master Marsh said. 'If I believe you are attempting to intimidate the witness, I will send you from the room.'

There was an awful silence. Even Captain Phillips looked shaken.

He opened his mouth, said, 'I . . .' but did not proceed any further. Corporal Arnold sat back as ordered, folded his arms and turned his gaze to a water jug which was held in a bracket affixed to the centre of the table.

Master Marsh said to Captain Phillips: 'It seems that we will have to reverse our earlier ruling and hear evidence about the spillage of the slops buckets.'

I realised that, despite their abilities and experience, they were not at ease with legal matters. They were, I think, practical men, both no doubt more comfortable out of doors.

Captain Phillips did not respond, so Master Marsh turned back to me and asked: 'I will put it to you this way, to save us the necessity of becoming becalmed on this issue. I take it that you would assert that Corporal Arnold pushed you, and this resulted in the buckets being spilled.'

I nodded dumbly, and he continued: 'So when the corporal accused you of deliberately fouling the decks . . . what happened next? The man Holt became involved?'

I nodded. 'Yes, sir. He told the corporal that we had all seen what happened. He sort of jumped at the corporal. I . . . I think he was trying to protect me.'

'And he hit the corporal?'

'I . . . Well, yes, he did, sir, but not very hard. I . . . He felt an injustice was being done.'

'We are not interested in your opinion,' Captain Phillips said smoothly.

'Does anyone have any questions for the lad?' Master Marsh asked.

Captain Phillips asked me: 'For what crime are you being transported, Fletch?'

'For theft, sir, of a purse and its contents.'

'And I suppose you would say that you are innocent of the charge?' he said in a tone that was unmistakably sneering.

'No, sir, indeed, I did steal it.'

'And what other crimes have you committed?'

I gulped. It was a big question, and an honest answer would reflect no credit on me. Thankfully I was saved by Master Marsh. 'By your leave, sir, I will rephrase the question,' he said. 'My understanding is that at English law a man cannot be compelled to incriminate himself.'

'You're deuced sensitive to these scoundrels, sir,' grumbled the captain, red-faced and staring up at the ceiling. I felt he did not have the courage to meet Master Marsh's eyes as he criticised him. Master Marsh seemed unruffled. He asked me: 'Have you been convicted of any other crimes, Barnaby, apart from the theft of the purse?'

'And its contents. No, sir, none.'

There was a pause. It seemed that no one else had any questions. Master Marsh nodded at me. 'You may leave, Barnaby. Can I trust you to return to your quarters unescorted?'

I suddenly felt a foot higher, that he would speak to me with such courtesy. 'Aye aye, sir,' I said as smartly as I could. He gave a little smile. I turned to go, deliberately catching Holt's eye as I did. I nodded and smiled at him, but he did not respond as I quit the room.

Chapter 30

ABOUT TWO HOURS LATER all convicts were marshalled upon deck. Master Marsh addressed us, as he had done on previous occasions, most notably upon the execution of Thomas Ffolkes. This time he was rather more peremptory in his remarks. He announced that the convict Holt had been found guilty by a properly constituted tribunal of striking a member of His Majesty's Forces. 'Such conduct cannot be tolerated, whatever the circumstances,' Master Marsh said. 'The prisoner is sentenced to forty lashes. Bo'sun, do your duty.'

I gasped in horror. Although this was the lowest number of strokes yet administered as a punishment during my time on the *Admiral Barrington*, I was overwhelmed by the injustice. My faith in Master Marsh was shattered. I gave a little sob as Holt was brought forward. He marched to the crosspiece which had been fastened to the mast. He looked more steady than I felt, even though I was not the one being punished. Upon his shirt being stripped from him and the order given, he stepped into the box which had been secured on the deck, and which was designed to keep his feet fixed and spread. His wrists were then fastened to the crossbar.

I have forborne in this narrative to describe a flogging, although I had already witnessed five on board the *Admiral Barrington*. They are vile affairs, and I am convinced that far from reforming a man, they are inclined to harden him and make him even more intractable. At any rate, this one disgusted every fair-minded prisoner on board, for by now all had heard the circumstances of Holt's arrest.

The bo'sun took up his position, ran his fingers through the cats to separate them, and then laid on. By the fourth stroke bright blood was beading on Holt's white skin, and by the seventh, trickles were running freely down his body. By the tenth his flesh was swollen and his back looked like a rack of lamb hanging in a butcher's shop. With each succeeding stroke the bo'sun found it more difficult to separate his cats, because of the clots of bloodied flesh sticking them together.

Through all this, Michael Holt uttered not a sound. I marvelled at the contradictory nature of a man who sobbed for his mother when he was seasick but could take a flogging without so much as a whimper.

Somewhere between the tenth and fifteenth strokes, something strange and without precedent happened. Several men in the front row of the parade of convicts slowly turned their backs on the spectacle. Almost instantly a dozen more followed their lead. Then others too did likewise. I was bewildered, not understanding the significance of it, until Carmichael nudged me, as he too turned his back. Then I sensed the import of the action and followed suit. As I did, I glanced at the assembled members of the New South Wales Corps. They looked bewildered, and almost a little frightened.

Standing so, demonstrating our disgust at the injustice visited upon Holt, gave me the most powerful sensation I had ever experienced. At one point I stole a glance at Master Marsh. He looked calm and serious, as he always did. Captain Phillips was approaching him, his expression agitated, and obviously desirous of a conversation. I did not dare to keep looking, but wondered what the upshot of their exchange would be.

I was left wondering, because nothing more out of the ordinary happened. The flogging proceeded. I could hear the hiss of the cat tails between each stroke, and the dreadful thud as they landed. The sound came to acquire a greater deadness and dullness with each succeeding lash. A seaman was keeping count, and his voice continued to ring out loudly and steadily. As he reached the thirties, Holt began to grunt and groan at each fresh impact. I realised that he would not be aware of our silent protest. When the punishment was completed, he gave a series of loud, dry sobs and then fell silent.

Master Marsh's voice, steady and strong as ever, gave the next order. 'Bo'sun, cut down the prisoner and dismiss the men.'

He had courage, Master Marsh, I give him that. Ninety-nine ships' captains out of a hundred would have been terrified of the situation that had developed, afraid that our behaviour presaged a mutiny, but I think somehow Master Marsh could read the mood of a mob. It takes a certain confidence to guide a ship halfway around the world, through storms and calms and rocks and reefs, with the constant threat of pirates, cannibals and rebellions, and I think this ship's captain had our measure.

The convicts gave no trouble. Silently we filed back below decks. As I passed Holt, I could see that Surgeon Gossam was tending to him, for which I was grateful.

Back in my hammock, and talking to Carmichael, I gave full vent to my rage at the injustice meted out to Holt. I did so in whispers, however, for a strange mood reigned in our quarters. Most men lay in their hammocks, as if mulling over the afternoon's events. A few were excited, talking wildly of overthrowing those in authority and seizing the vessel. I was alarmed at their impetuousness and expressed as much to Carmichael.

'Those blowhards!' he said. 'Can't you see how they are being ignored? They couldn't take over a graveyard. You have nothing to fear from them.'

I switched tack and launched into an angry peroration about the injustice perpetrated on Holt. Again Carmichael disagreed. 'But don't you understand what happened up there?' he asked.

'What do you mean? Of course I understand what happened.'

'Did you see Corporal Arnold's face when the captain announced the sentence?'

'No.'

Carmichael gave a short, humourless laugh. 'It was a sight to behold. Forty lashes for striking a member of His Majesty's Forces! Arnold knew what it meant.'

'Do you mean it was a light punishment?'

'Light! I know it seems a strange word to use for such a terrible ordeal as a flogging, but Michael should have hung for what he did. The best he could have hoped for was five hundred lashes.'

'Five hundred!' I exclaimed, thinking of the late Seamus O'Mahoney and his thousand lashes. 'How does a man survive such numbers?'

'He frequently doesn't. But usually they deliver the sentence in instalments. A man gets a couple of hundred, until his back is torn to ribbons, and then when it is healed they begin again.'

I shuddered with horror at the bestiality of such a punishment, though I believe no beast would treat another creature so.

'Then why did Holt get forty?' I asked.

Carmichael propped himself up on one elbow. He gazed me full in the face. 'You must have given good evidence,' he said. 'Master Marsh believed you. He knows what happened. He knows Arnold lied, that he deliberately provoked the whole thing. And Arnold knows that he knows. A sentence of forty lashes for such an offence is tantamount to an acquittal. It is a deep insult to Corporal Arnold. Any man of honour would seek leave to resign from the regiment in these circumstances. I doubt, however, if that thought would occur to Corporal Arnold.'

'Then why was Holt punished at all?' I asked. But I already knew the answer. Before Carmichael could say anything, I said hesitantly: 'Is it because Master Marsh thinks it would be too dangerous to let a convict off when he strikes a soldier?'

'Of course. He cannot risk this mob of desperados getting it into their thick heads that they can attack a soldier or sailor without fear of reprisal. He gave Holt the minimum punishment that he could safely give. Believe me, the only person angrier than Corporal Arnold today would be Captain Phillips. The reputation of his regiment has been impugned. No doubt when he gets to New South Wales he will fire off all sorts of official protests.'

'What will happen then?'

He gave his dry laugh again. 'Nothing, of course. A letter will go from Botany Bay to London, and it will sit there in an office for four or five months before a civil servant deigns to answer it. Then a few more letters will go back and forth and eventually the whole thing will wither on the vine like an unloved grape.'

It turned out that Carmichael was right about everything to do with the incident, as he generally was. Forty lashes was indeed, in judicial circles, deemed a light punishment. I was later to learn that some sailors on the First Fleet had been sentenced to as many as three hundred just for consorting with convict women who were on board their vessel.

In 1799 Governor Hunter ordered fifty lashes as the standard punishment for any convict defaulting from divine service on the Sabbath, aye, and he had the constables search the convicts' quarters every Sunday morning to seek them out.

Carmichael was right, too, about Captain Phillips. Upon our arrival in Botany Bay, as I found out much later, he went hotfoot to Government House to make his complaint about the contemptuous way in which Master Marsh had treated a member of the distinguished New South Wales Corps. An inquiry was held, statements taken, and the matter forwarded to London where it languished on a fine mahogany desk, no doubt, until it was long forgotten.

The urgency of Captain Phillips's concern about the insult meted out to Corporal Arnold and the honour of the regiment was diminished somewhat by subsequent events aboard the *Admiral Barrington*. Nearly two weeks passed without further incident. Michael Holt's back was gradually healing, although the scabs were awful to behold, and it was evident that he would bear the scars for life. Even I, at my tender age, had some inkling of what it meant to have a back crisscrossed by the cat-o'-nine-tails. A man might as well be branded 'Recalcitrant Convict'. Any time he removed his shirt everyone would know that he was a convict who had been flogged, and it would be useless for him to attempt to explain the injustice of the case.

A strange consequence of the whole thing was that as well as a great increase in the popularity of Michael Holt, which was only to be expected, I too found myself held in higher regard. I can only put this down to Holt's reporting of my testimony to my fellow prisoners. Although he was still, as ever, a man of few words, he evidently gave them to understand that I had declared before the tribunal that Corporal Arnold was a liar, and this was hailed as an act to be admired.

We saw a good deal less of Corporal Arnold, and we soon came to suspect that he was being given duties designed to keep him at a distance from the prisoners. However, the anger of the men towards him did not diminish.

Then dawned a day that I have never forgotten. Any concern felt by the ship's authorities over our silent protest during the flogging had no doubt abated, and once again most of us were allowed more and more freedom to go on deck for exercise. At least eight of the strongest and fittest convicts were now working every day alongside the crew, which gave the sailors much relief and seemed to bring pleasure to the chosen convicts, not least because of the regular glasses of rum issued to them as reward.

On a day which I believe was somewhere around the start of October, six bells had just sounded when I once again repaired above decks with night buckets. I had already, in company with four other men, taken most of the buckets up and emptied them, but two had inadvertently been left behind. Bowers, one of the captains of the deck, ordered me to undertake a second trip with the remaining buckets. I did so willingly enough. As a result I stumbled across a scene not meant for my eyes.

The ship was rushing along in a heavy squall and pitching quite wildly amid rough seas, but I had maintained my near immunity to seasickness and was not too discomfited by the violence of the movement. The wind was dead aft and all the foresails were set: the fore top gallant, the fore topsail, the lower fore topsail and the foresail. Since coming on board the *Admiral Barrington* I had learned enough about sailing to know that this configuration accounted for the considerable rolling motion.

On deck, as far as I could see, were just a couple of sailors up in the bows, and three of the convict sailors at the stern. The only suspicious thought I had as I emerged from the hatch and saw them was that there seemed to be something odd about the way the convicts were gathered. They looked to be waiting, and they looked furtive.

Coincidentally, as I took my first step onto the deck, Corporal Arnold emerged from the hatchway which led down into the cabins where the soldiers and sailors were accommodated. He could not see the three men, who were behind him, nor did he see me. He turned to come for'ard but almost at the same moment became aware of the men. He must have heard their footsteps as they rushed at him. He started to turn, but they were on him already. I was frightened by their speed and violence. They picked him up, ran him backwards and threw him over the stern rail, seemingly all in one movement. It was as though they had practised the manoeuvre.

They moved away quickly, then one of them started shouting and hallooing to the sailors at the bow. 'Man overboard!' I heard him yell. 'Man overboard!' The others joined in the chorus, and they all rushed to the stern, peering out at the vessel's wake, as though astonished by the sight of a man in the water.

The sailors at the bow ran the full length of the boat in seconds. Only then did the helmsman realise that something was wrong. In these southerly latitudes he was sheltered by a heavy canvas screen rigged by the ship's carpenter to protect him from the following seas that can so easily climb over the stern rail. Hence he had not seen anything of Corporal Arnold being heaved overboard. And perhaps his hat and oilskins had muffled his ability to hear the cry from the convicts, or perhaps he was deaf. At any rate, only now did he poke out his head to see what was happening behind him. Without thinking I too ran down to the stern. I could see Corporal Arnold, but I was shocked at how much distance had already elapsed between him and the *Admiral Barrington*.

He was close enough, however, for me to see his desperate expression. He waved at us frantically and shouted something. I thought it might have been the word 'Murder', but fortunately for the three convicts his voice was lost in the wind.

One of the sailors cut a lifebuoy adrift with the jack-knife that every sailor carries. He threw it in the direction of Corporal Arnold, but I was by no means sure that his intended target even saw it, for it landed in a trough between two large waves. The sailors turned away. One went to the helmsman, the other raised the hatch and shouted: 'All hands on deck! Man overboard! All hands on deck.' Out came the watch, and others besides, tumbling like ants from a disturbed nest. The captain suddenly appeared from his cabin. I wasn't aware that anyone had called him, but perhaps he had a sense for calamities on board his ship.

I heard him say to the helmsman: 'We must be doing eleven knots.'

'Eleven and a half, sir, last report I had.'

'Hopeless,' I heard the captain murmur. Nevertheless, he shouted a series of orders: 'Launch the number two boat there! Make sharp! Prepare to come about!' To the helmsman he said: 'Prepare for helms alee.'

He turned away and said to the sailor who had called out the watch: 'Who is it went over?'

'A soldier, I believe, sir.'

'Very well. Present my compliments to Captain Phillips and ask him to join us on deck.'

Only one of the convicts was still standing in the stern. The other two had gone for'ard to help, if help it can be called. Master Marsh called out to the man in the stern: 'Can you still see him?'

'No, sir, lost sight of him this moment just gone,' the convict shouted back. 'His head went under a wave and he hasn't come back up.'

'Fetch me a spyglass if you will, sir,' Master Marsh said to the bo'sun, who had just appeared on deck.

The bo'sun obliged and the captain stood at the stern peering through it at the turbulent waves, in the direction indicated by the convict. I should not have been surprised if the convict was deliberately pointing to quite a different place. After some minutes the captain shook his head. 'How came he to go over?'

'He was hanging over the stern rail, sir, sick as a dog, when the ship reared up and all of a sudden he was gone,' the man replied, smooth and glib as can be.

'Was he in uniform?'

'Aye, sir, that he was.'

The captain shook his head again and turned away. 'Hopeless,' he said again. 'Belay those orders!' he shouted to the helmsman and the crew. 'Nothing to be done. Prepare to make sail.'

I knew nothing of the sea, but it seemed that the time it would take to turn the vessel and sail back to the place where the corporal had gone over made the whole thing impossible. With no landmarks, no one would know where to look. Although, as I had observed, every wave is different, in a way, their ever-changing differences made them all the same. Weighed down by his uniform Corporal Arnold would already be sinking to the ocean floor.

I felt sickened by what had happened. I was the only witness to a brutal murder. It was not the first time I had seen sudden death, of course, but the speed of this, the violent reminder of how abruptly a man's life can be extinguished, left me shaken and shocked. Of course Arnold was a violent bully, but that did not lessen the impact of his death on me.

I realised that throughout the horrifying episode I had continued to clutch the slops buckets. The weight of them had cut into my hands, leaving vivid white marks and red ridges. I went to the rails and tossed the contents of the buckets overboard. Some people get flowers on their graves. It seemed that Corporal Arnold was to get nothing but shit and piss on his.

Chapter 31

ONLY HOURS AFTER THE corporal's disappearance, I was astonished to be witness to a procedure that even at the age of thirteen I considered macabre, though of course I did not then know that word. I was shocked to see the drowned man's possessions brought up from his cabin and auctioned off by Master Marsh.

I suppose, reflecting now upon these events, that it was another way of removing the contamination of death. Sailors are known to be the most superstitious men on earth, and I have heard stories of their becoming greatly perturbed when, for example, a cat dies on board ship, for they believe this to be a predictor of a storm. I found out, from the imprecations directed at me when I tried it, that they loathe whistling, because that too could provoke storm conditions, or so they believe. As we neared New South Wales a sailor told me that the cook on the *Admiral Barrington* had been forbidden to serve plum duff, because on a previous voyage, whilst most of the men were below, eating plum duff in the mess, one of their shipmates had been crushed to death by a boat which fell on him from off the booms.

At any rate, all of Corporal Arnold's worldly goods and chattels, so far as I knew, were sold quickly and efficiently by Master Marsh. His chest brought the best price, but his regimental comrades also competed enthusiastically for items of uniform, his travelling writing desk and even his spare boots.

And so ended my persecution by the honourable gentleman of the New South Wales Corps. I avoided his murderers as much as was possible. I spoke to no one of what I had seen, although I did attempt to raise the subject with Carmichael. As soon as he realised the matter I wished to broach he hissed at me: 'Not a word! I told you what would happen, and now it has happened. Not another word!'

No doubt many people had suspicions about the death of Corporal Arnold. The convict deck was rife with rumours, but no official doubts were raised. The captain held a short inquiry, at which only the six people known to be on deck at the time were called. The bo'sun asked me where I had been, but I said I had emerged from the hatch just in time to hear the cries of 'Man overboard!'

The captain announced that it was a 'death by misadventure'. I wondered if he had expedited the inquiry because it was Corporal Arnold, whom he clearly did not like and almost certainly did not trust. He may well have had his own suspicions, but no doubt he also surmised that it would be impossible to prove anything against anyone. My respect for the captain's acuity was such that I thought it likely he would prefer to consign the whole matter to an entry in the ship's log and be done with it than to have the stench of it contaminate the rest of the voyage.

But our journey was nearing its end. A couple of weeks after Arnold's drowning we had our first sighting of land, just after ten o'clock in the morning. I had smelled it as soon as I came on deck. I did not know it was land that I was smelling, but I knew it was the fragrance of trees and flowers, and about eight hours later I saw a brown and black hawk, which made me feel that the coast must be very close.

The unfortunately named Van Diemen's Land was our first landfall. Of course we now comprehend that the body of water called Bass Strait separates Van Diemen's Land from New South Wales, but it was not known for certain then whether the whole formed one complete land mass. Anyway, we did not concern ourselves too much with questions of geography. I think most of the men felt both relief and apprehension as the end of our voyage approached. We were all heartily sick of the cramped quarters on board the *Admiral Barrington*, tired of the monotonous food, and certainly fed up with each other. On the other hand the great distance we had travelled emphasised the vast gulf that now lay between us and our native home, and of course we had no real comprehension of the fate that awaited us at Botany Bay.

I noticed that since leaving Cape Town the tenor of our conversations had changed somewhat. There was no more boasting about crimes, and very little recounting of the misdeeds that had caused us to be transported. I think the men had heard one another's stories too many times for them to have any further attraction. Certainly once it was known I had been sentenced for stealing a purse, no one had taken any more interest in my wretched criminal career, as I am sorry to say that the persons of highest standing among our number were those who had committed the most atrocious offences. Only Carmichael had asked me for any details of my life or crimes, and I had not confessed even to him that I had set out to get myself transported. My experiences in Newgate and on the *Admiral Barrington* had already convinced me that my decision had been foolhardy. My need to get away from Mr Weekes was one thing, but I thought I would be a laughing stock if anyone knew that I had deliberately chosen to be sent to this savage land on the other side of the world, a place reputedly full of cannibals and monsters.

In the second half of the voyage there was much less talk of women, too, perhaps because none had been glimpsed since we left Portsmouth, save for a couple of older married women among the paying passengers.

No, the talk now was more about those gentler subjects which had been touched upon only in passing before, with men recalling, sometimes quite wistfully, episodes from their early years. It seemed that the further they travelled from their home country in distance and in time, the more importance memories held for them, and the more they strove to keep them in mind.

Much more repentance was now expressed for the false choices which had taken these men so far from the path of righteousness. John Bunyan himself would, I think, have been satisfied by the extent to which many of the prisoners now recognised that they had strayed along the tempting paths of Danger and Destruction instead of labouring up the Hill Difficulty. The unknown but dreaded perils that lay ahead seemed to concentrate their minds on their pasts, and sentiments laden with regretful allusions to mothers, fathers, sisters, brothers, sweethearts, wives and children were commonplace.

I knew nothing of France, so understood little of the life Pierre De Lafontaine had lived before coming to England, but now I listened in thrall to his tales of life as the son of a peasant on a farm in Bordeaux. He could talk for hours about his pigs, his chickens, the grape vines, the orchard. 'But zere were too many sons, too many boys,' he explained. 'My father and mother, zey 'ave thirteen children, and nine of zem are boys. When my parents die, 'ow can a farm divide among nine boys? So I say, "I will go," and I go to Paris to . . . what is this expression you 'ave? Make my fortune. But it is hard, so 'ard. I start to steal, the police, they chase, I go to London. But I still 'ave contacts in France. I arrange the smuggling. I make my fortune all right! But not for long! I spend it all. I smuggle again, but zis time I do not pay the custom men, I 'ave no money for the bribe, so of course they arrest me. What else they to do? And now look at me. I thank the good God my poor father and mother do not know what 'as become of me.'

'Do you thank the good God for putting you on the Hulks and then sending you off in this wormy old wreck?' asked Chris Norfolk. Pierre De Lafontaine looked quite perplexed at this response, and Chris added darkly: 'I don't think the good God is taking much care of any of us.'

Such blasphemous statements were rare, however. Men prayed more frequently, the pious group who met each day to worship grew in numbers, and the level of attention paid during divine service on Sundays was noticeably more marked.

As we sailed north, sometimes losing sight of land but never too far from it, groups of men exercising on the deck spent much of their time standing at the rails looking at the distant coast and musing on what it might portend. We were astonished at the extent of it. It seemed to go forever. Some of the cliffs appeared bleak and forbidding, but some, in their wild desolation, had a certain beauty. We argued over what appeared to be patches of snow on one stretch of cliffs, but many thought they were merely outcrops of a white rock. It had been cold enough at times for me to imagine a snowfall was possible. I was only slowly starting to become aware that everything on this side of the world was topsy-turvy, and winter occupied the months of June, July and August. We were now well into spring, but we had gone a long way south, and so there were days when the deck of the ship was still slippery with ice.

As we continued our journey north, the sailors reported that at night time they could see many fires inland, which they assumed were the cooking fires of the Indians.

It was the 14th of October when Master Marsh bade us take good note of the date, for he expected to make Botany Bay at about six o'clock the next evening. His optimism was premature however, for another squall hit us during the night. I awoke to find the ship pitching and rolling as before, and I had to grab the side of my hammock to avoid being tossed out unceremoniously. Others were not so lucky; I heard the crash of bodies and many curses as a number of my fellows were thrown to the floor. Thunder rolled and rumbled around us, then, some half an hour later, we felt the ship turning and running before the storm.

I would much rather have been on deck during wild weather, as it was hard not to feel terrified, trapped as we were in darkness, the hatches battened down, and ignorant of the conditions outside. Well we knew that were the ship to founder we would have poor prospects of escape. There would no doubt be a stampede for the hatch, and in view of my size and weakness, I would be either trampled underfoot or forced to the back of the mob. I felt my best hope in such circumstances would be to drop to my knees and pray with all the fervour I could muster, but I had little more trust than Chris Norfolk in the likelihood that the Divine was so closely shepherding us through our lives. Faithful Job had been far more worthy of His attention, yet God had neglected His devoted servant a long time before at last deeming him worthy of assistance.

On the morning of the 15th of October we found that the storm had been troubling indeed: our main yard had been carried away by the wind, which had apparently blown up with little warning. A heavy swell was still running, and I could see dull flashes of lightning in the distance, followed by an occasional murmur of thunder. Nonetheless, the boat had turned again and resumed its course for Botany Bay, and as the breeze started to swing around behind us we made good speed.

At dawn on the following day we were invited onto the deck most courteously, as if we were fine gentlemen, by the bo'sun, who was in excellent humour. There we viewed a sight which at times we had doubted our eyes would ever behold. We were approaching two capes, rather barren in nature, which evidently flanked the entrance to a harbour and which, the bo'sun informed us, was called Port Jackson. This had apparently become our destination, in place of Botany Bay. I found out soon enough that Botany Bay was a few miles to the south. It had been designated as the site for the first settlement, but rejected almost immediately by Governor Phillip in favour of Port Jackson, which he considered a more congenial location.

Many times I had, as I said, doubted my impetuous decision to solicit transportation. I had cursed myself for recklessness, and for putting my body, my soul, my life in peril. But now, as we gently progressed between the two capes and the harbour began to reveal itself, I felt overwhelmed by exultation. I hope it is not sacrilegious to say that I can only compare my sensations to those experienced by Christian in *Pilgrim's Progress* when he comes to the City and achieves the fulfilment of all his hopes.

Even those statuesque headlands, dun in colour and bare of vegetation, had a softness about them. One of them, off our port bow, boasted the first evidence of civilisation: a flagstaff and a lookout house, and a column of rocks painted white. As we approached we saw a man emerge from the house and quickly run a flag up the flagstaff, before turning to us, saluting, and then waving in a most friendly manner.

Later I found out that it was by means of the flag that the news of our arrival was conveyed to the residents of Sydney Cove.

Yet we were about to discover the true beauty of the harbour, for that beauty lay within. I trust my readers will forgive me if I say that the gradual unfolding of that inner beauty was analogous to an experience which was, by virtue of my youth, denied to me in those times but which was later to bring me both exultation and fulfilment. Having penetrated the heads, a whole new wonderful world lay before us. I felt that I could spend my life exploring the interior of this remarkable continent without ever truly understanding it. Beauty was mine that day. I incorporated a sense of beauty, an awareness of beauty, an appreciation of beauty into my understanding of the world in a way which I had never previously achieved. The blueness of the water offered sanctuary, as though this water were of an entirely different nature to the water contained in the dangerous and unpredictable ocean we had just traversed. Everywhere we looked were small beaches with sand invitingly white. Here and there we saw islands, rocky but intriguing and, to a boy's eye, begging to be explored. In all directions were further inlets, where entire navies could safely nestle. Proud trees, many majestic in their height, spread all the way down to the foreshores, thickly carpeting the hills and ridges. Yet even the highest points were not overly precipitous. Certainly the vista was one of wildness, but not threateningly so. I had the sense that we were entering something ancient, yet new; something rugged, yet gentle.

Fear and awe were on the faces of the men around me. The most hardened villains were as young children, their eyes wide and their mouths open, speaking only occasionally to point out some feature to their comrades. Carmichael, who had earlier expressed such hopes for his destiny in the new colony, was among those most moved.

'This could be paradise,' he whispered to me. 'It is all I dreamed of. I have never seen a sight more lovely.' Then he added mischievously, and uncharacteristically: 'Except perhaps for a Spanish señorita I met one night in Bournemouth.'

I was annoyed with him for making what at my tender age I regarded as a vulgar comparison, even though I had sensed something of the kind myself, with a dim understanding that the harbour had a distinctly female aspect. Nevertheless, I moved away from him a little, gazing across the railing at a group of large white birds far in the distance, circling a tall tree. Then I cried out in astonishment as a family of Indians suddenly appeared, walking onto a rocky outcrop. This was, not surprisingly, the first time I had ever seen anyone of so vastly different a nature to myself and I could hardly comprehend the sight. London had its share of people from different countries, but by and large they strove to fit in. Of course during the voyage I had heard many conversations and much conjecture from my fellow prisoners about the habits and customs of the natives of New South Wales, and I had understood that they would most likely be black in colour and might well wear a minimum of clothing. There had indeed been a good deal of salacious speculation about the appearance of the Indian women, and uncouth anticipation of what might ensue once we made their acquaintance. It seemed that for some men, the opportunity to see a bare-breasted woman walking about freely in broad daylight might of itself make the trip across the world worthwhile.

Young though I was, I must admit I too felt a certain frisson at the idea of seeing naked or semi-naked people. Life in East Smithfield had exposed me to many sights that would have outraged a moralist, but I had never seen people walking around naked, without shame, as though it were perfectly normal. These Indians were undeniably naked, completely so. They were true heathens in every way. I gazed at them red-faced. There were two men, three women, and half-a-dozen children, the oldest appearing to be perhaps thirteen or fourteen years of age.

In the bright, strong light of Port Jackson, a light which appeared to allow no grey, or shades of darkness, and with the group no more than fifty yards away, it was possible to see every detail of them. They stood sturdily and gazed at us. One of the men was a little apart from the others, and he struck an unusual pose, his left foot resting on his right inner thigh. He held a long spear, with one end resting on the ground. His stare was unrelenting and his face stern. An older man holding a spear and a piece of wood also gazed at us, with an expression that showed no warmth. The children watched us for a minute, but the younger ones soon lost interest and wandered away. I deduced that they had already seen a number of European ships, so that in their eyes we were no different from other white people who had invaded their sanctuary.

The watching convicts muttered various lascivious comments about the three women; about two of them at least, for the third was considerably older, and about her the men were vulgarly contemptuous. I moved away even further from their company. Some of the convicts were openly mocking the Indians, and the dignity of the latter was, I am sorry to say, in stark contrast to the behaviour of the men from the realms that would claim the virtues of civilisation.

I locked eyes with an Indian boy of about my own age who had not followed the other children and who returned my stare boldly. I wondered what it would be like to have a friendship with him, and whether such a thing were possible. No doubt he could teach me a great deal about life in New South Wales, and perhaps I could teach him a thing or two about our manners and customs.

The vessel continued on her course. I looked ahead, at the little settlement that we could now see clearly in the distance, and when I looked back at the Indians they were gone. I was surprised at how quickly and completely they had disappeared. Their dark skins no doubt helped them to merge into the shadows between the trees. They seemed to be part of the landscape in a way that I could not imagine possible for us pale-skinned folk.

As we moved on I saw half-a-dozen native canoes in the distance, each one seemingly occupied by a single woman engaged in fishing. Several had infants with them and I saw one woman with a baby at breast. Trails of smoke drifted from a couple of the boats, which led me to believe that they had cooking fires in their crude little craft. This struck me as a dangerous enterprise. Equally dangerous were the canoes themselves, which were tiny vessels and perilously close to the surface of the water. I wondered how the women restrained the infants from tipping the boats over as they frolicked.

Nearly half an hour later we approached our anchorage, the wind having dropped to a strength less than a butterfly could generate by a vigorous flapping of its wings. For the first time in more than six months we faced the prospect of stepping onto land, but I was not the only one on board feeling considerable apprehension at the thought. It was not just the Indians and the possibility of their being bloodthirsty savages. It was our fellow Englishmen, and the uncertainty surrounding their treatment of us. Would we be immediately locked up in the colonial equivalent of Newgate, with abominable food and wretched conditions? Or did a better situation await? I knew that when we stepped off the *Admiral Barrington* we would be stepping into an entirely new world. I hoped that it did not in too many ways resemble the old.

Chapter 32

THE QUESTION OF THE KIND of welcome we could expect from the
Europeans who had preceded us was answered almost immediately.
We were surprised but gratified to be received with remarkable warmth.
Various small boats, alerted to our arrival by the flag hoisted at the
headlands, came scurrying out to meet us. There were cries of pleasure
from their occupants, but few questions about events in England or
the continent, because, we were soon to learn, two other vessels from
the so-called Third Fleet had arrived in the preceding three days: the
Albemarle and the *Britannia*.

The boats brought some fish and bread, which were welcome
sights. There were also a number of Indians nearby, in their canoes, the
people just as naked as the ones we had already seen. I did not want to
be caught staring, yet I could hardly take my eyes off them.

The bo'sun blew his long whistle, summoning all hands to bring
the ship to her anchor point, and every seaman went to his station and
very neatly they worked to bring her up and moor her. And so our
long voyage was over! Though we knew nothing of what lay ahead,

we feasted our eyes eagerly on the sights of the port: the various small boats milling about the *Admiral Barrington*, the other ships which sat at anchor, the forested hills, the waves slapping gently against the rocks, and the settlement itself.

Of all these spectacles, I have to confess the settlement was the most disappointing. We could see a number of buildings, but very crude and poor they looked. Of course it would have been unrealistic to expect anything else, given the short time that had elapsed since the arrival of the first settlers, but it contrasted with the few other townships I had seen in my life, and the contrast was not in favour of Sydney Cove. London, for all its wickedness, teemed with life and had so many grand buildings; Portsmouth was very beautiful, situated so as to gaze across a harbour full of ships; Cape Town was a neat and pretty town framed by the rugged grandeur of the mountains. To be sure, the hills around Sydney Cove were verdant indeed, interspersed at various places by sandstone cliffs and well carpeted by trees, and the stream which evidently supplied the colonists with that most valuable commodity, fresh water, was a pretty sight. It had carved out a shallow valley about two miles across, and at its mouth trickled over rocks into the harbour.

Yet whilst it seemed that Nature had done all it could to embellish the scene, Man had added little in the way of improvements. There were buildings on both sides of the creek, and some looked quite substantial, but they had a rough and ready air. Most of the buildings were flanked by tents. On the left-hand side of the creek was the only building that appeared to have been constructed with any ambition of permanence. It was surrounded by palisades, but from the deck of the ship I could glimpse gardens within. I found out later that this was the residence of Governor Arthur Phillip, who, unbeknownst to us and probably to him too, was entering his last year of service to the colony.

We were mustered on deck by the worthy gentlemen of the New South Wales Corps. I had not realised that so many of them were already in the settlement, as I understood it to be a newly formed regiment. Apparently a number had come out with the Second Fleet, and their ranks had been further swelled by marines who had not wanted to go back to England and so transferred to the Corps.

The soldiers on board the *Admiral Barrington* had made a great effort to parade in their finest uniforms and were resplendent in red tunics, white webbing and brass breastplates. The members of the Corps who came on board in Sydney Cove were somewhat less proud, and many looked positively shabby: grubby silver braiding around the fronts of their hats, a couple of hats with badges missing, and boots that looked as though they lacked a coat or two of polish.

Nevertheless, there was much saluting and fine words as Captain Phillips handed us over to the tender mercies of his colleagues. Then the new men were let loose on us, and there was a deal of shouting as they marched up and down the ranks, inspecting us and making us aware of our shortcomings. It seemed that the shabbier the soldier, the more determined he was that we should not fall into his slovenly ways, and so we came in for a good deal of abuse from some of the most indifferently dressed men as they issued dire warnings of our fate should we not conform to the highest standards of behaviour and deportment.

We were, however, finally disembarked and the sensation of standing on firm ground was so novel that I found myself struggling to keep my balance. It struck me as odd that I felt almost more inclined to seasickness on land than I had done on the *Admiral Barrington*.

Conditions on shore contrasted quite sharply to the expectations I had after observing the bluster of the soldiers who had come on board, as they instead echoed the warm attitudes of the people in the bumboats.

When we landed we were greeted by a welcoming crowd of at least two hundred people. Quite a few of the convicts were reunited with old friends who awaited them, and it seemed a simple matter for them to obtain permission to go with their comrades to be fed, and even to stay overnight. The rest of us were mustered again and then escorted to the largest of the men's camps, near a place called Dawes Point.

If this were a prison, I told myself, it would suit me fine. No one attempted to solicit a bribe; we were not divided into a private area and commons area; we were not confined to stinking squalid cells. We were not even chained or shackled. The residents did not seem in terror of headhunters or giant beasts. We had considerable freedom of movement, although there were stockades for those who abused the Governor's hospitality, and a curfew for all. We were told that our rations were one pound of rice a week, and four pounds of pork, alongside greens and other vegetables, but that these were dependent upon our working to earn them.

As we gathered around the cooking fires, the old hands told us stories of how close the colony had been to starvation. Astonishingly, no farmer or gardener had been sent out on the First Fleet, yet the settlers had been provided with various grains and farm implements, as well as livestock, and in consequence of being issued with these supplies were expected to become self-sufficient in a very short time. As a result of the lack of farming experience and skills, many crops had been planted in the wrong season and had failed. The livestock did not fare much better. Cattle had run away or been driven off by escaped convicts or the natives. A majority of the pigs and chickens had died. Some of the pigs had been speared and taken by Indians.

Of the native animals, kangaroos and opossums seemed to make the best eating, but there was constant competition between the Indians and us, their uninvited guests, for the available wild animals. Fish were often in short supply. At one time there had been an abundance of turtles, but few now were found.

It was disconcerting to be thrown into this new mix of men and boys, and I kept close to Carmichael that night for comfort and security. In the morning we were mustered again, and many of us were told to fall out and wait at the camp gates. I was pleased to find that my old shipmates Carmichael Lance, Pierre De Lafontaine and Michael Holt were numbered with me in this group. As well, I saw Chris Norfolk, whom I liked well enough, despite his unattractive habits, and Marmaduke Wyatt, the man who had lied so outrageously about his string of felonies and whom I liked not at all.

We were allowed a couple of minutes to gather our meagre possessions – not a difficult task for me – and then marched down to Farm Cove. A few craft had been warped in for us to board, which we did, and upon pushing off found ourselves on the water once more, bound for a destination unknown to us all until the night before, when we had been advised by the old hands of our likely assignment.

It seemed we were to sail up a river to a place called Rose Hill. I shall, however, henceforth refer to it by the name of Parramatta, as it was renamed such by Governor Phillip just after we arrived there. The name Rose Hill was then applied to a neighbouring area, a change which caused some confusion.

Farms were apparently being established at Parramatta at a great rate. The soil around Port Jackson had been adjudged unproductive, but the Parramatta soil was considered much superior.

Although there is always a sense of dread, or at least nervousness, when en route to a destination about which little of any substance is known, it was nonetheless a pleasant trip, with much to see. I had been told on the *Admiral Barrington* that the swans of New South Wales were as black as the Indians, and I had disbelieved it, imagining I was being teased. But it seemed that on this other side of the world everything was upside down and topsy-turvy, even the swans, for before long we had disturbed a flock of at least a hundred, and certainly they were blacker even than the natives I had seen.

It was hard to imagine men wanting for food, because shortly after sighting the swans we saw geese, and later a flock of a huge white parrot-like birds, wheeling around a dead tree and screeching at each other as though all the demons of hell were in pursuit of them. I had never heard such a raucous noise, outside the streets of East Smithfield at any rate. They were so loud that I put my hands over my ears, which made Carmichael smile and say: 'They are like the crowds who mill around the gallows at a public hanging in London.'

'But they look like angels,' Chris Norfolk said, and I was bound to admit he was right, for I do believe they were the whitest creatures or objects I ever did see.

The trip to Parramatta proved a short one, and by mid-afternoon we found ourselves surveying a pleasant prospect. The temperature was comfortably warm, leading me to renew my faith in the opinions of the returned convict I had met in the Pie and Peas, and certain it was that most men had their shirts off as they luxuriated in the temperate climate. The land in every direction had a park-like aspect, with attractive grasses and tall trees, but plenty of room to walk among them without difficulty. Quite a number of acres had been cleared already for farming, and various houses and barns erected. Far in the distance, to the west, towered a mountain range that had no apparent end in either direction. It looked wild and rugged, a barrier both deterring and tantalising.

We were not, however, permitted to stand and gaze about, but instead forced at a quick pace to a group of huts and tents which we were soon made aware was to become our home. Many of our number complained about the rude nature of the accommodation, but to me it was, apart from the comfortable cottage of the Piggotts', the best home I had ever enjoyed. I was assigned to a hut of bark and timber, with its own fenced kitchen garden. I shared these salubrious conditions with thirteen other boys and young men, the first time the authorities had made any effort to segregate me from older prisoners. Despite the crowded conditions, I thought it vastly superior to the solitude of my existence in St Martin's and Hell, back in faraway London.

The next morning at seven, without the luxury of any further time to accustom ourselves to our exotic new surroundings, or to recover from the gruelling voyage from England, or to get used to being on dry land once more, we were put to work.

I make no complaint about this. We understood already that the colony was at a critical point in its short life. Since the arrival of the First Fleet, none of the settlers knew whether each ship that arrived would be the last. The drain on the public purse in England for food and other supplies to support the colony was a heavy one indeed, and every person of sense was aware that His Majesty's Government might at any time throw up its hands and cry 'Enough!' Already the entire venture, and every man, woman and child in it, had come close to foundering; in other words, to death by starvation. The spectre of that experience continued to hover over all.

Chapter 33

DESPITE THE FOREGOING, IT was soon clear that many among the convicts would as rather condemn us to the Everlasting as do any work. I do not believe that this was a conscious choice, an act of collective suicide on their part, though it may have been for some. Self-slaughter was far from unknown among the transported convicts in New South Wales and years later I became aware of the stories emanating from the ghastly penal settlement on Norfolk Island, where men drew lots to decide who would murder the other, by which means both were enabled to slip the knot of life; the one who was murdered, and the other, who would then be executed by the authorities for the 'crime' he had committed.

At times I worked at Parramatta and Rose Hill, and other times at Constitution Hill, renamed Toongabbie by the Governor in 1792. Owing to my age, I was given a task which was relatively undemanding, that of delivering water to the men performing jobs which were at times literally backbreaking. The buckets I carried were indeed heavy when full, and for many weeks my shoulders were sore and blistered from the weight of the pole I bore across them, but I could not complain when I saw older men yoked to ploughs, or rooting out tree stumps, or engaged in road-making or tree-felling. There was much ill feeling between the convicts who worked hard at these jobs and the men who shirked. The former were aware that their tasks were more taxing because of the indolence of the latter; the latter were disparaging of the former's compliance with their masters' wishes. And so the malingerers called the hard workers 'nightingales', because they sang too sweetly to the authorities, or, at other times, 'catch-farts', a term used in England for a foot boy. It seemed that this vulgar term originated from the practice of a foot boy following exceedingly closely behind his master.

Although I came to some understanding, or so I suppose, of the reasons for many men doing so little, it was nevertheless difficult at times to restrain my anger at them, particularly because most of my friends came from the group who worked fairly willingly. I would say the extreme reluctance of some to perform their assigned duties was a way of demonstrating passively an objection to a system which had ground these men, and women and children too, down from the day they were born, working relentlessly to reduce them to creatures without will, without spirit, without autonomy and, cruellest of all, without hope. I could see that, I had sympathy with their situation, but I also saw two good men crushed to death under a tree because others had not exerted enough effort to keep the strain on the rope which would have saved them. And I resented carrying water long distances under the hot sun to men who had not raised a sweat and who invariably drank carelessly, not caring how much they spilled. Some even tipped the bucket over their heads to cool themselves, thereby wasting the precious liquid which I had laboured to procure for them. Almost without exception I could tell the hard workers from the others by the way they treated me and my buckets.

My interest in this subject was made personal for another reason, which was that the other person designated to carry water was an old lag named Alec Mildren. He undoubtedly belonged to the first group, for he was a professional skulker. As lean as a greyhound, he spent most of his time trying to cadge tobacco. His eyes were lively and alert, but his face was lined and wrinkled. He did not know his age, guessing it to be about sixty. He knew every trick for getting out of work, but when a soldier hove into view no one could have been more industrious. Everyone liked him, including me, but I quickly became aware that I carried six pairs of buckets to every one carried by Alec, and when the men cursed me for being too slow with the water I burned with a sense of injustice at the unfair division of labour.

The cooler the day, the less work there was for both of us, however, and on those days I enjoyed listening to Alec spin his yarns. He had come out on the Second Fleet, after getting a fourteen year sentence for receiving stolen goods. He called himself a slip-gibbet, and he had to explain to me what that was. 'I'm a man for whom the gallows groans, Barnaby my boy,' he said. 'I'm one who could have gone to the gallows half-a-dozen times.' He had a colourful way of expressing himself, and used a lot of words I didn't know. He was the one who told me what a 'nightingale' was, and how 'catch-farts' got their name. He blamed women for all his troubles, and claimed he had three wives in England. 'But I haven't taken a wife out here, Barnaby boy,' he said. 'I've learned my lesson. Not like some of these other lads. If you spit with the wind behind you any day here, you'll hit at least three men who have a wife in England and another one in New South Wales. The ocean is as good as a widow-maker to these lads. When England slipped over the horizon, their wives slipped out of their ken.'

I was a little shocked at this information, and hardly understood when he went on to say: 'Docking is all they care about, Barnaby my son; they'd marry laced mutton if it'd get them into a woman's commodity.'

Many of the convicts who worked hard did so because they hoped to get pardons. Some wanted to return to England, some hoped to take up land around Toongabbie or Rose Hill where, according to Alec, the Government was 'handing out land like they were making new swathes of it every day'. Alec had no such aspirations. His only interest was his own comfort, and because he did not want to farm land for himself or anyone else, he avoided the attention of the authorities as much as possible. 'I'm as lazy as the tinker who laid down his load to fart,' he told me one day, and I could not disagree.

I had no real aspirations myself. I just had a vague idea that one day I would be free and then life would be much better, but I was unable to appreciate what form freedom or 'a better life' would take.

Of the four men from the ship whom I knew best, Pierre De Lafontaine, Michael Holt and Chris Norfolk were all assigned to hard labour in the fields or forest, or on the roads. Carmichael, however, with his learning and book knowledge, secured a position as assistant storekeeper and soon made himself indispensable, disbursing everything from grains, salt and sugar, to boots, shovels, sewing twine and nails. His record-keeping, so neat and meticulous, contrasted with the blotted and ill-spelled entries of those who had come before him. In the late afternoon, when I had been discharged from my duties, I would sometimes visit him in the store and thumb through the books in fascination, having never had such an opportunity in my life before. The late Mr Ogwell had never allowed me to look at his records.

The sheer numbers amazed me. The First Fleet had brought 747,000 nails. I was surprised that the weight of those alone had not sunk the boats. They brought seven hundred wooden bowls, eight thousand fishhooks, and forty-four tons of tallow. I marvelled at the planning which went into these ventures.

They also carried with them twelve ploughs and two thousand one hundred hoes. There were seven hundred of the wide weeding hoes, seven hundred West Indian hoes, and seven hundred of the narrowest variety, the grubbing hoes, which were supplemented by additional stores from the boats which arrived in the Second and Third Fleets. The men called the hoes 'long-tailed monkeys', but they proved to be infinitely superior to ploughs for the conditions prevailing in New South Wales, and indeed, they are still preferred by most to this very day. The rocks and stumps and tree roots were too difficult for the ploughs, and besides, not enough horses were available to pull the latter. The hoes were easy to use, and well suited for cultivating maize, a grain which I found pleasant enough to eat, although it was not popular with many of my fellow convicts. The natives quickly became very fond of it, however.

Carmichael took advantage of my presence in the store and my interest in the records to continue with my reading lessons, and I was happy enough to be thus employed. In his spare time he was often asked to act as a scribe for convicts wishing to write petitions or letters or suchlike, and he always obliged, which helped ensure his good standing with his fellow prisoners. His reputation with them might otherwise have been threatened by his easygoing cooperation with the authorities.

It was a proud day for me when I was asked by a lad of seventeen years, one James Chester, to write a letter home to his mother on his behalf. Seeing me thus engaged, other convicts then sought me out for similar tasks. I was sometimes given food as payment, sometimes tobacco, sometimes just a muttered grunt of thanks. I was thankful for the food, and I passed the tobacco on to Alec.

When the departure of a ship for England was imminent, soldiers, marines, convicts and for all I knew free settlers as well, embarked upon a frenzy of letter writing, so anxious were they to maintain connections with their families, friends and sweethearts back home. Scribes were in great demand at such times. If two ships were leaving at around the same time I would sometimes be asked to make copies of the letters, so that each ship could take one; insurance against the possibility of disaster befalling one of the vessels.

There are many stories told nowadays of the cruelties practised at the Constitution Hill or Toongabbie settlement. People have said that upwards of eight hundred died there in just a few years. I have even heard the figure of one thousand bandied about. It is claimed that convicts were buried whilst they still had breath in their bodies, that men ate grass to survive, that they were yoked to ploughs like beasts of burden and made to pull them across the rocky fields. In particular I have heard the story of the fellow thrown into a mass grave whilst still alive, of how he begged the overseer not to cover him with dirt and the overseer sneered: 'Damn your eyes! Why should I go to the trouble of pulling you out now when I'll have to throw you back in before the day is done?'

There is some truth in most of these stories, though I never heard tell of the last one until I was thirty-one years of age. There were many deaths at Toongabbie, partially occasioned by the practice adopted by the authorities of sending gravely ill convicts to the hospital there. Sometimes, when more than one person died in a day, the bodies were buried together, as indeed happened often enough in parts of London. At times there were shortages of food, as there were throughout the colony, and our rations would be cut to levels which made our survival uncertain and forced us to take whatever measures we could to find food in the rivers and forests. Certainly during these times of hardship there were men who experimented with different grasses, including making soups from them, but I never heard of anyone who had much success at this. We did not find much in the way of edible plants, although the lily pilly trees had a sort of pink berry which we liked to eat, despite its sourness.

As for being yoked to ploughs, that did happen, but not as often as the old lags tell it, because ploughs were generally not favoured, for the reasons I have mentioned. And if men were used in this way, what of it? The ground needed to be cultivated, sometimes the plough was the most efficient way to achieve this, and if men were strong enough, why should they not draw a plough behind them?

I do not seek to deny that there was cruelty. Wherever men are put in positions of power and other men are deprived of their rights and liberty, cruelty will manifest itself. There was the sanctioned cruelty of floggings and executions, and there was the concealed cruelty of certain turnkeys and overseers. Conditions were exacerbated by the adoption of Toongabbie as a place of punishment, so that a man or woman transported from Britain to New South Wales for a crime could then be further transported from Sydney Cove to the New Ground at Toongabbie for another crime. Thus the worst of the worst gradually congregated in the area, and some overseers adopted a 'rule by rod' approach to manage them.

I wondered as I grew older whether many of the convicts might have been better prepared by the authorities for the situation in which they found themselves in New South Wales. For decades past some of the old lags had hardly spent a day out of strict confinement, surrounded by prison walls and watched over by keepers, forced to adhere to a code which prescribed every detail of their lives. At Sydney

Cove, Parramatta and Toongabbie, they found themselves without man-made barriers. There were plenty of natural barriers, those of the forest, the ocean, and the rugged mountains to the west, but these did not present the same aspect. Indeed, to many, they seemed benign compared to the cold stern walls of places like Newgate. In New South Wales men could wander quite freely at times, even into the forest, from whence many made their escape. Although convicts were forbidden to construct boats, they sometimes stole them. Yet over time, these natural barriers proved to be effective prison walls indeed, and few succeeded in penetrating them.

Food rations were issued on a weekly basis, and again, to prisoners not used to managing their own affairs, this system had inherent defects. Just as on the boat, it was not unusual for men to gamble away part or all of their rations, whereupon they had the choice of starving for the rest of the week, or stealing food, or making do with what they could forage. Men sometimes traded food for grog or tobacco. And sometimes they were simply not able to control their impulses. I remember an older man named Alfred who, on at least one occasion, received his week's issue of grain and used all of it to make his cakes upon a cooking fire but then ate them on the spot, leaving him with nothing for the rest of the week.

Many of the overseers seemed bewildered by behaviour which to us did not seem unreasonable. Their response was to brand all convicts as incorrigible, reckless, irresponsible and beyond rehabilitation or redemption.

I certainly suffered at times at the hands of the overseers, but I also suffered at the hands of my fellow convicts. It was not always easy to determine which group was worse. We boys in our hut, which the others had nicknamed St James's Palace long before I arrived, got along tolerably well much of the time, but only a fool would put down an apple or a melon and expect it to be there when he returned. The constant thieving did cause much bad blood.

The boys whom I befriended particularly were George Bruce, sometimes known as Joseph Druce, and James Chester, whom I mentioned earlier, the illiterate lad who had solicited my services as a scribe. As well there was a younger boy named Isaac Rose, a cheeky lad, who must have been the youngest convict in New South Wales, having been transported for seven years for the theft of money. It turned out that he had stolen it from the poor box in a church. When we older ones reproached him for such sacrilege he explained ingenuously: 'Ah, but I was poor, so who was it meant for if not for me?'

He did not know how to stop talking, young Isaac, and I some-times thought ruefully of Carmichael's comments on board the *Admiral Barrington*, about people who were 'talked out' and therefore made bad companions. There were times when I wished Isaac was talked out and so give us some peace. Sometimes we sat on him to silence his babbling tongue, but even that had little effect.

George was a water carrier like me, whilst James, who was a strong lad, worked for a brickmaker named Wheeler, who had been tasked with making 40,000 bricks and tiles a month. For this, Wheeler had twenty-two men and two boys to help. It was heavy work: they had to cut the wood, dig the clay and fetch it two hundred yards to the kiln, keep the kiln fires going and load the carts with the bricks when they were done. Wheeler was a hard taskmaster who wanted the best results. He was forever complaining that the clay was not good enough; it was too brittle, compared to the bricks he made in England which fetched at least thirty shillings a thousand.

The four of us, George, James, Isaac and I, eventually managed things so that we squeezed into the smallest room in the hut together.

One of the reasons I liked this arrangement was that we four were the only ones who did not interest ourselves in the vices practised by the other boys, who disported themselves with each other in ways that were at times quite shameless. But then, whoever imagined that shame was a characteristic of the transported convict?

Chapter 34

CARRYING MY BUCKETS INTO the forest, to bring water to groups of men working there, was fraught with hazards. Among these were the wild creatures. Despite the stories told on the *Admiral Barrington*, no one seemed sure whether the snakes of New South Wales were venomous. Certain it was that the Indians would not eat them, though they ate almost everything else. These people, who had presumably inhabited the country for some considerable time, reacted to the serpents with the greatest terror and loathing, which indicated to me that there was much to be feared about them.

I heard tell of a convict who was bitten by one and who appeared to suffer nothing more than he would if bitten by a dog. Yet I also heard of a dog bitten by a snake; the dog swelled up, twisted and contorted in agony, and was dead within the half-hour.

James, who was a country lad, taught me how to catch the snakes of New South Wales by swiftly pinning them down with a forked stick behind their heads or, if such an implement were not available, by pressing a stick across their necks and then killing them at leisure, with a rock or similar. He cautioned me to sever the head from the body and not to touch the head, for fear that the creature might strike with its fangs after death. He said he had been taught this intelligence by a Chinaman.

In St James's Palace we consumed snakes on at least a dozen occasions, although it was hard to render them as tender as chicken or pork. They had many little bones, which made the eating of them difficult.

The native dogs were sighted frequently enough, and although I have seen them bring down a kangaroo, they had enough discretion to keep away from us. The kangaroos could fight if they were cornered, kicking with their powerful hind legs hard enough to disembowel a man if he were too slow on his feet. For the most part, though, they were timid creatures. The soldiers tried to hunt them, but with limited success. The kangaroos grazed in flocks of twenty or thirty, and at the slightest disturbance lifted their heads and gazed at its source. They would do so for many seconds, and if a soldier was close enough to fire it was then that he stood his best chance; if he did not seize the opportunity the kangaroos would suddenly, with one accord, break away and hop deep into the forest. Their speed was deceptive; they seemed to go at an almost leisurely pace but within seconds were out of sight. Governor Phillip's greyhounds, of which he was very fond, could occasionally run a kangaroo down, but were sometimes much wounded in the process.

The chief cause of my discomfort in the forest was the insect population. Unless the wind blew hard, mosquitoes were common, and seemed attracted to my soft skin. Ants were numerous, and many of them could sting, particularly a huge ant the size of the two top joints of my little finger. George showed me how to take the immature bud of the bracken fern, squeeze it and rub the juice onto the bite, which gave almost instant relief. He had been shown this remedy by one of the Indian lads.

Despite our fears of headhunters, and despite the stories we had been told of their savagery, the Indians only occasioned fear in me two or three times. They wandered around the huts and tents quite freely, often looking for victuals, of which they sometimes stood in great need. It puzzled me that they suffered such hunger, for I wondered how they had survived in the area so long if they could not easily find food, but no doubt the arrival of several thousand Britishers had put a strain on their resources.

One of their chief methods of hunting game was to set fire to the forest and then wait downwind to spear the animals as they fled. This system, lazy though it seemed to me, was efficient enough in its own way, but did not serve their long-term interests well, as it meant the population of animals was much reduced, not to mention the birds' nests that were destroyed in the blazes.

The boys of St James's Palace and I were forever on the lookout for ducks' nests, and those of other birds too, raiding them at every opportunity and thereby guaranteeing ourselves a good source of additional nourishment.

The Indians seemed more dangerous to each other than they were to us, although they could certainly turn on the white man quickly enough if seriously affronted, for example by the theft of their fishing or hunting tools, or by improper attentions paid to their women. They themselves were extraordinarily brutal to their women, going so far as to knock them unconscious with a club if they gave cause for displeasure. Many of the women had old scars, and almost every time I looked at them I could discern new wounds, particularly around the scalp area.

When a man caused offence to a member of another tribe, the two tribes would meet, and with bodies and faces painted advance on each other with much gesturing and shouted threats, flinging spears and at the same time using their shields to deflect attacks. Eventually the one who had caused the offence, or one of his relatives, was speared by the enemy – most commonly in the leg, and if the offence were very great, speared a number of times. This seemed to discharge the tension to the satisfaction of all concerned, and the wounded man would be hauled away by his tribe to receive the ministrations of whatever primitive medicines his witch-doctor prescribed. There were times, however, when the spearing was fatal, though I formed the impression that this never happened unintentionally. I could only assume it was done as retribution for a crime most serious.

I suppose that when all is said and done, these barbaric battles were not entirely dissimilar to our civilised European custom of fighting duels with swords or pistols at daybreak, to settle some real or imagined score, or indeed the meeting of two armies on the plains of Marathon or Abraham.

At any rate, I became less fearful of the Indians as time went on, and gradually I even became accustomed to their nakedness, although I could not help noticing, young though I was, that some of the girls my own age or thereabouts were quite comely. It was hard not to stare at their nubile charms.

However, neither the snakes nor the native dogs nor the kangaroos nor the Indians posed as much danger as did our own kind, and in particular the convicts who had fled from the confinement of the settlement. Indeed, 'confinement' seems scarcely the word when comparing the conditions in New South Wales with the conditions reputed to exist in the Hulks and the conditions I had experienced in Newgate. I was one of many who had never imagined such openness, such vastness as was to be found in this country. The sky was inconceivably immense, the forest stretched forever, the oceans were infinite and the mountains towered in the distance, all combining to impress us with our insignificance. We felt dwarfed by the magnitude of our surroundings. 'Hast thou perceived the breadth of the earth?' the Lord asked Job, and here on the other side of the world, so far from civilisation, I felt that we had a glimmering of understanding of that breadth. 'Whatsoever is under the whole heaven is mine,' said the Lord, and instead of feeling exhilarated by being permitted to stand erect in that immensity, many cowered under it, and ran away, seeking to hide from the presence of God like Adam and Eve in the garden of Eden.

Just a few days after the *Admiral Barrington* had dropped anchor in Sydney Cove, twenty-one convicts from previous shipments, including one woman, had fled from Rose Hill northwards into the forest. Most were retrieved within a comparatively short time, some surrendering themselves because of hunger, but a couple were never seen again and were thought slaughtered by the Indians. The members of this group believed, as they confessed when they were recaptured, that could they travel but a hundred miles they would find themselves in China! I heard this story told and retold many times, sometimes with doubt cast upon it, but I can attest to its truth, for I was told it by one of the soldiers who stood guard over the escapees in the hospital. And although I joined in the mirth at their expense, my own ignorance of geography was so complete that no doubt back then I too could have easily been persuaded that China was just a brief span up the coast.

There were doubtless others who struck out for far-distant destinations, and there were also many who went but a short distance into the forest and lurked there, committing depredations upon free settlers, soldiers and convicts alike. Theirs was an unthinking existence, for there could be no future other than a lonely death in the wilderness on the one hand, or a flogging and a more severe imprisonment on the other. Occasionally, it is true, an escaped prisoner would be adopted into a native tribe, and of course we shall never know how many such instances occurred, but I believe them to be few and far between. The native people rarely welcomed the attentions of escapees and at times treated them quite brutally, perhaps, it is thought, as some kind of punishment for crimes committed by others, as their perverted system of justice prescribed.

Yet there were also many instances of their kindness to our people. It seemed impossible to find a consistency in their behaviour.

When I started fetching water to the men working in the forest, my fellow carriers George and Alec cautioned me that I might encounter renegade convicts. But, George confessed and Alec concurred, they had never seen any, and so I suppose I did not take much notice of their warnings. I was therefore quite confounded soon after dinner one day, when I had resumed my duties and was making for a stand of timber perhaps a mile from Toongabbie Creek, to have an apparition suddenly appear from behind a tree, holding a wooden club above his head in a most threatening manner.

He was a tall man, but very thin, with a prominent Adam's apple, and no head hair at all. He had a thin straggly beard of recent growth, was dressed in nothing but a pair of ragged trousers and had cuts and scratches and scabs all over his legs and arms and torso. He stared fiercely at me but seemed to have trouble speaking. I stared back into his blue eyes, feeling desperately afraid but trying not to show it.

Eventually he rasped: 'What have you got?' He waved the club as he said it, as though to emphasise his question.

'Only water, sir,' I replied. 'Would you like some?'

I had the feeling that he was not in his right mind and I should be careful not to offend or anger him. He nodded, to indicate that he would like water, and I filled my pourer and gave it to him. He drank thirstily, but without taking his eyes off me, then gave the pourer back and gestured that he wanted another serving, which I was glad enough to provide. His eyes seemed to burn holes in me as he drank this second draught, staring at me from above the lid of the pourer. Then he threw it down. I eyed it as it lay on the ground, wondering how I should get it back.

'Food,' he croaked.

'I don't have any, sir,' I said, trying to appear calm and unconcerned, although truth to tell my heart was beating quickly.

He suddenly let go of the wooden club, lurched forward and grabbed me around the neck. I dropped the bucket and felt the water spill across my feet as he shook me. I was surprised and shocked by his speed and strength. He felt around my clothes but I had nothing in my pockets except a parrot's feather, a smooth rock I had found in the creek and a slingshot George had made me. He let me go, pushing me back so that I nearly fell. Then he studied the slingshot for a moment, before thrusting it into the only pocket in his trousers which looked intact.

'You understand,' he said, 'I'm desperate for food. Come back here tomorrow. Bring me food, for God's sake.'

'I . . . I'll try, sir,' I stammered. 'No one has much food, as you would know.'

He shook his head and for the first time his eyes wandered away from me. 'I don't know how long I've been out here,' he muttered. 'It's been so long. You can't live without people, boy. No matter how bad it is, don't run off, you understand?' He began mumbling then, and I could not understand what he was saying. I backed slowly away, but just as I felt I was at a safe distance from him he suddenly turned and trotted off in the opposite direction, leaving his club behind. I saw the tell-tale maze of white scars on his back, the sure evidence of one or more floggings, the mark of the convict. I picked up the pourer and the empty bucket and headed quickly back to Toongabbie Creek.

Chapter 35

I SPOKE TO NO ONE, not even George or James, of my encounter with the man. I knew well enough what would happen if I were caught helping him. So far I had avoided a flogging, and I dreaded the thought of having my back cut to ribbons by the dreaded lash.

The next day I was in an agony of apprehension as to what course I should pursue. Having been among the abused and downtrodden all my life I had a natural sympathy for others in the same condition. Yet the hold self-preservation has on us cannot be underestimated. Leaving our residence the next morning, I paused, irresolute, then thrust some bread and a potato into my pocket, not sure whether I would offer them to the man, should he find me again, or eat them myself.

Mid-morning I delivered water to the convicts working in the stand of trees to which I had been paying twice-daily visits. It had apparently proved difficult at first to find good quality timber in the forests of New South Wales, and I had heard much grumbling about immense trees which had taken great exertion to fell, only for the axemen to find them rotten to the core. It was true also that many of the gums were knotted in such a way as to make them unworthy for certain uses, but the blue gums, the red gums and the trees that we came to call stringy barks all proved suitable for boatbuilding, furniture making and shingles for roofs, as well as their most important function: the construction of houses.

Having made the outward journey safely, I returned in a more serene state of mind, only to be startled as abruptly as the day before by the reappearance of the sepulchral figure in front of me. If anything, I was even more frightened of him than I had been the first time. Certainly he looked even more desperate. He stepped out suddenly from behind a tree and came at me, carrying what seemed to be the same wooden club. He dropped it again as he reached out to grab me. I stepped backwards, pulled from my pocket the potato I had brought, and offered it to him. He seized my arm in a death grip with one hand and took the potato with his other. His eyes burned fiercely as he bit into it.

'Eat it slowly,' I urged. I had learned a thing or two about hunger in my time, and I knew that this was the best way to assuage it.

He glanced down at me, and I saw him making a conscious effort to do as I had suggested. Nevertheless, the potato seemed to be gone in a moment.

'Water,' he demanded, but I had none left and told him so.

'More food,' he said, and I gave him the two hunks of bread. He took a bite from the first one and glanced at me again. 'You're kind,' he said. 'You're a good boy.'

I shrugged. I feared that my kindness might cost me dearly. Although I could argue with myself that I was helping him out of fear, the truth was not quite so simple. He did frighten me, but I could have avoided him by taking a different route through the forest. I could have reported him to the soldiers who guarded us. Given my youth, and his obvious frailty, I could probably have run away from him. I did not know why I had done none of those things, except for my feelings for a fellow creature. Perhaps the kindness displayed me by the Piggotts and the Revd Mr Haddock back in London served as some sort of inspiration. At any rate, I did not regret giving him the potato and bread.

'I have to go,' I said. 'They'll be looking for me soon enough.'

'But you mustn't give up on me,' he croaked. 'For the love of God, come back tomorrow.'

I shrugged again, fearing that I was being dragged into a quicksand which would sooner or later engulf me. He did not attempt to stop me as I picked up my buckets and turned away, walking through the trees as quickly as I could.

I did indeed bring him food again on the following day, and for all but one of the five days after that. The amount varied. Food was difficult to obtain at the best of times, and only once could I manage a decent quantity for him. Half-a-dozen sheep, apparently killed and mauled by the native dogs, had been brought in to be butchered. We had all eaten well and I had been able to secrete at least a pound and a half of meat for him. 'But,' he confided to me, as he gnawed at a bone, 'I believe my stomach to have shrunk, because it takes so little to fill it now.' It was true: he ate only half of what I had brought, then loped away into the forest, clutching the remainder of his provisions.

Just those few sporadic meals had brought about some change in his condition. He did not look any less gaunt than before, but he seemed calmer, his eyes less fevered. He no longer threatened me with clubs or words, but waited anxiously for me in the same place at the same time each day.

After a week of this, my talkative little friend, Isaac Rose, who loved information and would scurry down any burrow like a ferret after a rabbit if he thought there was gain in it for him, said to me slyly: 'I know you're stealing food, Barnaby, and I can guess why you're stealing it.'

'Oh can you just?' I said, thrown badly off guard by this unexpected sally. 'Well, listen to me, my lad, generally them that thinks doesn't know much, and them that knows a lot don't need to think.'

I had heard a man say this on the *Admiral Barrington*. I wasn't quite sure what it meant, but in my confusion over Isaac's remark I thought it might buy me time while he tried to sort out the tangle of words himself.

He did look somewhat disconcerted and skulked away, saying merely: 'You better watch out for yourself, that's all I'm saying.'

Later I saw him talking to George Bruce and wondered at the subject of their conversation, as they both looked somewhat furtive. I liked George Bruce, or Joseph Druce as he later called himself, for he was a smart lad with a keen mind and a great curiosity about the world. Like me, he had picked up some sort of education, in bits and pieces. He had a great interest in insects, and although he had not been long in the colony, he could already speak with authority upon them. Quite a few of my fellow convicts were able to make good money by gathering specimens of unusual creatures, bones, shells, rocks and vegetation, which eventually made their way back to collectors in Europe. George was already so employed, whenever he had an opportunity, and often added to our food stocks with the proceeds of his enterprise. I sometimes gave him curios I picked up in the forest or along the river, but so far he had treated them all with scorn. 'Got thousands of 'em,' he would grunt. Yet once in a while he would slip the item into his pocket even as he disparaged it, which made me doubt the authenticity of his contempt.

He was a devout lad, George, constantly invoking the name of the Lord in his daily affairs and capable of preaching with the fervour and eloquence of an adult. Yet I had noticed that in a number of ways his actions did not match his words or his professed beliefs. Much as I enjoyed my conversations with him, and much as I admired the knowledge he had acquired of the country, yet I did not altogether trust him and hence maintained a certain reserve when with him, never more so than when I commenced my dealings with the desperate escapee in the forest. It was George, after all, who had warned me of the possibility that I might encounter a runaway, and he had done so in words that conveyed no sympathy for the plight of these renegades.

Old Alec Mildren, too, though he was a likeable scoundrel, was a scoundrel nonetheless, and I kept well away from him during the days of my dealings with the man. Because George, Alec and I were engaged in the same occupation, sometimes taking the same routes, I had to be particularly careful that they did not witness my nefarious meetings. I believed I had been successful in this, but after seeing George converse with Isaac I became somewhat suspicious and so the next day deliberately missed my rendezvous with the convict. The stand of timber was very nearly exhausted anyway, so it seemed that I would only be travelling through that particular section of forest for a couple more days.

When I next met the man, on the following day, I told him I was unlikely to be in a position to continue his deliveries of food.

He had not reproached me for missing the previous day, but now he looked at me in some panic and dropped the ladle from which he was drinking. 'Don't speak to me so,' he cried. 'I have nothing without you. You'll not be deserting Johnny now?'

It was the first time he had told me his name. I opened my mouth to answer, but before I could utter the first syllable I saw a movement among the trees, over Johnny's shoulder. I did not know what it was, but it seemed unnatural. I paused, looking at it, trying to discern what I had seen. Johnny, whose time on the run had perhaps heightened his senses to an acute degree, responded to my changed expression and swung around fast, moving to his left at the same time. I saw a glimpse of scarlet, a colour never to be found in the landscape of New South Wales, except on the plumage of certain parrots, and real- ised that we were in danger. Then a man's voice, to my left, called something, and in a moment the forest seemed to spring alive with soldiers as though they were part of the flora, large scarlet flowers with deadly intent.

Johnny darted away to the right now, towards the thickest timber. I hesitated. The soldiers paused as one and lifted their rifles to their shoulders, as a man with sergeant's stripes bellowed: 'Stop or we shoot!'

I had been well instructed by my ill-famed compatriots aboard the *Admiral Barrington*. One of the lessons they had impressed upon me was that people in authority use their voices, and in particular the volume of their voices, to control others. 'They shout to frighten you,' they gravely told me, 'they shout to paralyse you.'

For an instant of time I felt that paralysis, a response, no doubt, to the shocking appearance of the soldiers from their hiding places, but also to the booming parade-ground voice of the sergeant. However, the tuition I had received from my companions in infamy helped me resist the sergeant's shout, for it was but a moment later when I turned and followed Johnny.

Considering his physical condition, Johnny had moved with remarkable agility and was already twenty-five yards away. I went after him as smartly as I could. The sergeant bellowed again, 'Halt!' and then a moment later, 'Fire as you will! Bring 'em down, boys!'

It appeared that we were to be treated as nothing more than targets in a contest of marksmanship. When the first shots rang out I gave an involuntary leap that seemed to take me as high into the air as the length of my stride, even though that itself was of unnatural duration. I am sure I heard a guffaw of laughter from one of the soldiers, reinforcing my impression that they saw this as good sport and we had no more value than kangaroos or native dogs to them.

Shots continued to pop around us as, gasping for air, I followed Johnny into an undergrowth of medium thickness. Luck was on our side, for although it seemed that we were completely surrounded by soldiers, Johnny had by chance chosen a weak spot in their defences. The man who confronted us looked so young as to be barely of age for his first shave. He was fumbling to reload his gun, having evidently discharged one round of shot without success. As Johnny reached him the young soldier held his gun crossways, in hopes of using it as a club perhaps, but the momentum Johnny had achieved enabled him to charge straight through this weak attempt at defence.

The soldier jumped aside at the last moment but was still in my path. Slightly built as I was, I realised I would be less likely to succeed with the tactic Johnny had employed, so I swerved at the last minute, leapt through a prickly bush, ducked under a low branch and raced away at a diagonal angle. I lost sight of Johnny during this manoeuvre, but I was only concerned with escape and so continued on my path, half rolling, half sliding down a gully and then climbing rapidly up the other side. Looking over my shoulder, I saw the young soldier and one of his colleagues in pursuit, but they were hampered by their heavy uniforms and their muskets, and so I was gradually able to gain the advantage over them and make good my escape.

At length, puffing and panting, my chest heaving, I came to a halt in a small clearing. In the anonymous forests of this strange land it was difficult to get a sense of north or south, east or west. In escaping the soldiers I had zigzagged and altered direction many times. As well, each deviation of the landscape had forced me to take a different path, until after just a brief time my disorientation had become absolute. I did not know now whether I was facing the settlement or whether it was behind me. There were no landmarks, just the giant eucalyptus trees, each aspiring to the heavens in its own way, each boasting its own peculiar distortion of branches.

For all I knew I might have run in a large circle and been close to my starting point again. Or I could be hopelessly lost in the depths of the forest. I stood for a while, bent forward, hands on my knees, listening intently, until at last I was satisfied that I had shaken off the hunters. I felt momentary relief, but soon the enormity of my situation began to make itself manifest to me, and I let out a sob of despair. Alone, entirely without shelter or tools, food or water, ignorant of my location, and an outlaw in this alien land . . . I had nothing, I was nothing, my future had suddenly been rendered hopeless. It was a bitter feeling, and bitterly did I reproach myself for ever having shown kindness to the runaway convict named Johnny.

Chapter 36

I WANDERED THROUGH THE FOREST for upwards of an hour, completely without purpose. I had an idea that sooner or later I might glimpse a camp or a settlement or some evidence of the presence of white men. I saw no clue of any such. Always it was the same: trees, grasses, bracken, other plants and rocks. The ground was generally flat but with occasional slopes and dips. Everywhere were logs, some lying flat, others at angles across each other. Some were old and rotten, others fresh. Quite a few were still alive, with new green growth springing from them.

It was often possible to reconstruct the history of the fallen timber: I could see how a branch had ripped away from its parent, leaving a scar, and plunged earthwards. In doing so the branch would frequently have crashed into another tree, perhaps knocking the whole of it down, or part of it, so that a tangled mess eventually settled on the ground, Nature in a wrecked state, a bewildering maze of timber. Time and time again I had to clamber over and through these immense knots. The biggest trunks were often too high for me to scale; I had to make my way up or down the length of these giants until I could get around their roots or climb them at their thinner reaches.

In time my mind settled down a little and I was at least able to consider my position with more clarity. It seemed to me that I had four choices. To find civilisation and give myself up, upon which I would be sentenced to, at best, a severe flogging. To find a tribe of Indians and attempt to ally myself with them, as according to rumour, other escapees had done, some successfully, some not. To strike out for the coast and attempt to get a French ship or some other vessel to take me away from this accursed land. To seek out other renegade convicts like Johnny and live off the land as best we could, outlaws forever.

I had developed a morbid fear of the cat-o'-nine-tails, and was sure that I would rather put an end to my own life than submit to its horror. So it seemed that my first option was unthinkable. The other three offered nothing much, no realistic hope of freedom, prosperity and a long life, all the things I had dreamed of in the days before this. Yet they were all I was left with.

I came to a stream that was not running but had settled into a series of pools, and I drank gratefully. As I finished and sat back on my heels, I was startled beyond measure to find that I was being observed. A man sat on a rock opposite, looking calmly at me. It was Johnny.

'Nice spot this,' he said. 'I never seen it before. Nice drop of water.'

I was deeply grateful and relieved to see another human being, even one who had got me into such dire straits, but all I could do was start crying. I sobbed and sobbed. Johnny crossed the stream and came to where I was sitting. He stood beside me looking down at me, almost as though he were curious. After a while, when he had said nothing and shown no particular sympathy or concern, I managed to get control of myself. There seemed so little point in crying. Eventually I got up. 'What are we going to do?' I asked him, quite calmly.

He didn't answer, just turned on his heel and set off across the stream again. Yet I had the feeling he was expecting me to follow, so I did. We went up the hill and over the ridge, and started through the forest. Johnny didn't look around once, but he clearly knew I was behind him.

I got very tired. I think it was the tiredness that comes from shock and fear, because the walking wasn't hard, even though we went quite a distance. I had no idea where Johnny was taking me but he appeared to have a destination in mind. I had no plan of my own, no ability to think for myself. My mind was no longer working. I followed blindly, stumbling quite often, until my companion stopped and I nearly walked right into him.

We were at the edge of a cliff. I moved out beside Johnny and peered down the drop. It was not as steep as I had feared, perhaps thirty yards. Johnny led me to some rocks about halfway along the escarpment and carefully made his way downwards. I watched until his head was out of sight, then followed. To my surprise he had completely disappeared. I scrambled down, grunting and panting, frightened by my renewed isolation, but I soon found the explanation for Johnny's whereabouts. I came to a dark hole, not much wider than me and smelling of moist earth. I squeezed through it, into complete darkness. I could hear, from scrapings and shufflings, that Johnny was in there somewhere. Then I heard the familiar sound of a flint striking steel and saw a couple of sparks dropping into a tinderbox. A small flame flared, and as he blew on it I saw his face, intent upon his task. I felt comforted by his calm concentration. The flames increased; he tipped the little fire gently onto the earth, and as I watched he carefully added fragments of bark and small twigs. The fire got bigger and the cave gradually warmed. I welcomed the warmth, for the cold of fear was through my body and it is a cold that cannot easily be comforted. I had no idea of the new direction my life was now to take; all I knew was that I would be lucky to survive, that from now on every decision and action would have to be taken with survival in mind, and the time left to me was likely to be numbered in days or weeks, months at best.

I sat there with my knees to my chest, my arms wrapped around myself, trying to stop trembling. This was not the future I had envisaged when I first formed the intention to come to New South Wales. Johnny did not say a word but after a time he left the cave and I could hear the scrambling sounds of his feet as he made his way back up the steep incline. I did not wonder where he had gone, nor did I care, but after a while I let myself slip over sideways, whereupon I curled up and slept beside the little fire.

I was awoken by Johnny's return and had no idea of the length of time I had been asleep. I was shocked at first, and then deeply grateful, when he thrust a couple of medium-sized carrots at me, and an apple, then put half a loaf of bread and a ceramic vase containing water beside me. I did not take much notice of the vase at first, as I busied myself with the victuals, and only after I made great inroads into the food did I attempt to quench my thirst.

As I picked up the vase I felt something sticky on it, and looking down at my hand saw that it was smeared with blood. 'Why Johnny,' I said, 'did you cut yourself when you were getting this?'

Looking up at him I saw guilt written large upon his face. 'Johnny,' I said, putting the uneaten bread down. 'How did you get this food?'

He did not answer, but looked stricken. I gazed again upon the vase and saw that it was a fine object indeed, purple flowers that I now know to be irises, against a green background, with long leaves wrapping around the neck. The colours were muted but to my ignorant eye it seemed finely done. This was an object which had travelled a great distance across vast oceans, protected and cherished, brought to a strange land, placed no doubt in a position of honour in whatever raw new building now housed it, only to be stolen and carried off into the wild forest for no other purpose than to hold water for a worthless runaway convict lad . . . and what was its fate now? To be cast down upon the floor of the cave and left lost among the dirt and rubble of millennia, never to be gazed upon by the eyes of man again?

And what other damage had been done by its procurer in the annexation of it? I looked up at Johnny again but before I could say anything I heard a shout in the distance. It sounded far away, but we were in a cave, where every sound was necessarily muted. Johnny heard it too, and his composure deserted him. He looked terrified. I put the vase down carefully and went past him to the entrance. Looking out I caught a glimpse of the familiar scarlet jackets, only two soldiers, but horribly close and coming in our direction with a purposeful air. One of the men paused, and with his right arm made a sweeping movement to someone out of my sight. By this I knew that there were more than two.

Aghast, I looked around at Johnny. 'Is there a back way out of the cave?' I asked him. He shook his head. 'Well, we had better make a run for it,' I said. 'It's another batch of soldiers. They're getting closer. I think they know we're here. They must have followed you.'

He nodded dumbly and came forward to join me at the mouth of the cave. I peeped out further and saw another scarlet jacket away to my right, working his way around the rocks. I realised we had to go now or we would of a certainty be trapped. I pointed to Johnny, to go to the left, and he nodded again. It seemed that I was in charge. I had no idea of course whether the left offered better prospects than the right, or whether straight ahead might have been an even better choice; all I knew was that those two latter options were already closed to us.

Taking a deep breath, as though jumping into the Thames, I leapt out from the mouth of the cave and immediately broke to the left, running as hard as I could. Pounding footsteps behind told me that Johnny had followed. I soon came to the end of the shelf of rock that lay out the front of the cave, and took a jump off the brink, sensing, from the fall of the land, that the drop would not be too great.

Whilst in midair I heard a shout from a soldier who was labouring up the face of the cliff. Thankfully I was right; the drop was not too great, but it was enough to jar me from my feet up to my neck, and it threw me off balance. Johnny landed behind me, so close that he fell against me. I was not able to regain my balance and went sprawling onto sharp rocks, with Johnny falling a moment later on top of me. As I struggled to get up I heard another shout, this time from the left of the cave, in the direction we were facing, and this provided me with added incentive to regain my feet. When I did so I ran with furious intent down the slope. Musket shots exploded on both sides, almost at the same time, upon which I started taking giant leaps, at great peril. I neither knew, nor, I confess, cared whether Johnny was behind me. Life, to be sure, had little enough to offer me at that time, but nonetheless I wanted to preserve mine. Like Job, bereft of all life's blessings, I still clung to an unknowable solid presence, perhaps the one that men call hope.

I saw a soldier running to cut me off, from my left, and I veered sharply away from him and put on speed. To my surprise I was suddenly overtaken by Johnny, who cast nary a glance in my direction, and so was evidently as little interested in my fate as I was in his. But he was a man and I a mere boy, and he was able to outrun me. I changed my course again to follow him, for I surmised that he knew these woods better than anyone and would perhaps guide me in the best way. So it proved, for shortly I could see, looking back, that the scarlet uniforms were well behind us. Their heavy clothing no doubt weighed them down, and perhaps they had little stomach for a long run in hot weather. There was not much in it for them; for us there was everything: liberty, of a kind, but more importantly, life itself.

Chapter 37

A FEW DAYS LATER FOUND us in a pitiful state. By then Johnny had told me the truth, so far as I could tell, of the episode where he had stolen the food. It seemed that he had broken into a house to procure some victuals, not for the first time, but had been disturbed in his endeavours by the lady of the place, who had come into the parlour just as he was leaving, panicked, as indeed she was entitled to do and, screaming, had rushed towards the door. Fearing that she would be successful in summoning help, Johnny had seized a poker from the fireplace and struck her across the back of the head, whereupon she had fallen insensible to the floor.

'Was there blood?' I asked, listening in horror and trepidation to this story.

Johnny gave a little nod. 'It started to spread,' he said. 'I staunched the flow as best I could, with a scarf, but I was too afeared to stay. I knew it would be the gallows for me if I was caught.'

He told this story on the third night of our trek into nowhere, our escape into the great inland nothingness of New South Wales. Huddled into Johnny, for protection against the cold and the savages and the beasts of the night, I shook with fear and remembered how Christian had preached to Hopeful that Moses would rather have died where he stood than go one step without his God. And I remembered how Christian and Hopeful, having reached a crossroads and become uncertain of their direction, had been persuaded to follow one who promised to take them to the Celestial City. Instead he had led them astray, until eventually they found themselves caught in a horrible net in which they were pitifully and hopelessly entangled.

> *Come hither, you that walk along the way,*
> *See how the Pilgrims fare that go astray;*
> *They catched are in an entangled net,*
> *'Cause they good counsel lightly did forget . . .*

I could not credit how the stolen food had not choked me with every mouthful, and I bitterly rued the day I had shown kindness to Johnny, for it seemed he was the one who had led me away from the future that Carmichael and the Revd Mr Haddock had shown me, and in consequence I was now to be punished over and over again.

Indeed it seemed before much longer that the punishment was to be a capital one. The next day we reached the foot of the cliffs that formed such an impenetrable barrier to the colony's expansion and, despairing of tackling the mighty sandstone ramparts in our weakened state, turned north. It was difficult walking on the broken rocks, but the vegetation to our right was too thick to penetrate, and so we struggled on. With every passing hour the desire for food grew stronger, and the lack of it sapped our limbs of strength and our bodies of energy. It was now our third day without food. Even in the cruel streets of London I had never gone so long without some trifle to eat. We did find a few bushes, more like small trees perhaps than bushes, with little orange fruits hanging from their branches. Some pretty crimson and green parrots, of a type I had seen before, were feeding from them, so we took the risk that they would be palatable for humans and filled our pockets. They were somewhat bitter and not at all tasty, but they seemed to do us no harm and doubtless were better than nothing.

That afternoon we came to a waterfall which, had we been in a healthier state, we might have appreciated as a superb example of Nature's magnificence. The water thundered down upon our heads when we ran into the torrent, the drops striking us with force. We had to shout at each other to make ourselves heard. Bubbles foamed around us as we luxuriated in one of the shallower pools at its base. We drank greedily, refreshing ourselves inwardly and outwardly. Although I could not spare the energy to appreciate the spectacle of the cascade, yet I was grateful for the nourishment the water provided.

Just a few miles further on, however, we came across water of a very different sort. We reached the banks of a broad river and stood in dismay looking out across it. Just under the surface were many green weeds and the water flowed fast across them. As if to further emphasise its speed, Johnny threw in a stick and it was swiftly borne away, being out of sight in less than a minute.

It seemed to me that my life continued to mirror that of Christian's, for I could not help recalling the great darkness and horror that fell upon him when he found himself in the river, just short of the celestial gates. I told Johnny of this. He stood for a moment ruminating upon the story and then said to me: 'This fellow, Christian, he was taken then, by the river?'

'No, indeed.' I shook my head. 'He had faith and was saved.'

'Well then, we need not be too despairing. If he was saved, there is hope for us.'

I thought, but did not say: But we are wicked sinners. The waterfall seemed to have given Johnny new energy, and he began to trek eastwards, along the bank. I followed. A few days earlier I would have said that I had more strength and endurance than Johnny, but now, hungry, exhausted and frightened, I found myself looking more and more to him to take the lead. Besides, he was a man and I was yet a boy.

Nevertheless, by nightfall we were both done in. We had failed to find any way of crossing the river. As is the nature of rivers, it became broader as it spread across the plains. It became slower too, but that was little consolation, as neither of us could swim, and the flow was still quick enough to intimidate us.

We crept into a hollow that had been created by the roots of a tree. The rumblings of my stomach almost drowned out the susurration of the river, but eventually the gentler sound lulled me into a sleep that lasted until dawn.

When Johnny roused, we dragged ourselves up and staggered on our way. Within an hour or so I found myself struggling to take each successive step, so weary were my limbs and so heavy my body. Although Johnny was still in the lead, he appeared to be in no better shape. By mid-morning we had reached a stage where we frequently tripped and fell over disturbances in the ground that ordinarily would have gone unnoticed. A rock, a tree root, a clump of grass . . . these were becoming almost insurmountable obstacles. The worst were the fallen logs, which were numerous. On the first day of our journey, nourished by the food Johnny had stolen for me, and driven by fear of the soldiers, I had easily scaled giant logs that were almost twice my height. Now the effort required to clamber over a sapling no more than a foot

in diameter seemed impossible to muster. Most times now when I came
to a fallen tree I shuffled off the track towards the topmost branches and
went all the way around rather than lift my leg a few extra inches.

I did not even notice when we came to an area where the river
spread out across a vast area of shallow water and rapids. I did notice
that Johnny had sunk to the ground just ahead of me, and when I came
up to him I slumped down too. Without speaking he nodded at the river,
which already felt like our inescapable companion. I glanced in the
direction he indicated and realised at once that our way to the northern
bank lay open.

The awareness gave me a little more strength. After a short rest we
dragged ourselves down the bank and breasted the water. I was shocked
at how deep it quickly became, but I struggled forward, as I could see
that if we survived the first few yards we would have an easier time of
it. However, just a couple of steps later I lost my footing and was swiftly
carried away. I struggled to keep my head above the water and at the
same time flailed with my arms to try to get out of the current. Looking
back, I could see Johnny waving wildly, but I had no idea what message,
if any, he was trying to convey. Certainly he made no attempt to come
after me, to save my life, and I was filled with bitterness at the awareness
of how truly alone I was.

I soon realised that I had no hope of swimming against the current
to reach the bank on one side or the shallower water on the other. All I
could do was allow the flow of the river to take me and at the same time
try to ease myself in my desired direction in the hope that I would reach
safety before I was sucked under. Already I was so waterlogged that my
face was the only part of me not submerged. The wash kept covering
my nose and mouth, causing me to inadvertently imbibe large quanti-
ties of water. I was in desperate straits when the back of my head struck

an object with stunning force. I realised it was an old grey dead tree branch, of great immensity, stretching either side of me, and I somehow found the strength to reach up my hands and take hold of it. Before I lost further strength I dragged myself painfully along it. The water, cheated of its prey, continued to pull at me, but it was impotent now, and at last I found myself standing on a spit of sand and gravel, up to my knees in water so mild that I might as well have been on land.

I spent some time retching and coughing. My head rang with the force of the blow from the tree. I had no interest in Johnny's whereabouts and did not look for him until a splashing noise caused me to lift my head, and I found him approaching, and just a few yards away. Unable to speak, I merely shook my head, but I was surprised at his emotion when he grabbed me by the shoulders and stared into my face. Looking at him, I saw that his face was working with deep feelings, and there appeared to be tears in his eyes. I straightened up further. 'Thank God you're all right,' he said. 'I thought it was all up with you.'

I merely nodded, still unable to speak, but I was impressed at the depth of his feeling. We had been thrown together by such strange circumstances; we had exchanged few words since our first meeting, and even fewer since our escape from the soldiers, and yet I suppose being outlaws from the whole of society caused us to form a bond in a place that was beyond civilisation, where the normal laws and customs did not apply. We had entered a world where we made our own rules.

In the early days of my illicit contacts with Johnny, I had formed the impression that he was barely sane, but now that I had spent all this time with him, I was coming to a different conclusion. He was reticent, not a man for conversation, a self-contained man, but he was clever and resourceful and had a certain strength of mind.

It took us some hours to ford the river. It was by no means as easy as it had appeared from the bank, as indeed I had proved in those first few minutes of terror. There were other deep sections which caused us to make long detours, and some of the rapids were so fast that we were afraid of them. As we neared the northern bank we realised that the same conditions prevailed as on the southern bank. Once again the water was deep and fierce-flowing. We waded upstream, on another sandy spit, hoping to find a place to cross, but were unsuccessful. Eventually the spit ran out and we were facing impossibly deep water again. Heavy of heart, fearing that our venture was doomed to fail, we turned and retraced our steps. At least now the water was with us rather than against us. We continued downstream hundreds of yards until Johnny pointed to another fallen log that straddled the fast current, and by its means, using it as a bridge, we made our clumsy and faltering way across to the refuge of the bank.

Although I call it a refuge, and although I felt a sense of achievement and relief to reach it, what in truth was our achievement? We had no purpose, no destination, no plan. We had certainly outstripped the pursuit by the soldiers, but where were we to go and what were we to do? We had not discussed giving ourselves up, making our way to the nearest settlement and surrendering to the authorities, but the thought was there, in my mind, and with every passing hour of our flight it became more persistent. I did not dare mention it to Johnny, because although the consequences would be awful for me, they would almost certainly be fatal for him. If nothing else, my youth still gave me prospects of escaping the gallows.

Of course there was no certainty that we could even find a settlement in time to stave off the awful ravages of starvation and exhaustion. We had fled in fear, with no thought of our direction, so we were thoroughly lost. We could head eastwards, towards the coast, which was the only direction that might lead us to our own people. The chances of stumbling upon one of the outposts of the colony, however, were no better than the chances of finding the stick Johnny had thrown into the river hours earlier.

Without a word to each other, we resumed our grim journey. We were still heading northwards, but only because the country seemed more open in that direction. We followed tracks that were doubtless made by kangaroos or some other large creature. There was no discernible purpose or pattern to them, and they frequently crisscrossed each other, but some were as good as London footpaths. The ones to which I had been accustomed, at any rate. Nonetheless, as dusk fell, we had both reached the limit of our endurance. Malnourished and weak at the beginning of our trek as we were, we had now exhausted our meagre resources of strength. We fell down at the base of a huge eucalypt tree, and eventually, under the shelter of its protecting arms, I drifted into an uncomfortable and uneasy sleep.

Chapter 38

I FELT SOMETHING PRODDING MY side, and as so often happens in sleep, I incorporated the sensation into my dream. My dream was of the sons and daughters of Job who had been eating and drinking wine in their eldest brother's house when a great wind came from the wilderness and smote the four corners of the building, so that it fell upon Job's children and killed them. Somehow I found myself wandering around the ruins, trying to lift the heavy beams in hope of finding some survivor of the disaster.

The prodding in my side became, in my dream, a broken roof rafter which kept knocking against me as I tried to fight my way through the tangled wreckage. Eventually it became too insistent; it woke me, and I realised I was not in the land of Uz but lying on the inhospitable ground of a New South Wales forest, and the annoying poking in my side was not from a broken piece of timber but from Johnny's fist.

I sat up, pushing his hand away and at the same time brushing my hair from my face. Thus it was that my eyes fell upon a line of four naked savages looking upon us. All were men, standing with such perfect stillness and silence that they seemed as much a part of the land-scape as the trees and rocks that surrounded us. Exhausted though I was, I was startled enough to jump to my feet. Johnny followed my example, though more slowly. We stood looking at these extraordinary primitive figures. I had of course seen Indians from the ship when we arrived, I had seen them around the colony, I had seen them wandering freely through the settlement; but out here, they were different. It seemed that wherever we British went, we quickly laid claim to the territory and rendered all others into trespassers. In the labyrinthine forest, these bearded men with their wild hair and dark eyes took on a new stature. Their gravity matched their surroundings. The little I had seen of the English countryside led me to suppose that it was a soft and comforting environment. On the way to Plymouth I had seen farms and cottages tucked into nooks and crannies in ways that made them seem warm, protected, snug. The countryside of New South Wales did not convey those qualities. It was not cruel, in the way in which I imagine the desert may seem cruel, in which the ocean can often be cruel. It was just indif-ferent. It cared for nothing. It went on forever, unchanging, untouched by the hand of man, retaining no imprint of man's footsteps. It shrugged off man's puny attempts to make his mark upon it.

So too the aboriginal people of this country seemed largely indif-ferent to the new, white residents. They reacted to us when we came into contact with them, of course, but they did not initiate contact with us. I had the sense that if we were blown away one day by a mighty storm they would resume their ancient way of life in a moment. Perhaps a few stories would be told about us, perhaps we would appear in a few of their paintings on rocks, of the kind I had seen in sheltered places along the cliffs near Toongabbie. Yet we would have as little impact on them as Johnny's stick had upon the river.

So it was with a sense of inferiority as well as fear that I gazed upon them that morning. Would they kill us, as trespassers? Would they butcher us for food? Would they brush us off as we were forever doing with the ubiquitous flies? Would they welcome us as brothers? Surely, looking at us now, they could not see us as a threat. We were gaunt, weak, barely able to stand. We had no weapons; indeed, no possessions of any kind. We were almost as naked as they were: just a few ripped garments clinging to our bony bodies. I hoped that they would recognise our inadequacy as meat for their dinner pots. We had as little to offer as a pair of crows, and everybody knew that crows were the one bird the Indians of this land despised to eat.

Having surveyed us for some minutes, one of them gestured towards us with his head and said something to the others, upon which an excited jabbering broke out. All the men clustered around the first speaker, offering their different opinions no doubt. We were at a loss to understand the nature of the discussion, except that we were evidently its subject. At length Johnny interrupted them by stepping forth and saying: 'Please take us with you. We need food.'

At the same time he pantomimed the action of eating and rubbed his stomach. The men looked at him somewhat uneasily, and there was further conversation between them, this time more muted. Finally one of them turned to us and indicated by a gesture of his hand and an inclination of his head that we should follow them. They offered us no assistance, but instead set off at a fast pace. We had no choice but to do as he suggested. For all that they were so far removed from us, we still belonged to the same species. They were the first humans we had seen in many days – I had lost count of how many, but it was either six or seven. If we separated from them there was no certainty that we would ever see another human being again. Anything was preferable to a cold and lonely grave out here in the vast unknown.

It was, however, only with the greatest difficulty that we kept up with the men. They did not appear to walk at a fast pace and yet somehow they covered the ground with such ease as to make it look effortless. When the kangaroo bounds through the forest he does so with great pounding heavy thumps. Yet these aboriginal inhabitants seemed barely to touch the earth. Within minutes both Johnny and I were panting and sweating and stumbling. Not one of the men we followed looked around even once to ascertain our condition.

We were soon struggling to keep them in sight. I was very afraid that we would lose contact with them. We were saved, however, by the appearance of another group of Indian men, three in number, who converged with these fellows from our left-hand side, from the west. When the two groups met they gathered in a crowd, and much delight was evinced by our newfound friends at the fact that a man in the second lot had a dead beast slung over his shoulders. I had only seen a few of these creatures before; they were evidently a type of kangaroo, only smaller, and reddish-black in colour. The tail also appeared to be longer, at least in proportion to the size of the body.

This one appeared to weigh about forty pounds. The hunting party, when I indicated to them my interest in its name, told me it was known to them as 'bagary'. Because of its colour, the colonists called it the red kangaroo, although later the name 'wallaby' was accorded to it, I believe because it was known as such by some other native tribe. That is the name I shall use for it.

I muttered to Johnny: 'Good news that they have food. It means they are less likely to eat us.'

He gave a mirthless smile in response. I think he was too done in to speak.

The men who had now joined us seemed no more interested in us than were the first group. They threw the animal onto the ground, on its side, and proceeded to cut open its belly with one of their knife-stones. The efficacy of these tools was impressive; however, they could not rival the steel blade used by the European, and I fancy that as much was accomplished by the sheer strength of the hunter as by the sharp-ness of the 'blade'.

The man who appeared to be chief among them, a huge, power-fully built fellow who had been carrying the wallaby, then pulled out the gut of the animal and, to my disgust, proceeded to drink some of its blood. The other men all followed, but neither Johnny nor I, weak and malnourished though we were, cared to partake of this ceremony, in spite of being invited to do so, in an offhand sort of way, by one of the men.

The big man then squeezed the animal's faeces out and replaced the gut in the stomach. He pushed a sharpened stick through the stomach, hoisted the creature back on his shoulder, and signalled that we should resume our journey.

It was a goodly time before we came upon the campsite of the tribe. By then Johnny and I had once again almost lost sight of the hunters, and we were greatly relieved when we realised that our day's journey was at an end. As we approached I saw quite suddenly that there were bark shelters everywhere, but they were difficult to discern against the natural colours of the trees and ground. A couple of small fires burned in roughly arranged fireplaces. Native dogs skulked around, looking at us warily.

Although the men had seemed to find the wallaby of more interest than they found Johnny or me, the women and children of the camp paid us somewhat more attention. Most of the women gathered around us, feeling our scanty clothes and mauling us with their dirty fingers. Hiding behind the women, the children peered at us with bright eyes, full of curiosity. They seemed especially interested in me; they had quite possibly seen white adults before, but not a white child.

As preparations for the evening meal began we were left to our own devices. This did not displease us at all. The campsite was near a stream; we went down there to drink, for we were both thirsty. I was surprised that we were accompanied on this little excursion by two men, still carrying their spears: they themselves did not drink but merely watched us, as though ensuring that we had no nefarious purpose.

Returning to the campsite was an ordeal. Although only a short walk, the energy that had sustained me as I followed the hunters was now completely depleted. Johnny was in no better condition. We went to a place under a tree, at a respectable distance from the biggest cooking fire. I felt dizzy and sick. There was nothing in my stomach to vomit, except water, but I wondered if I might faint at any moment.

A woman threw a couple of yams to us. They were raw, but they represented some form of nourishment. I had reached the stage where, starving though I was, I could barely find the energy to eat, but I made myself nibble at the vegetable. It took ten minutes or so to finish it, but it did help revive me, a little.

I tried to take more interest in my surroundings, still fighting off the sensations of dizziness and fainting. In an effort to get warmer I inched closer to the fire. Wherever these people travel they take fire with them, from camp to camp, carrying firesticks which smoulder all day. I had to admire their ability to manage this forbidding environment in these subtle ways. Johnny and I were as good as helpless in it, but the native people seemed to me adroit and clever.

I watched with some squeamishness as the wallaby was prepared for cooking. The men did this work. Several of them dug a kind of pit and lined it with dry grass. One of the bigger men then stood on the buttocks of the creature and broke the hind legs, at the ankles. With a confidence and ease no doubt born of long familiarity, he pushed a stick into the legs and removed the tendons, which he wound around the stick and put to one side. These, I was to find, would be used later to bind sharp stones to the end of spears, to make the killing points.

The men then set fire to the dead grass in the pit, and another of them, holding the wallaby by one front leg and one rear leg, swung it repeatedly through the flames to burn off the hair. At the completion of this task he broke the legs completely away from the body, cut through the tail and put all the parts of the animal, including the gut, beside the main fire, covering them with hot coals. Later, the women threw their contributions onto the fire. These appeared to consist of a number of different roots, as well as grubs of several varieties.

No matter how disgusting it may appear to be, food which is cooking has an aroma that is irresistible. To Johnny and me, sitting there in our starved condition, the smells had our heads spinning until I would almost have leapt into the fire and pulled something, anything, from the coals and crammed it into my mouth. However, fear of the reactions of my sable companions kept me from doing anything so foolish. I attempted to divert myself by studying the members of the tribe in which we found ourselves, in an effort to differentiate their various personalities.

It was by now evident to me, as I indicated earlier, that the man who carried the wallaby, and who had presumably been responsible for its spearing, dominated this group of thirty or so persons. Taller than the others by a full head, and weighing perhaps thirty pounds more, he cut an impressive figure. Like all the men, his chest bore raised ceremonial scars, only his were greater in number and size than any others. He had a magnificent head of tangled black hair and a massive black beard; his eyes were fiery and alert. He would have been a formidable opponent in battle.

His dignity was remarkable. He took no part in the butchering of the wallaby, ignoring the scene completely, as he ignored everyone most of the time. At no stage had he taken any notice of Johnny and me. The only member of the tribe for whom he seemed to soften was a lad, perhaps six years of age, who had run to him as soon as he returned to the camp and had dogged his footsteps ever since. I took this boy to be his son; I later found out that his name was, as best as I can reproduce it in the English tongue, Mudaree, and the father was the famous warrior, Chaginnini.

Mudaree was a slightly built lad, not particularly robust, and with little to say, but whenever his father's eyes lighted upon him, a fondness crept over the face of the big man, and he murmured words of endearment to the child. Young though I was, and ignorant of any first-hand knowledge of the bonds between parents and children, yet it was a touching sight to witness this father and son together and to observe the same sentiments as might be found in the most fashionable thoroughfares of London.

The leader among the children was a lively and quick youngster, about ten years of age, whose name I was to discover was something like Nama-Nama. He was a dextrous lad. Like all the boys he fashioned toy spears out of any materials which came to hand. They used these weapons continually in their games to hurl at any target, including each other. Nama-Nama threw with more strength and accuracy than the other boys, and this aptitude alone would no doubt have given him great status with his fellows, but his popularity was further enhanced by his sense of humour, for he loved to laugh and seemed able to find a jest in every situation.

The group seemed to comprise about nine men, twelve women and thirteen children. I had doubts about the capacity of one wallaby to satisfy the appetites of so many, but he was a fat little beast, and the meal was enhanced by the grubs and roots obtained, apparently, by the women. When the meat was dragged from the fire it was placed on sticks laid close by, presumably so it could cool. It was then apportioned according to protocols which took me some time to work out, but the first thing I noticed was that the cooked gut, and the fat around it, was given to the oldest men. Fat appeared to be much valued, for that which was not given to the old men was given to the hunters who had been responsible for the slaughter of the creature.

Access to the meat was gained by cutting open the back of the carcass. Whilst one man pushed a stick into the animal's anus, thereby enabling him to lift the body clear of the ground, another broke off the ribs. He made a small hole on each side of the animal and used this to loosen the hipbones. The ribs, the hipbones and the backbone were then cut from the flesh, and the backbone broken in the middle. I noticed the care with which they cut the neck; for some reason they appeared to have a great fear of damaging the Adam's apple. In the absence of any reasonable explanation I was forced to put this down to superstition.

The neck was then broken off the backbone. The various parts were laid upon the cooling sticks again, in an order which appeared to be strictly prescribed and showed much respect for fairness and equity. One leg was placed in one row, the second in the other. The same procedure was followed with the two rib parts and the two sections of the backbone. The stomach, the neck, the head, the hipbones, the tail and the tail end of the backbone were carefully placed according to some etiquette that was beyond my comprehension.

The food was then further divided among smaller groups, at the discretion of the men, and at last the eating began. Nothing was offered to Johnny or me. I believe I groaned aloud several times with the agony of the hunger in my belly, and with my sense of the injustice of it all. If I did, it evoked no response from anyone. At last, when most of the natives had eaten, a woman threw us a few remnants of backbone. We flung ourselves upon them with a fervour only the starving can understand. They were still warm, but only half-cooked. It mattered not to us. I glanced at Johnny as we ate, and it struck me that the two of us, squatting there in the dust, tearing ferociously at the bones, filthy and ragged as we were, had been reduced to nothing better than wild animals ourselves. The Indians, so at home in their natural surroundings, had a grace, and easy manner, which put us to shame. It hardly needs saying that I was beyond caring about our degraded state.

When we had finished the meat, the same woman brought us some of the cooked roots. A few of these had quite a pleasant nutty flavour, but most were bland and lacked taste. I was surprised at how quickly my belly had shrunk, for I could only eat half-a-dozen before feeling too full to continue. Glancing at Johnny I saw that he had reached the same point. He had lain down the root on which he had been nibbling and was now slumped backwards against a rock. He looked utterly exhausted.

As no further notice was taken of either of us, it seemed that we were free to do as we wished. The Indians had their bark shelters, under which they slept, but we dared not abuse their hospitality by going close to those. We found a comfortable enough area of grass and nestled up together against a dead log, endeavouring to keep each other warm. I believe not even the log could have slept more soundly than I did that night, in those strange and fearful surroundings.

Chapter 39

THE WOMAN WHO HAD fed us the night before was named Baroo and she showed us more kindness in the days that followed. Johnny alarmed me considerably by suggesting that she was fattening us for the cooking pot, but I hoped this was mere facetiousness on his part. The natives showed no sign of animosity towards us. However, we were careful to conduct ourselves with modesty and deference, and in time their indifference seemed to give way to something resembling friendliness.

This began with the children, who were more open to our presence than were the adults. They seemed particularly interested in me, being closer to them in age and no doubt less of a threat. Yet their ways were extraordinary to me, as indeed they would be to any God-fearing person. It took me a deal of time to adjust to their pagan customs. I blush to recount some of the behaviours freely indulged in by those as young as two or three years of age, but I will be as true to my chronicle as I can. I crave my readers' indulgence if I mention some of the less savoury aspects of these savages' lives.

And yet, 'One calls "barbarism" whatever he is not accustomed
to.' It is hard to conceive of customs more barbaric than the procedures I witnessed in London for the punishment of criminals, many of
whom had done no more than steal a little food to keep hunger at bay.
It is hard to conceive of anything more barbaric than the conditions in
Newgate and on the Hulks. Mr Ogwell was a God-fearing gentleman,
but his treatment of his four-year-old daughter Josephine could not be
compared with the tender and affectionate way these natives treated
their infants. The behaviour of Corporal Arnold towards me and others
on the ship was coldly and cruelly barbaric – and so was the punishment meted out to him. And nothing could be so savage, so inhuman, as
the practice in our civilised society of inflicting hundreds of whiplashes
upon the back of some poor fettered soul until his skin and much of
his flesh lies in shreds on the ground and still they flog him upon his
raw and bloodied body. I am told that the natives with whom Governor
Phillip and the first colonists had intercourse shrank away in horror and
revulsion from the spectacle of men being flogged or hung, even if they
were being punished for crimes committed against the natives themselves. Doubtless they thought the white man a most primitive creature.

Pope has it thus:

Lo, the poor Indian! whose untutor'd mind
Sees God in clouds, or hears him in the wind;
His soul proud Science never taught to stray
Far as the solar walk or milky way;
Yet simple Nature to his hope has giv'n,
Behind the cloud-topp'd hill, a humbler heav'n;
Some safer world in depth of woods embrac'd,
Some happier island in the wat'ry waste,

Where slaves once more their native land behold,
No fiends torment, no Christians thirst for gold!
To be, contents his natural desire;
He asks no angel's wing, no seraph's fire:
But thinks, admitted to that equal sky,
His faithful dog shall bear him company.

Yet Pope's lines did not reflect my observations of the Indians of New South Wales either. They were kept company by their faithful dogs, but the dogs were a miserable collection of half-starved mutts who would as likely snap at the hand that fed them as accept a scratch behind the ear. I sought in vain for some sign of the workings of a divinity in the lives of the dogs' masters. They appeared to keep no religious observances, to worship no Creator, to bow their knees to no all-powerful Father. They were most mindful of their surroundings, the woods, the cloud-topp'd hills, the wind, and the sky at night. They told stories and acted them out in their dances, for which they decorated themselves in all kinds of queer ways, and although these narratives were often all but incomprehensible to us, yet they had a strange and compelling fascination, so that I came to look forward to the performances. Still, the natives themselves seemed oblivious to the idea that their destiny was in the hands of the mysterious One to whom we Christians believe we are beholden for our lives, and who shall determine the manner of our death and our fate thereafter. The dogs, in the way that they deferred to their human masters, seemed to have a greater appreciation of the meaning of worship than did the natives in any relationship they might have with their Maker.

As the poet says, 'to be' appeared to represent the extent of these people's ambitions. Pope surely spoke the truth when he observed that they did not thirst for gold, nor did they aspire to the study of science. As far as I could tell, they simply existed, as much a part of their surroundings as every other manifestation of Nature. There was a rhythm to their lives, although I did not dwell with them long enough to discern the patterns of it. They got up in the mornings, whereupon the men repaired and prepared their spears. They used tendons such as those taken from the legs of the kangaroos and wallabies they had killed to tie sharp rocks to the shafts of the spears; the spears without such accoutrements were put in hot ashes to make them more flexible, so they could be straightened. The men then set off on their hunt. The women took their woven baskets and went searching for food, generally yam roots, or other roots including those of ferns. The children helped the women, or played. The tribe moved from place to place according to whim, or for reasons that I did not comprehend. As the wind moved through the trees, bending the branches and rustling the foliage and then was gone, leaving no trace of its passing but a few leaves on the ground, so these people traversed the land.

Much of this perspective has come to me in later years. As a young boy, ignorant of the ways of the world, I was not perhaps so measured in my response to the customs of the tribe. From the first morning, the children started drifting closer to me, but it did not take long for me to feel astonished by the way they conducted themselves. 'One calls "barbarism" whatever he is not accustomed to.' The play of the children of this tribe, free of any apparent moral strictures or divine laws, appeared to me barbaric in the extreme, but it seldom strayed into acts of violence. They seemed to play at but two games, which had in common that they were both imitative of adults.

One of these games was hunting, by both girls and boys, and housemaking, generally by the girls alone. In the hunting games the children used their fingers, or long pieces of grass, or sticks, to attack each other or to attack rectangles of bark that the defenders held as targets. They chased and fought and duelled, and in so doing the boys at least were no doubt learning the skills they would need to become successful hunters and warriors who could fight for the tribe. Frequently they played a game where one held a bark shield, catching in it the pointed twigs thrown by another. When the thrower's stock of twigs was exhausted, the shield bearer collected the twigs and the tables were turned: he threw them back at his opponent.

If a child, in the middle of this mock battle, wanted to pick up a twig that had fallen to the ground, he or she would do so with toes only, conveying it to the hand without once taking his or her eyes off the further onslaught of little spears, and thus continuing to successfully deflect the attack. They always stood side on in these encounters, so that they presented the narrowest possible targets to their opponents.

Boys stalked and killed insects, then brought them 'home' to the girls, as if they were kangaroos or wallabies or opossums. The girls, when not engaged in spear-fighting, occupied themselves by pretending to cook the insects brought to them by the boys, by building shelters from eucalyptus leaves, by nursing sticks that they called their babies and carrying these wooden infants around in bark vessels. Watching them, I used to think of the spoilt little rich girls of London, wheeling their elaborately dressed, exquisitely made dolls in expensive peram-bulators along the streets and through the parks. How they would have despised their dark-skinned cousins from New South Wales, and yet the latter seemed to derive more pleasure from their simple twig-dolls than did the proud little misses in Hyde Park from their porcelain creations.

The Indian girls carried their house-making games to such a degree that they frequently argued and fought like jealous older women, hitting each other over the head with the sticks they used for collecting roots, and screaming abuse. Not infrequently, they would knock down the eucalyptus leaf shelters in their mock rage, then suddenly squat in the sand poring over the positions of the fallen leaves as though able to see all kinds of prophecies in their patterns. They reminded me of an old gypsy woman I had seen in London, who claimed she could tell the future by studying the tea leaves left in the bottom of a cup.

The other game played by the children was the one that both Johnny and I found immeasurably shocking, for it was the imitation of adults in a different aspect of their lives. I did not have to look far to find the exemplars for this precocious behaviour, for men and women disported themselves publicly in ways that I found embarrassing, disturbing and, at the same time, I must confess, compelling. Approaching as I was the time when my own maturation was imminent, I could not help but be excited as much as repelled by the way the adults of the tribe flaunted themselves. Sometimes I thought of the Revd Mr Grimwade at St Martin's, and how he would have viewed their promiscuity. I have no doubt that he would have predicted the fieriest tortures of Hell as their inevitable destination.

Certainly it was true that the children, inspired by the debauchery around them, were endlessly fascinated by their own private parts, and those of others, and were constantly acting out scenes of coition. Sometimes these were mere play; at other times they appeared to be achieving something closely resembling the practices of their elders. They had little compunction about using parts of the body I cannot bring myself to name to explore one another, paying little regard to such trivialities as gender. During games, the boys at times ran at other children, holding their organs of generation as though they were weapons, as though they were attempting coitus, and hence causing the other children to run away, giggling and screaming. Nama-Nama was not alone among the boys in urinating at children whom he wished to chase off. On one occasion the older children pulled a little boy, who could not have been more than three, away from a baby girl who looked to be only twelve months or so old, and with whom he was obviously attempting connection.

I could not be sure when childhood ended for these people, because there were no boys whose age corresponded closely to mine. I had the feeling that the natives were puzzled by me, in one respect at least. It was evident that at some stage boys were operated upon in ways which must have been very painful, but which were necessary for them to become full adults. One part of this process I had already observed: the cicatrices seen on the chests and arms of adult males around Botany Bay and Toongabbie, and in the tribe among whom we now dwelled. On men like Chaginnini these scars were fierce indeed. A second operation performed on boys was already familiar to me, and is almost universal practice in my own country, except that we inflict it on males when they are still infants. Among the aboriginal people of New South Wales, however, it appeared that the operation took place at a more advanced age. I was still intact in this respect, which was unusual enough among English lads, and seemed to perplex the natives greatly, as I was probably past the age when they would have expected the operation to be performed.

The third procedure was one that I had heard discussed by the convicts at Toongabbie, where it had been the subject of fascination, mirth and fear in approximately equal proportions. Amongst the people with whom we now dwelled I had my first opportunity to see the results of this primitive rite at close quarters. I refer to the practice known as subincision. I have said that the members of the tribe went naked, but although that was true for the women and children, the men, when in the company of women, wore a tassel which I had first thought was donned as a modest cover for the male organ, but which, I eventually came to realise, was to conceal the evidence of subincision. They were mortified when women, on occasions, were by chance able to view these quite dramatic cuts, which again appeared to be associated with initiation into manhood. I thought it a rather dreadful sight myself, and shrank at the thought of the pain it must have involved.

Although Johnny satisfied the requirements of manhood in one respect, he did not, of course, in the other two; and I failed on all counts. Fortunately for us, however, the natives made no attempt to remedy these defects.

Almost equally extraordinary and abhorrent to me was the custom among the women of cutting off the top two joints of the little finger on the left hand. All adult women suffered this amputation. Apparently it served a similar purpose to the wounds inflicted on the men: a kind of initiation ritual. The practice was called by the people 'malgun'.

Perhaps the lack of these gruesome wounds helped account for the apparent reluctance of the tribe to admit us into their ranks. Perhaps previous encounters with escapees and runaways had not been happy experiences for them. Or perhaps they were simply not interested in connecting with people who obviously had so little to offer and who taxed their already meagre resources. Whatever the reason, we were with them many weeks before we felt reasonably well accepted into their midst. Although they had quickly dropped the habit of following us if we appeared to be moving out of their sight, for a long time we felt of little more value or status than the miserable native dogs that skulked around their camp.

Chapter 40

GRADUALLY THE INDIANS SHARED food with us more readily and more generously. Little was asked of us in return, and so as time went on we put on condition, and I for one started to feel some energy and strength returning to my limbs. In the absence of much warmth or interest from the adults, I found myself settling into the role of a sort of older playmate to the children and spent some hours each day in their company. With my experience of doll-making in London, I thought I would try my hand here in the primitive forest, and so I borrowed a stone knife from a man named Kutuku. It was awkward for me to handle at first, but I soon became used to it and found it surprisingly efficacious. However, it proved extremely difficult to find any wood worth carving: most of it was too hard or too soft or too brittle. Eventually I hit upon a few good pieces, particularly when I found some driftwood on the banks of a broad and slow-flowing stream.

I completed the first doll and gave it to a group of girls one afternoon when they returned from a food-gathering expedition with their mothers. They were completely astonished by it, and quite fearful, stepping back and huddling together, looking at it apprehensively. When one of the bigger girls, a lass named Rainja, finally found the courage to take it from me, she immediately turned it upside down and back to front, inspecting its posterior closely. She seemed alarmed by what she found, and pointed urgently to the others, showing them that something was lacking. They chattered among themselves in great agitation and excitement. I formed the view that they wanted to ensure it could defecate. This was an issue that did not seem to concern them with the twig-dolls they chose for themselves, but no doubt this was attributable to the fact that they made no attempt to give these twigs any resemblance to real children. I took back from Rainja the doll I had carved, and with a pointy piece of hardwood drilled into the soft driftwood in the appropriate place to make something resembling the necessary anatomical correction. The girls seemed greatly relieved by this small piece of surgery, and then adopted the doll with enthusiasm. They seemed to play with it, and to talk with it, as though it were a real infant. They gave it orders, and chastened it when it did not obey; they took it to the creek and made it 'drink'; they put it into a bark cradle and took it with them wherever they went.

Johnny and I also made spears, using the same materials and techniques that we had observed employed by the hunters. Our early attempts were vastly inferior to those of the natives, to the men's great amusement, but we still used them for practice, whilst at the same time trying to improve upon our prototypes. We were soon making quite passable weapons, and the accuracy of our throwing developed too, although we could not match the Indians for distance. The range they achieved was prodigious, most of them exceeding thirty yards with ease, yet still hitting their targets. With the spear throwers, or 'woomeras' as they called them, they could get twice as far.

Nonetheless we were delighted to be invited one evening to accompany the tribe upon a major hunting expedition. The moon was full, which seemed to give them the confidence to find their way through the forest at such a late hour. This was the first time I had seen such a united endeavour, and the first time I had seen a night-time hunt. Food had been scarce for some days, and clearly in their minds the time had come for decisive action.

We walked for about an hour. I did my best to tread silently, but Johnny, who was in front of me, made as much noise as a drunken tinker in a cobblestoned alleyway in London. In contrast, I could not hear the natives at all. Yet when we paused in the middle of crossing a stream Johnny said to me: 'Can you not make less noise, Barnaby? Compared to our dusky friends, you sound like a draught horse dragging a wagon-load of beer barrels.'

'I thought you were the one making the noise,' I stammered back in astonishment.

'Hah,' he ejaculated, and said no more.

When we reached the appointed spot, we waited to see what would happen, but it gradually became obvious that nothing in particular was planned in the near future. This was the way of these people. They did not seem to mind if something took a long time or a short. The children would sometimes spend almost an entire day searching for witchetty grubs, which they found by digging under certain plants where the discarded shells lay and then breaking into the thick roots to pull out the treats. The grubs were certainly exquisitely delicious, tasting something like creamy scrambled eggs, but left to myself I would not have spent an entire day looking for them.

However, as the night wore on, the great man Chaginnini roused the others, and the men began to construct a fence from dead logs, fallen branches and torn-up bushes. It became clear that they were planning an ambush. The women and children set off in the moonlight, in an eastwards direction, and were soon out of sight. I was relieved that I had not been classified as being among their number; it seemed the tribe had decided that, although I lacked the insignia of initiation, I could be safely accorded the status of man rather than child. This pleased me greatly. It may seem to my readers that an English lad is degrading himself and his proud race by paying any care to the rank he is accorded by savages, but our long residence within the tribe, my affection for the children, and my growing respect for the manners and customs of the people with whom we dwelled had wrought a change in my sentiments. And they had, after all, saved Johnny and me from certain death.

As we worked on the barricade I asked one of the men by sign language the purpose of it, and he responded with an excellent imitation of a kangaroo, and the word 'patagaran'. So I knew then the prey for which we lay in wait. A great comfort of life in New South Wales was that so far as I could tell – and this was borne out by the accounts of other colonists – the country was not inhabited by lions, tigers, bears or other savage creatures. The kangaroo was known to be capable of inflicting great damage with his powerful hindquarters, and although the Governor's greyhounds were a little faster than the kangaroos, as I have said, the latter fought fiercely when cornered, and not many dogs came away from the battle without a few lacerations. Humans, however, had nothing to fear from these creatures, who much preferred discretion to valour, and grazed entirely on grass.

When the fence was completed, the men, including Johnny and me, took up positions behind it, each according to his preference. There was nothing of the British military system about their organisation; they did as they liked. The night passed slowly. I dozed for most of it. The forest in this remote country seemed very quiet at night to me, although I had no experience of British conditions with which to compare it. Occasionally I heard the double hoot of an owl, and once there was a mad scramble by some animal high in the treetops, but other sounds were few and far between.

I trusted to our sable companions to rouse me should the occasion demand it, but it was Johnny who eventually prodded me into full wakefulness.

A grey light at the edge of the sky showed that dawn was imminent, but the full moon continued to illuminate our surroundings. Around me the men were stirring, and taking up their positions. I moved to the best spot I could find and crouched behind the barricade. The warriors appeared to hear something before I did, for suddenly a surge of energy ran along the line, and every man took a tight grip on his spear or spear thrower and raised his arm. I did likewise, and a moment later heard the distinctive thumping of kangaroos in full flight, and beyond them the indistinct cries of the native women and children. Clearly it had been their job to flush out the prey.

As the kangaroos appeared, I could understand why the Indians had chosen a full moon for their hunt. It would have been impossible to discern these grey creatures at any other time. But suddenly I saw the distinctive head and pointed ears of one, then another, then another, coming straight towards us, silhouetted against the skyline. To my left, Chaginnini rose to his full height and threw a spear with tremendous force. It impaled a large kangaroo through the neck; I saw the spear emerge from the other side; the creature took a great leap and fell straight to the ground.

This was the signal for a shower of spears. To my right Kutuku hurled his with deadly accuracy. I saw it bury itself in the chest of a smaller kangaroo, which turned, staggered, and then slowly toppled over. I fixed on a target, an animal about the same size as the one Kutuku had felled, and threw my spear with all the force I could muster. To my chagrin, I missed by about a yard, and was only consoled by the sight of Johnny's spear missing his target by an approximately equal margin.

The drove of kangaroos, taken completely unawares, now swerved indiscriminately to left and right. Spears continued to follow them, and I saw two more felled before the survivors disappeared from my view.

As we emerged from cover and began to inspect the fallen animals, the women and children arrived, sweating and panting and laughing, evincing great pleasure at the success of the hunt. The men, too, showed obvious delight. Nine adult creatures – only one a male – and two young ones had been brought down. Many of the men customarily carried wooden clubs, some of them of considerable size and weight, and they now used these to crush the heads of any unfortunate beasts who were still alive.

As soon as full daylight was upon us, Chaginnini and a couple of other hunters began to inspect the ground, and found something that had them jabbering to each other in excitement. Following them, I realised that they had discovered a trail of blood, and with a steady loping gait they now set off to seek its source. I followed for a few minutes but was unable to keep up with them, and so returned to the others. Within an hour the hunters came back with the body of a young male kangaroo. Judging from the state of its skull, I assumed it was still alive when they had caught up with it, but its end would have been swift when Chaginnini arrived.

Chapter 41

AS MIGHT BE IMAGINED, much gaiety and feasting followed the successful ambush of the kangaroos. This was accompanied by dancing and music-making. I confess I now found much of the latter form of entertainment quite interminable. They seemed to have many songs, which covered a variety of themes, but my deficient understanding of their language, and the monotony of the music, had gradually diminished the appeal of these to me.

The dances were a different matter however, as they had a more varied repertoire. War, the weather, hunting and love seemed to be common topics, in which respect they differed little from their European counterparts, and no doubt from people the world over. Yet I had never seen anything in London which much resembled the dancing of these natives of the New World. Out in the dark forest, under a sky alive with glittering stars, with the leaping flames of a fire as backdrop, hunters or women, their skin painted with brazen white stripes or dots or circles, their brown eyes deeply beautiful in the semi-darkness, sprang fiercely towards me, stamped repeatedly on the ground, then sprang away again. It was both frightening and exhilarating. Many of the dances seemed designed to intimidate. Others were clearly charged with a sexual energy which had my cheeks burning red from more than just the reflection of the fire. The dancers were tremendously agile, none more so than Chaginnini. I found it hard to hold my ground when he came at me, brandishing a huge wooden club, his hair embellished by long pieces of bone, but I felt that a show of fear would cost me what little respect I had gained in these people's eyes, and so, difficult though it was, I maintained my outward composure.

Yet minutes after he had retired from a warlike dance, I saw him sitting on the ground cradling his young son Mudaree, murmuring tenderly to him and displaying the gentle affection that he always showed the boy.

Following on from a dance celebrating the kangaroo hunt, the most popular dance, which was called for repeatedly, was the creation of Kutuku and a man named Arnapata. It took Johnny and me only a few moments to realise that we were the subjects of this performance. Every notable incident in which we had featured since our arrival in the midst of the tribe, and in particular our attempts to learn spear-making and throwing, climaxed by our ignominious failures at the ambush, was impersonated by these two men for their appreciative audience. The boy Nama-Nama played the part of the kangaroo in the final scene, and he danced about brazenly in front of the men, daring them to spear him. When the twigs they threw missed him by impossible distances he turned and bent over and waggled his hindquarters at them, but still they could not hit him, and he finally bounded away triumphantly, to the delighted laughter of the spectators. Some of the children in particular rolled on the ground in uncontrollable mirth whenever this dance was performed. Johnny and I gritted our teeth and laughed along with the rest. I comforted myself with the thought that at least we were providing the tribe with entertainment, in return for our board and lodgings.

Arnapata afforded me much less amusement a week or so after the hunt, however. Several of the native men had two wives, and as if that were not enough, they were happy to bestow their favours even more widely, as was particularly apparent during and after some of the dances. One of Arnapata's wives was Baroo, the woman who had been kindest to us when we arrived in the tribe. The least attractive aspect of the Indians to me, as to many other convicts and colonists, was, as has been well documented, the treatment of the women by the men. There was not a woman in the tribe who did not exhibit the effects of this ill treatment, in the form of both old scars and current wounds, which were sometimes horrible to behold. When a man was annoyed by a woman, his almost invariable reflexive response was to deliver a savage blow to her head with whatever weapon came to hand, be it a rock, a club, a fist or, on one occasion I witnessed, a kangaroo tail. A man thought nothing of hitting a woman with the full force of his hand, or kicking her should she aggrieve him. Frequently I saw a wife staggering away from her husband with blood streaming down her face, or a woman stretched insensible on the ground from such a blow. Although the men could be tender and sentimental in their approaches to women, it seemed that their mood could quickly change, and on these occasions they showed no interest in the distress of the victims of their blows, and certainly no remorse. I had witnessed, it is true, similar scenes in London on numerous occasions, but not with the casual indifference displayed by these men.

An area not far from the camp was used by the Indians for the purpose of defecation, although not all observed this nicety. There was complete tolerance of the children when they squatted around the campsite; in fact, during our first few days with the tribe some children seemed to make a point of passing bowel motions in the very near vicinity of Johnny and me, looking at us with an expression of mischievous triumph when they did so. At any rate, Johnny and I certainly used the assigned area scrupulously.

Late one afternoon, right on dusk, as I returned from this place, I stumbled into an ugly scene. Arnapata, it appeared, had just knocked Baroo down, and as I came up behind him, he reached for his spear, which was leaning against his bark shelter, and with the speed and fluidity customary to these fine hunters made to hurl it at her, all in an instant. I believe he was aiming for her leg. I reacted instinctively to her expression of terror, and threw myself forward, crashing into Arnapata's back. Thrown off balance, he missed her, though only by a matter of inches.

Now it was his expression to which I reacted. The savage does not trouble to hide his feelings, and Arnapata glared at me with such malevolence that I fled, leaving Baroo to her fate. Such behaviour was hardly in accord with the traditions of the British race, but I had not been given the benefit of an upbringing that inculcated me with nobler sentiments, and although I was at last showing signs of beginning the journey towards manhood for which I had yearned for some time, I had nothing like the muscle development or strength of a fully grown native warrior.

I ran straight to Johnny and told him what I had done. 'Well,' he said when I had finished my necessarily brief account, 'there's no telling what will come of that. But you know the custom of these savages is to spear the person who has offended them. In the leg usually. You're expected to stand there and let them do it, and then all is forgiven and it's back to business as usual.'

'I know that . . .' I quavered. 'But do you really think he will want to do it to me?'

Johnny looked as worried as I felt. 'Who knows what these beggars are capable of?' he said. 'It sounds like he was going to do it to Baroo, and so he might well do it to you instead. Maybe it's time we thought of quitting these comfortable digs and looking for new quarters.'

'But where could we go?' I asked.

'Now how can I answer that? But let's find out what your black friend is planning. You leave it to old Johnny, and I'll go and talk to a few of my crewmates.'

He wandered off, leaving me scanning the camp anxiously for signs of danger. I trusted Johnny though. In all our time together this had been one of our longest conversations, but as he had gained in health and strength, both physical and mental, I had observed many skills in him, and many signs of a kind and true nature.

He was back within half an hour or so. When I saw his comfortable smile I relaxed. 'Is everything all right?' I asked hopefully.

His smile became broader. Through clenched teeth he said: 'You look far too nervous, Barnaby. That's never good. I'm smiling so as to put them off guard. There's an ugly mood about. None of the hunters would come near me, but I talked to Baroo's sister.'

I tried to smile back at him. I knew the woman he meant. We called her Baroo's sister, because she appeared to be in some kind of family relationship to Baroo, but the kinship arrangements in the tribe were too complicated for us to understand.

I also knew that Johnny's conversation with the woman would have been mostly in sign language. He had learned more of the native tongue than had I, but we were both still sadly deficient.

'And?' I asked.

'She was mightily afraid to be with me for long, but she gave me to understand that some mischief is planned. We seem to make trouble wherever we go, Barnaby boy. It might be time for us to go and make trouble somewhere else.'

'Perhaps Arnapata will calm down in time,' I ventured.

'Well now,' he said with a loud chuckle, which I knew was for the benefit of any observers, 'I got the distinct impression that things are rather serious. No, I rather think we need to leave tonight, and with no handshakes or verses of "Rule Britannia".'

It was the first joke I had heard him make, so I knew things must be serious indeed.

We had our own gunyah, or shelter, these days, made in the same style as those of the tribe. We crawled into it and discussed plans, at the same time keeping a close watch on any untoward movement in our direction. But all was quiet.

In discussing our getaway we had to take into account the fact that our movement through the forest was clumsy and noisy compared to our dark-skinned hosts, and those same hosts possessed extraordinary tracking skills. Having seen them at work many times, I was of the belief that they could track a moth through air, twenty-four hours after it had flown from their sight.

'Water is our only hope,' said Johnny. 'We must get to the river as quickly as possible and launch ourselves into it. Anyone can be silent in a river, and not even Chaginnini can track us there.'

Chapter 42

THE SMELLS OF COOKING drifted through the evening air. The natives were still feasting on the kangaroos, killed more than a week ago. The slaughter of such a large number of animals had given them a long respite from their usual routine of hunting and collecting food. I believed this to be a mixed blessing for the women, as the men, with so much more time on their hands, had been free to turn their minds to other activities. 'More fighting and more . . .' as Johnny had laconically described it, using the crudest imaginable language to conclude his epigram.

We waited until we felt it likely that they would be replete from their evening meal, knowing there would be little activity for an hour or so as they digested their feast. At last, when it was almost dark, we slipped out from our gunyah, taking with us nothing but a couple of knives we had made, a couple of spears likewise, and a wooden club I had pulled out from the ground 'ready-made', being nothing more than the root ball of a young tree that had died.

Our shelter was on the outskirts of the native camp, signifying our status as outsiders. So in the space of fifteen yards we were already entering the fringe of the forest. Everything seemed quiet, and I was optimistic about our chances of a discreet departure, until we met with an unexpected distraction. Suddenly the young girl Rainja loomed up on my right-hand side.

Johnny had been teasing me more and more in recent weeks about this girl and her supposed liking for me. I had to admit that she had been behaving in an increasingly flirtatious manner. I had observed many instances of the Indian women acting as coquettishly as their European counterparts, when it suited them, and Rainja seemed to be following the lead of her elders. She had sidled up to me on a number of occasions, offering little gifts such as witchetty grubs, flowers, and driftwood for me to make into dolls. She had insinuated herself between me and Johnny several times during the corroborees, the native dances, and I have to admit that I found the sensation of her naked skin bumping or rubbing against mine almost unbearably intoxicating.

At first I had found the smell of the native people quite repugnant, unless they had recently bathed in the river. But the old man who had been assigned to water-carrying duties with me at Toongabbie, Alec Mildren, had given me a different perspective when we were discussing the matter one day. Being something of a lecher, he took a keen interest in the native women. 'Do you know, Barnaby boy,' he said, looking at me with his sharp, twinkling eyes, 'we smell as bad to them as they do to us.'

'How do you know that?' I asked.

He laughed. 'I asked them,' he said. 'I asked one of my dusky girl-friends one day, "Do we white folk smell bad to you?", and she made a face like she had just swallowed dog droppings.'

I had been more tolerant on matters of odour since that conversation.

As for beauty, the native women, in my humble opinion, ranged as much as did their white sisters, from comely to repellent. Rainja was definitely at the comely end of the scale. Although not much more a woman than I was a man, her cheerful black curls, her soft brown eyes, and the swell of her youthful breasts were a bewitching combination, and I was struggling not to fall under her spell. It was possibly not a coincidence that she had been lurking so close to our gunyah, and seeing her now, I hesitated, realising that I was leaving her forever, and feeling an acute pang in my heart at the thought.

She smiled at me, but her expression quickly changed as she noticed the items Johnny and I were carrying. She looked at us quizzically, nodded to our weapons, then the forest, and asked a question in her own tongue, which was clearly 'Where are you going?'

I shrugged, tried to smile back, but inexplicably felt tears sting my eyes. Although I had not been in love with Rainja – indeed, I had found her irritating most of the time – now, suddenly, I did feel love for her. I think the true fact of the matter was that I felt desolate at the idea of leaving the tribe. We had been with them for months, and after their initial diffidence they had treated us well, even warmly. For the first time in my life, apart from my brief sojourn with the Piggott family, I had been a member of a group in which I felt safe and secure. Now we were plunging back into the unknown.

All I could do was nod and give her a brief wave, then hurry to catch up with Johnny, who was twenty yards ahead of me and waiting with obvious impatience. Unfortunately I did not know enough of the nature of the female when spurned, for even at her tender age Rainja did not want to let go of what she coveted. She let out a screech like one of the cockatoos to which I had become accustomed since my arrival in the colony. In front of me Johnny convulsed in horror, took a nervous look over his shoulder and began to walk on hurriedly, ever increasing his speed and then breaking into a trot.

Rainja rushed at me, still screeching, and with importunate haste I set out after Johnny. I did not like the situation at all. The two of us went as fast as we dared in the dim light, through the lightly timbered forest, over the broken ground. We had the great advantage that the warriors of the tribe could not use our tracks to follow us in darkness, but if it came to a straight-out race I would not give much for my chances of beating Chagannini on his own turf.

Fortunately Rainja abandoned the chase quickly, but she continued to cry her distress as she stood looking after us. I glanced back and saw her dark figure among the dark trees. A minute later she was out of my sight, but we could still hear her voice. 'This way,' Johnny cried to me, swerving to the left. I knew that the path would take us away from the river and into the hills, but before I could ask Johnny his plan he explained it anyway. 'They won't be expecting us to go uphill,' he called. 'Come on.'

The kangaroos made many paths through the forests, and these were usually distinct and well trodden, although they formed endless mazes of crisscrossing tracks. They had no doubt been used for thousands of years. The natives employed them all the time, and we were on one now.

Before long we were panting hard, struggling with the uphill terrain. Our pace slowed substantially, but I felt as though I had been struck by lightning when I heard the deep booming voice of a native man not far behind me, shouting to a companion. It was a cry of triumph and undoubtedly indicated that he was on our trail. It was so close that I knew he had somehow discerned the path we had taken, and was on it himself. Johnny heard it too, and cried out to me: 'No good, we must change our tactics.'

Within moments we came to another intersection of kangaroo tracks, and instead of continuing uphill, Johnny took one that went downhill, but at an angle, away from the direction of the camp. I followed faithfully. Over his shoulder he called softly: 'It's the river or nothing now.'

I realised that we were in the situation I had feared, having to beat the natives in a race through the forest in which they had spent their whole lives. Desperation lent speed to my feet, and I went downhill at the charge. No sooner had I begun my descent than I heard a strange whistling noise, and an instant later a spear flew past my nose with tremendous velocity. Had I been one step, or even a couple of inches, further down the hill, my brain would have been pierced by that spear, and it would have been all up with me.

If I had been running fast before, I now somehow seemed able to double my speed. I took vast strides, hoping desperately that I would be able to see fallen timber or other obstacles in time to hurdle them. In a few places I leapt down steep drops. Our path seemed to be taking us down a longer hill than the one we had been climbing a minute or so earlier. I could hear Johnny behind me. I had overtaken him at some point, but I did not dare look around to ascertain his whereabouts. I had to concentrate entirely on trying to reach the river without breaking my neck.

Alas, my concentration was not enough to preserve me from harm. Running recklessly down a grassy slope that appeared reasonably clear, I tripped on a small log and flew through the air, turning as I travelled and landing on my back with a tremendous blow that drove the air from my lungs and left me completely winded. Johnny raced by me, calling, 'Come on, Barnaby,' and grabbing at my shoulder to encourage me to get up.

I staggered to my feet, somewhat dazed and shaken, and set out after him. My vision was blurred, but we were now in the darkest section of the forest, so vision mattered little.

At last the ground began to flatten and the vegetation to thin out. The light improved slightly. I had glimpses of Johnny, who was about twenty yards ahead of me again. Then I saw the glimmer of water in the distance. At the same time I found I was suddenly running on the characteristic rounded stones of a riverbed instead of the dry grass of the forest. We had emerged much closer to the river than I had expected. Yet at the very moment a tiny wisp of hope unfurled in my brain, a huge native stepped out from behind a tree in front of Johnny. He carried a club as big as me, and with a grunt of triumph he swung it around his head.

It was Chaginnini. Johnny stopped with a sudden lurch, tried to step back and change direction all in one movement, realised it was hopeless, and went into a half-crouch, holding up one arm in a futile attempt to ward off the blow that would crush his head like a hammer on an empty eggshell.

I had no weapons left, having dropped everything in my desperate flight. With an instinct perhaps as ancient as those of the aboriginal people of this country, I picked up a rock as I ran and hurled it straight at Chaginnini's face.

It struck him in the temple with great force, helped no doubt by the momentum with which I had invested it as a result of my speed. He had been holding the club with both hands, but now one hand slowly fell away from the dreadful weapon and the club was both checked and deflected in its descent. For a few moments the fate of both Chaginnini and Johnny seemed to be in the balance. Then the great hunter toppled forward and fell slowly to the ground, in much the same manner as I imagine Goliath fell when struck by David.

There was no time for celebration; indeed, it would not be seemly to celebrate the downfall of a warrior for whom I felt nothing but respect, but behind me came more shouts, from Indians in pursuit, and now their cries seemed tinged with a new passion, for they had seen the leader of their band fall, and the sight evidently filled them with wild shock and grief.

Johnny and I ran together to the bank of the river. We found ourselves on a small cliff about ten feet above the water. As a spear whistled past my ear and disappeared into the darkness, we threw ourselves without hesitation into the black water below. Thanks be to God, we did not land on a rock or log but in a deep pool. Agitating our limbs like dogs, we swam forward with all the vigour we could muster. Within moments we were swept over a small waterfall. Still alive, but coughing and choking from our immersion, we resurfaced in a whirlpool and continued our perilous journey downstream, at the mercy of the current. When we believed we had put a considerable distance between our pursuers and ourselves we found large pieces of wood and thrust these under our stomachs to aid our progress.

Much later, shivering violently with cold and barely able to move, we dragged ourselves out of the river onto a sandbank, where we dug holes into which we could crawl and await the morning.

Chapter 43

D ESPITE THE COLD, WE re-entered the river early the next day and continued to use it as a thoroughfare until we were satisfied that we were a long way from the territory occupied by the tribe. Only later did it occur to me that I never knew the name of the group to which we had been attached for so long. To Johnny and me they were just 'the tribe', and perhaps that is all they ever called themselves, like a couple of convicts who had been on the *Admiral Barrington* and who, never having previously left their birthplaces in the whole of their lives, knew only that they lived in 'the village', without learning the name other men gave it. Only gradually, as they made the long journey to New South Wales, did awareness dawn on them that, should they ever return to their native shores, they might be unable to locate their homes again.

The river gradually broadened and slowed, as is the nature of such beasts, and we left it at some time in the afternoon, at a place we deemed suitable for a camp. It was an unseasonably cold day, and we had been warmer in the river than out of it. Upon quitting the water, we felt the bite of the wind so keenly that we decided a fire should be our first priority.

Using the method employed by the Indians when they did not have their firesticks, we plucked a reed, shaved the top flat, nicked into it to find the pith, then rotated a blunt stick in the incision as quickly as possible to create a flame. We had done this often enough with our previous hosts to become quite dextrous at the process, but even the natives could take a long time to succeed at it, and we, with our shaking hands, found it almost interminable on this occasion. We took turn about, and I will say that at least the effort required helped to warm me a little.

At last, however, we had our fire, in a discreet corner among the rocks near the river, and this, combined with the weak rays from the sun, enabled us to at last still our chattering teeth. The quest for food was of course our next priority. Johnny went wandering along the bank of the river, peering into its depths. After twenty or so minutes he called me to him. I found him crouched beside a pool in a side eddy. 'Look at this, Barnaby boy,' he said with some evidence of glee. I peered into the water and could faintly discern a dark shape about as long as my arm.

'Is it a fish?' I asked.

'It is indeed,' he answered.

'It's a very big one. But can we catch it?'

'We can that.'

'But how?'

'In much the same way as our friends caught the kangaroos,' he said. He led me to the point where the water emptied from the pool, 'Fetch me some rocks,' he said. 'The bigger the better.'

I saw his intention at once. It was a clever scheme. Through the artful construction of a dam wall we made our trap in remarkably quick time. I was glad that Johnny took the initiative after that, for I felt somewhat nervous at the idea of wrestling with a big, slippery fish. Johnny had no such fears, however. He jumped in. The water barely reached his waist. He waded to the fish and lunged at it. It eluded him, once, twice, three times, but on the fourth attempt he grabbed it and threw it out onto the bank, where I found the courage to pounce on it and drag it well away from the water.

We ate well that afternoon, and had more of the same for our evening repast. The flesh of the fish was white and delightfully juicy; it was as fine a meal as ever I have had. Lounging by the coals of the fire I congratulated Johnny on his resourcefulness.

'Have you done much fishing before?' I asked him. I had been impressed, not just with his plan to catch the creature, but with the way he had cleaned and gutted it, using improvised tools we fashioned from stones and sticks from along the riverbank. He was an entirely different man these days from the incoherent, haunted figure who had first confronted me in the forest when I was taking water to the timber getters.

'Oh yes, quite some,' he said. 'I was brought up on the river. My folk have always been fishermen.' He threw another stick in, and it drifted idly away. 'This is my kind of river,' Johnny said. 'Not like the wild torrents we have experienced hitherto, young Barnaby. I feel more at home here.'

I realised, somewhat belatedly, that I knew nothing about Johnny. We had never talked about our past, only what was happening at the time.

'Where did you grow up?' I asked him. 'Which river was it?'

'Why, the Thames,' he said. 'I know that river like the back of my hand. I spent more time on it than I did on land.'

'How did you come to leave it?' I asked. 'Is that when you got arrested?'

'No,' he said slowly. 'No, that came later. I left the Thames because I was a fool. All young men are fools, I suppose. All we can think of is love and adventure. By the time we reach a better understanding . . . well, sometimes it's too late.'

'What form did your foolishness take?'

'Drink was my first folly,' he said. 'I became a slave to Madame Geneva. She is not a good mistress, indeed she is not.'

He shook his head. 'I had a good home, as good a family as any man could ask for. But I became infatuated with Madame Geneva, and as if that were not enough, before long I fancied I was in love with a bar girl as well. Drunk or sober, I wanted to be in her arms. One night I didn't go home. I stayed with her the next day, and the day after that, and so on. I knew my family was looking for me, but the girl told them I had been shanghaied by a press-gang and was gone to sea. I laughed when she told me what she had said to them. I felt that I was a free man at last.'

A terrible recognition of Johnny's story was growing on me. I waited in agonised suspense for what might come. But he was silent for so long that I finally had to ask him. 'Please . . . what happened next?'

He looked at me in surprise. 'Why are you so interested?'

I shrugged nervously. 'I don't know. We've been together a long time and I know so little about you.'

'Aye, that's so. Well, I'll tell you my story and then you can tell me yours. So . . .' He looked embarrassed. 'I'm afraid I wasn't faithful to Becky for too long. She caught me cheating on her and threw me out. Smartest thing she could have done. But there I was, no home I could go to, no money, not a true friend in the world. So what do you think I did?'

Trying to keep my voice steady I said: 'Joined the Navy?'

He looked startled. 'Aye. Did I tell you I was in the Navy? It's what I did, all right. I thought, well, Becky had me signed up in the Navy when she met my father, so I might as well make her lie come true. So off I went and found a recruiting sergeant. They were pleased to take me, but I soon decided it wasn't much to my liking. I've never taken kindly to being told what to do, and in the Navy there was nothing but being told what to do, every waking minute. And then one night, off the coast of Scotland . . . me and the Navy got separated you might say.'

'What happened?'

'Quite a storm was blowing. I was on deck, on watch. I got sent amidships, to take in some sail. But a huge wave came over the rails and washed me clean overboard.' He glanced up from under his eyebrows. 'It may be that I wasn't entirely sober at the time, so I mightn't have been steering the straightest course. To tell you the truth, I don't think the wave was quite as big as all that. Anyway, there I was in the water, doing my best to stay afloat, knowing I had no chance, knowing that this was the end of a misspent life.'

He mused for a moment. 'I don't know why a man keeps struggling when he has no hope. I don't know why I worked so hard to keep my head above the water, to prolong my miserable existence for another few minutes. But just as I was starting to gulp more water than air, just as I felt myself slipping under the waves, something came along and bumped into the back of my neck. Bumped! It hit me so hard I felt dizzy. I turned around and found myself staring at a broken spar that the Lord God decided to throw me at the last minute. It seemed that He wasn't ready to take me yet.'

He laughed. I could not laugh, for I was sure now I knew who my Johnny was. 'What happened next?' I asked.

'I drifted right onto the rocks of Bonnie Scotland. I got fearfully bruised and cut, but some skivvies found me and took me to their hut. They were kindly folk, and looked after me better than I deserved. When I got better I did some work for them and then lit out for Glasgow.

I'd decided that the time had come for the Royal Navy and me to part company. No doubt they thought I was drowned, and there didn't seem much sense in telling them otherwise. I got a job building fishing boats, and worked at that for a couple of years, then drifted down south. By the time I got to Liverpool I had no money left. Just to make a bad job worse I'd fallen in with a pretty gang of cutthroats and thieves, and one day we banged an old fellow on the head and relieved him of his purse. I was in drink at the time, but the next day, when I recollected what I'd done, I repented it and went back to find him and give him my share of the booty. As soon as he saw me, though, he started shouting, "Thief! Thief!" and before I could explain my intentions his friends had jumped on me and trussed me up and off they took me, to the magistrates.'

'So you got transported?'

'Yes indeed. And a hard voyage we had of it, on that hell-ship the *Hillsborough*, may her name be forever cursed. By the time we got off the ship at Sydney Cove only two men in three were still alive, and most of those had to be carried off. Even the worst of the turnkeys were appalled at our condition, and our losses. At least I walked down the gangplank on my own two pins. I wanted to show those murdering bastards that they couldn't kill me that easily.'

'What did they do with you?'

'I got sent up the river and assigned to a lime kiln, which is work not fit for a man in my opinion . . .'

'What's a lime kiln?' I asked.

'You know they use lime to make mortar? And whitewash? Well, you get the lime from burning oyster shells or limestone. Either one. You run out of oyster shells pretty quickly, so mostly it was limestone we used. We spent our time cutting out blocks of the stuff, fetching it down to the kiln, dropping it in the oven, then scraping the lime out the front of the thing, through an opening. Bloody hard work it was, and hot, and dangerous. You'd forever be getting burned.' He grinned. 'It'd be typical of the Government, wouldn't it? You take a man who's been in boats most of his life and send him inland to work in a lime kiln. If I'd been a coalminer they would have sent me out to sea to go fishing.'

'Is that why you ran away?' I asked. 'Because you didn't like the job?'

'No, no, I stuck it pretty well. But a new foreman came along and started throwing his weight around, and like I said, I've never taken to that too kindly. So one day I gave him a tap on the head with my shovel, and I thought, that's it for me, I'd best take myself off.'

'Did you kill the man?' I asked naively.

'No, no, I'm not a murderer, lad. Just laid him out for a little sleep. It was the wrong thing to do, I know that, but I've been that way since I was a young 'un. My father was a strict man – a good man, mind you – but he didn't take kindly to contradiction, and I never could stand to have him tell me what to do, so we had some terrible disagreements. I regret it now. I let my parents down, aye, I let them down badly. They deserved better.'

'Would that be Silas?' I whispered. 'And Abigail?'

The effect on him was something terrible. He had been picking at his teeth with a fishbone while he talked, but now he jumped up and backed away from me, shrieking like a madman. I ran to him, though I was half-afraid he would strike me down. I gripped him around the upper arms and fortunately he did not hit out at me. 'What kind of devil are you?' he gasped. His eyes were staring, almost out of their sockets. I let him go, and he groaned and shook himself and beat himself in the chest with his fists. Then he fell to his knees on the sand. I had never seen such a dreadful desperation in a man before.

'How do you know their names?' he howled at me. 'How do you know them?' Over and over.

'Johnny,' I said to him, pleading for his attention. 'Johnny! I have slept in your bed. Your father plucked me out of the Thames when I was as close to drowning as you were off the coast of Scotland. Your father, and Thomas too. Your mother nursed me back to health, like the skivvies who looked after you. I awoke in your bed one day and saw a new moon on the wall above me, a moon with a nose and lips and a face that looked down upon me every night for weeks thereafter.'

Still kneeling on the sand, he pulled at his hair and swayed to and fro. 'Yes, yes,' he groaned, 'I made that carving. Ah, cruel, too cruel. One life to live, and see what I have done with it.'

He was inconsolable. I went to the river and fetched him water in my cupped hands, then sat with him murmuring words of comfort as one might to a baby. When he seemed calmer, I told him everything I could remember, including the information that his parents believed him drowned. He nodded fiercely when I said that. 'Yes, yes,' he said. 'I thought the Admiralty would give them that news. At the time I believed it would be for the best. I didn't want more grief heaped on their heads from my wanton behaviour. I thought they had suffered enough, that they were better off believing me dead. But all I've done is add to their woes.' He rocked backwards and forwards again. 'Ah, to see them one more time, to be able to tell them how bitterly I repent my wrongdoing. And Thomas too. He was a sweet and gentle lad. He deserved a better example from his older brother.'

I made a bed for us both and led him to it. He sobbed quietly for a little while, but I was relieved when eventually the deep and heavy breathing of sleep overtook him. I could not sleep. I lay awake, looking up at the bright stars of heaven and wishing I could somehow bring about the reunion of the Piggott family, as Johnny so devoutly desired.

Chapter 44

WITHOUT PLANNING IT, WE seemed to drift slowly down the river, day by day, sometimes only moving a few hundred yards, sometimes a mile or so. We had no definite goal, we discussed no purpose, but we seemed to be drawn towards the coast. I suspect that something in our hearts yearned for contact with our fellow Englishmen again, perilous though such an aspiration must be. It was certain, however, that white settlers would be found in greater numbers along the coast than inland, and that if we continued downstream we might eventually make contact with them.

Most days we ate quite well but some days we went hungry. Where sizeable tributaries joined the main river Johnny taught me to explore up these streams, looking for pools in which fish might linger. He taught me a trick he had learned in Scotland, of feeling under the banks of the pools and tickling fish that lurked there. The first time he told me about it I thought he was teasing, but he had the last laugh when he landed a trout that must have weighed three pounds. It was of a type I had never seen before, with a brown speckled body, a big mouth and an overhanging upper jaw. It had a dark blue stripe running from its nose almost to the gill, and was delicious. From then on this was our preferred method of fishing, and it was a fine day for me when I landed a two-pounder myself.

Now that he had opened his life's book to me, Johnny became an even better companion, proving to be a man of many talents, and much learning that he had picked up in the course of his adventures. 'The darling of all who knew him,' Silas had said, and I thought it significant that Silas had not mentioned any old wounds between him and his son. So often one remembers but the other forgets. I felt now that I was seeing the Johnny whom Silas had described. A bond had already been forged between us by our shared hardships, but the connection with his family had created a new and, I felt, more enduring friendship. It was articulated by Johnny one evening, when he said to me, as we crouched over our little fire, 'You know, Barnaby, I feel you are my brother now. God sent you to me for a reason. You have no family, and I will never see my family again. We only have each other.'

'I feel that too, Johnny,' I replied, and no more was said between us on that topic, but I had the strong sense from then on that it would take more than the Royal Navy and Royal Marines, let alone the worthy soldiers of the New South Wales Corps, to separate us.

Yet our destinies were about to take another unexpected turn. We had endured a cold and dark morning, with thunder grumbling and rumbling about us, and heavy raindrops falling, followed by a monumental downpour that lasted two or three hours. Strong rain had already fallen the night before, but we had holed up in a providential cave. These days we followed the custom of the Indians and carried a firestick, so when we found a hole in the back of the cave which gave access to the outside, we lit a fire, using the hole as a chimney. We were quite snug in our hideaway, and I dozed for most of the morning.

When the rain cleared we moved back down to the river, which was now running hard and fast. It thrilled me somehow to see the water rollicking past, carrying all manner of tree branches and logs, smashing into boulders with clouds of spray, and spilling onto land which had hitherto been dry and out of its reach. I made sure not to get too close, for I was wary of its speed and ferocity.

We detoured around a small waterfall and went less than a hundred yards further downstream when my attention was drawn by a little island created by the torrent. Judging by the bushes in the water on the other side I felt confident that the island had not been there the night before, for I could see the bushes were bent over by the rushing water, and for the most part were completely submerged by it.

Johnny was a little way ahead of me, and I continued to follow him, picking my path carefully among the rocks. As usual we had no particular end in view. As I passed the island I took one more glance at it and almost kept going without another look, except that a small patch of white drew my attention. I confess I took little interest in the sight, for I imagined it to be a piece of wood, or perhaps some white stone. Then, just as I took my eyes off it, a breeze caused it to flutter slightly.

This intrigued me a little more. I glanced at it several more times as I made my way through the rocks. It fluttered again, and I could see now that it was probably a piece of man-made material.

A thing of slight interest to those who dwell in Europe perhaps! But consider, it had been many months since Johnny and I had seen anything made by white hands. We had long since lost the last remnants of our clothing, and these days were as naked as the Indians. So it was with some excitement that I called to Johnny: 'Come back here!'

He did not hear me over the roaring of the river, and I had to run forward and shout from just a few yards behind him before he turned around. 'Come with me,' I said. 'I've found something.'

He followed willingly enough. We stood opposite the island and peered at the white patch. 'It could be just a plant,' he said doubtfully. Then the breeze caught it again, and he was forced to admit: 'It does look like a piece of clothing.'

'I want to get it,' I said.

'That won't be easy,' Johnny said. Then suddenly he grabbed my arm with such fierceness that I cried out in pain. 'Barnaby! Are my eyes failing me?'

'Let go,' I said. 'I don't know if your eyes are failing you or not, because you haven't told me what it is you're seeing.'

Without looking at me, staring at the island, he said hoarsely: 'I'm seeing the shape of a fellow creature, Barnaby Fletch.'

In astonishment and horror I stared at the patch. And yes, I thought I could just discern the shape of a human head in the grass. Or was it that Johnny had put this picture into my head?

'We have to get over there,' he said urgently.

We both looked around in desperation. 'If we go back up to the waterfall,' Johnny said, 'and find some decent sized logs, we could ride them down to the island.'

'But we could miss,' I said. I was, however, unable to think of any better suggestion, so I went with him to the churning pool at the bottom of the fall. It was too dangerous for us to attempt to enter the pool itself, but a number of logs had jammed just below it. Wading in, until the water was up to Johnny's waist and my chest, we worked furiously to separate them. The first couple were torn out of our hands as soon as we loosened them, and away downstream they galloped, but we learned from that and were able to control the third more successfully. By then we were both desperately cold and barely able to talk.

'What now?' I called to him.

'You take this one,' he called back. 'I think I can get the next one out on my own.'

I was too cold to argue. I knew we could not endure this for long. I tried, foolishly, to mount the log as if it were some kind of horse to be ridden. Johnny snapped at me: 'Not that way.'

I understood his meaning, and taking a deep breath launched myself into the river, holding the log before me and praying that it would not immediately be ripped out of my hands. Johnny let go of his end and I was immediately swept away with ferocious speed. I lost my grip on the log with my left hand but, after several frightening seconds, was able to regain my hold. I had no control, but was dragged over boulders and hit by other pieces of wood. For one long stretch I was completely underwater and feared I would be drowned, but at last I managed to get my face to the surface and draw in great gasps of air. Surely the island must be close? I looked around and saw that it was indeed dreadfully close; another few moments and I would be swept right past it. At least here, a good way downstream from the waterfall, with the river widening somewhat, the force of the current was slightly weaker. With all my strength I steered the log to my left and kicked madly. A piece of wood struck me hard in the nose and blinded me briefly, but I continued kicking. Suddenly I felt my chest and knees grinding on a rough material and realised that I had landed on a spit of gravelly sand at the very tip of the island.

I let go the log, pleased to discard that which I had clung to so affectionately for so long. Such is the fickleness of humanity. I staggered up onto the grass, looking around for Johnny. I was in time to see his log crash into a boulder just a few yards upstream of the island. He let go of it at the last moment, trying desperately to swim around the rock, but was thrown into it. Tumbling end over end he was rushed along by the river. I did not know if he was dead or alive after his collision with the boulder, but I stepped out as far as I dared into the water and, leaning out, reached across to him.

Our eyes met, and I was relieved to see that he was conscious. He wriggled through the water somehow, towards me, and our fingers made contact. I grabbed him around the wrist and, digging in my feet, tried desperately to stop both of us being swept away. Inch by inch, I dragged him to me, until our other hands met and then it was comparatively easy to get him ashore.

We both fell back onto the grass gasping for air. As soon as I could, I turned onto all fours and staggered upright. Looking at Johnny and then at myself, I could see that we were in much the same condition: covered with grazes and cuts. My nose felt swollen and bruises were already starting to form all down the front of my body. No doubt my back was equally afflicted. Johnny dragged himself to his feet and, walking like a pair of drunks, we went looking for the object of our search.

I thought the most likely outcome would be the ignominious discovery of some variety of native flower or heath. If it were not that, I expected to find a piece of clothing, perhaps washed downstream from the camp of an explorer. I had no real confidence that the head we believed we had seen was anything more than a rock, or a trick our eyes were playing on us. Yet I knew also that it well behoved us to investigate the white patch. Hardened criminals as the law had ajudged us to be, yet neither of us was so lacking in humanity as to walk away from what could have been the body of a fellow creature.

I was the first to reach the place. It took some moments for my eyes to draw out from the surrounding grass and gravel the figure that lay on the ground. It was like trying to define a kangaroo against the background of eucalyptus trees and rocks into which they blend so successfully. Hardly any wonder it took me so long to recognise what I saw now, however: who would have expected to see a white child, a little girl, lying insensible in front of them?

From behind me came a hoarse cry from Johnny, as he too recognised the nature of our discovery. He was quicker to act than I. He dove in beside me and put a hand on the child's forehead, at the same time picking up her nearer arm. She seemed to stir and shake her head slightly.

'Is she alive?' I said stupidly. This seemed even more unlikely and astonishing than the fact that she was here at all.

'She is, or we're all in another place together,' Johnny said grimly. 'But whether she'll stay alive is another question.'

'What are we to do?' I asked.

'She's too cold,' he said. 'I don't know what else may be wrong with her, but she's too cold.' He thought for a moment, then came to a decision. 'Take her in your arms, Barnaby, and hold her like she's a baby. You may be cold yourself, but you're warmer than her. I'll try to get a fire going.'

I did as he directed. It felt strange to hold a child like this. I tried to transmit what warmth I could to her; I tried to will her into life; I tried to redirect my strength into her limp body. From time to time I glanced at Johnny to see what progress he was making. He had to use the Indian methods again of course; our firestick was on the other side of the river. But I could see what he was doing: searching among the bushes for tiny twigs that had been protected from the rain, especially the ones that grew straight upwards and so were drier than the ones which grew horizontally.

Several times the little body in my arms gave a great shudder, and each time a terror ran through me, for I thought it might be the child's last breath. She felt thin. Her face was very pretty though. She had dark brown ringlets and the sunburnt complexion of all those who had been in the colony more than a few months, so different to the pale skins of those who dwelled in England. The white material that had caught my eye was her dress, which so far as I could judge, was made of linen, or possibly linen and wool. It was flared somewhat at the bottom, and had an elaborate stitched border of red, brown and green lines, made to simulate vines or creepers and highlighted at regular intervals by a pretty arrangement of flowers on stalks that almost resembled a peacock's tail. It looked expensive, and I thought that she might be from a rich family. Both the sleeves of her dress had been torn; one was torn almost completely off, the other had a long rip from the elbow to the wrist.

I wondered how long she had been wandering alone through the forest, separated from her parents, no doubt, by some mischance. At the same time I kept looking to the two banks of the river, half-expecting to see a search party, and I wondered what our fate would be should such an eventuality occur. It seemed to me that a great rage might be visited upon me, should, for example, the child's father find me, a naked runaway boy, cradling his infant daughter. From my terrible experience with Mr Ogwell, and then the conversations I had been exposed to since joining the world of convicts, I had learned enough to know that such a situation harboured dark possibilities which would not have occurred to me when I was younger.

At last Johnny got the fire going, and I wriggled closer, still holding the girl. 'What do you think?' I asked him.

He shrugged helplessly. 'I don't know what more we can do,' he said. 'We can't get her off this bit of land until the river goes down. We've got no food to give her, and the way she is at the moment, she couldn't eat it anyway. All we can do is what we're doing.'

I could not disagree with him, for I had nothing better to suggest. He built up the fire. Each time the blaze permitted, he put another damp log on it, which quieted it for a time, but as the log dried out the flames burned more fiercely. I felt the little body in my arms gradually becoming warmer.

After a time, however, my arms grew too tired to hold her any longer and we exchanged places, Johnny nursing the child and me feeding the fire. We continued to alternate our duties throughout the evening. As night fell, Johnny rolled up a big rock, then hauled in logs to make a kind of frame or structure to support me as I slept, so that I could continue to hold the little girl. Had we been better guardians we might have stayed awake all night to care for her, but our exhausted and aching bodies demanded rest, and we were too weak to hold sleep at bay.

Chapter 45

A S THE SUN ROSE I opened my eyes, feeling very sore from yesterday's battering, but my first thought was for the child. To my great
relief she was still alive. My concern was not only for her; I had woken
several times during the night with the dread that she might be dead, for
I had a great horror of the idea that I might be sleeping with a corpse in
my arms.

However, I had a fancy she was breathing more easily, and her
colour was undoubtedly healthier. Johnny was already awake and
building up the fire. I ventured to suggest to him that the child looked a
little better, and he agreed. Neither of us expected, though, that within
a minute her eyes too would be open and she would be fluttering in my
arms like a tiny bird caught in a boy's cupped hands. Yet that was what
happened. I was so startled that I almost dropped her. To my further
surprise she spoke almost immediately.

'I'm hungry,' were her first words.

'I'm sorry to hear it,' I answered. 'But I'm afraid we haven't any
food.'

Her face puckered up and she let out a thin wail. 'We'll get you some food as soon as we can,' I assured her, but she continued to cry, sobbing, 'I want my mummy.'

I felt helpless, and looking at Johnny gave me no confidence that he would be any more use than me in this situation. 'Have a drink of water,' I suggested. 'Sometimes that makes hunger a little easier to bear.'

When she did not respond I helped her up, took her by the hand and led her to the edge of the river. She did then lap up some water, and it seemed to calm her. 'We're hungry too,' I said. 'When the river goes down we'll be able to get some food.'

'Are you Indians?' she asked me.

'No indeed,' I said, smiling a little at the notion.

'Then why aren't you wearing any clothes?'

I thought quickly. 'We've been in the forest a long time. Our clothes wore out.'

She seemed satisfied with that answer and followed me back to the fire. Johnny said to me: 'You know, the vines over there look like the midiny that the Indian women dug up.'

I went to where he indicated and was excited to see the familiar heart-shaped leaves and papery flowers that characterised the yams which we ate frequently when we lived with the tribe. We both got digging sticks and set to work. Despite the rain, the ground was quite hard and dry, once we got down a few inches. But we continued to dig, and eventually were rewarded by finding half-a-dozen tubers, each similar to a medium-sized potato. We washed them in the river, then put them in the coals. After her initial burst of energy when she awoke, the little girl seemed to have gone into a decline. She sat at the fire, but her eyes were half closed and she kept tipping over. I was afraid she would tip right into the fire. She would not now permit me or Johnny to touch her, shrinking away from us when we tried, but I modified the structure Johnny had made the night before, to support her.

While the yams were cooking, Johnny searched for some stones with sharp edges. He found only one that was in any way satisfactory. It took much patience on both our parts after we had pulled the yams from the coals to wait for them to cool enough for him to peel them, and further patience while he scraped away at them with his stone. When the first one was done, I took it to the river, washed it again, then brought it back to the child. She still seemed in a state of semiconsciousness, but I borrowed Johnny's stone and used it to strip off pieces of the root in the way that I had seen the native women doing. Then I forced a piece into the little girl's mouth. She seemed too insensible to know what it was, but I gently worked her jaw to encourage her to chew, and after a few moments she seemed to ingest the vegetable.

I had a better idea then, and again following the practices of the Indian women, I chewed some yam into a soft mass and transferred it to the child's mouth. This seemed more successful, as I was convinced that she swallowed the food voluntarily. Like a mother bird I continued to feed the fledgling, until she had eaten an entire yam. 'Maybe give her a rest for a little bit now,' Johnny suggested. 'If she hasn't had food for a while, she might not be able to take much.'

At last this gave me licence to make a meal for myself. I had been sorely tempted whilst chewing for the child but had suppressed my own hunger in the hope of bringing about an improvement in her condition. To my great joy, as I began my breakfast, the little girl opened her eyes and sat up. 'More potato,' she said, and the words were sweet to my ears.

From then on, her recovery was quite rapid. After eating another yam she became more talkative. We tried to elicit from her details about her identity and current predicament, but she was too young to communicate much information. She said her name was Sophie and she lived in a new house, and they had chickens, and a pig called Roger. She said they had been for a picnic in the forest when her father and mother had fallen asleep, so she 'went for a walk' and got lost. She didn't know how long she had been lost. She cried and said her father and mother would be angry because they had told her not to leave their sight. Then she had another fit of shyness and wouldn't speak to either of us.

The river was going down quite quickly again, as is the habit of some of these New South Wales rivers after a violent storm. I thought that we would be able to cross to the shore by the middle of the day. I had deliberated on our best course of action and I told Johnny I thought we should take Sophie down the river until we saw some colonists, and then we could point them out to her and trust her to walk to them while we ran off into the forest.

Johnny, however, was thinking of an altogether different approach. He cut me off before I had finished, saying: 'Barnaby, don't you realise what we have here? This child is our ticket to forgiveness. She is like an angel of deliverance. She represents the first stroke of good fortune I've had in a dozen years.'

I started to grasp his meaning and said slowly: 'Do you mean we'll be let off our punishments if we return her to her folk?'

'That's exactly what I mean.'

I felt a surge of excitement in my chest. Despite Johnny's company, I had been feeling a great loneliness: just the two of us out here in the vast forest, sharing the space with an occasional kangaroo or opossum . . . and in some ways the loneliness was not the worst thing. I was too young to put a name to it, but I found it disheartening to have no purpose, no meaning in my life. I did not want to spend more months or years wandering aimlessly, preserving my life simply for the sake of preserving it. I wanted to be back in a world where I had something to work towards, even if my goals perforce had to be long-distance ones.

I looked across at Sophie. She was idly pulling shreds of bark from a stick that had been washed onto the island by the swollen river. Was it cynical to use her in the way that Johnny had suggested? It probably was, but now that I had a glimmer of hope of returning to civilisation I was tempted to snatch her up and run full pelt down the river, looking for the first outpost of the colony that we could find.

'Of course, there are no guarantees,' Johnny warned me. 'They could still stretch us.'

We had to wait until mid-afternoon to cross to dry land again. If Johnny and I had been on our own we could have left earlier, but Sophie was too fearful of the water. We eventually constructed a sort of pathway of logs, but even then it took a great deal of coaxing and patience to persuade her to make the journey.

When we finally got across we were both eager to keep moving. We hurried Sophie along as best we could, going downstream, but she was painfully slow. She complained incessantly of hunger; we had found and baked a few more yams, and kept one for her, which we now fed her, but it was hardly a decent meal.

Eventually we gave up and made an early camp, then tried to catch a fish. The heavy rain had changed the nature of the pools in which we generally sought our prey, and the best we could do, after a long search, was a small green and yellow fish with an almost elliptical shape, which we found in a pool left isolated by the receding floodwaters. Hungry though Johnny and I were, we gave most of it to Sophie, in the hope that it would help her regain some strength.

Chapter 46

I T DID NOT TAKE me long the next day to become extremely irritated
by Sophie's petulance and dilatory progress. I had never really had
any contact with a little girl before, apart from Josephine Ogwell and
the native children, but I rapidly came to the conclusion that if Sophie
were typical of the species I would do my best to stay away from them
in future.

Though she found herself in a difficult predicament she seemed
incapable of showing any of the spirit or resilience that had characterised the Indian girls. One minute she would tell us she was too tired
to walk and she wanted to lie down; the next she would dash off into
the forest in pursuit of a butterfly. She complained incessantly, particularly about hunger, but she rejected much of the food we found for her.
Around midday Johnny killed a large lizard, so we lit a cooking fire and
baked it, but she found the whole procedure disgusting and would only
eat a few slivers of the meat.

Sometimes she accepted my offers of rides upon my shoulders;
at other times, with apparent capriciousness, she declined them, even

though she would not walk for herself. She flatly refused all such over-tures from Johnny.

She told us that we were 'mean' when we wanted her to walk, and 'rude' because we were not wearing clothes, and 'cruel' because Johnny killed the lizard. She cried when her dress tore as she was getting over a fallen log; she cried when she fell and got her hands covered with mud; she cried when we wanted her to ford the river again.

We were steadily losing height and getting closer to the coastal plains. The river twisted and turned considerably, which meant that we no doubt covered much more ground than necessary, but we were afraid to get too far away from the river's comforting presence. It was, however, becoming wider and shallower, so fording it was by no means an insur-mountable challenge. I had to carry Sophie across, for she refused point blank to traverse it herself. Unfortunately I slipped halfway and fell on my back, so that she landed in the water and was thoroughly soaked: an outcome she probably would have avoided had she used her own legs to make the crossing. This incident provoked screams of rage, and many threats of 'telling Daddy' and 'telling Mummy' directed at me, so that I began to fear my sentence would be doubled by the time we delivered Sophie back to civilised society and she had finished her litany of complaints.

Johnny's characterisation of her as our 'angel' was starting to appear wide of the mark. There were times when I felt like putting her in the pouch of a kangaroo and telling it to deliver her to her parents. The situation was not helped by Johnny's abdication of responsibility for her; for the most part he kept well away and left it to me to manage her progress, a task for which, as I have said, I was singularly ill-equipped.

We camped that night on the flattest land we had seen for many a long day, and were more successful in obtaining provisions: our usual standbys of fish and yams. After this, the best meal we had yet been able to provide Sophie, she seemed in a better mood and went to sleep quite quickly.

Our dreary progress continued the next morning, but did not last long. After about two hours we saw a thin trail of white smoke rising in the still sky. We hastened towards it and soon came to a fence. A fence! What a symbol of civilisation it is! I looked at it quite stupidly. I had almost forgotten the nature of fences, their function, the very concept of them. I felt an unaccountable wave of melancholy. For all the licentiousness of the natives, despite the savagery with which their men so often treated their women, I nevertheless had found something noble about the way they roamed freely through the countryside, living with the land, not from it. I was willing to swear that not a single aboriginal person of this country had ever built so much as a yard of permanent fencing.

We found a gate, and passed through it. My melancholy was replaced by the sickness of fear as I realised how much we were gambling on the return of Sophie. If she did not buy us a pardon for Johnny's attack on the woman, and our escape from lawful custody, we were certain to face at best a flogging and an extended sentence; at worst, the gallows.

A track led us to another gate, and another fence, and through it we saw a simple log cabin, less than a mile away. The smoke we had observed earlier was rising from its chimney. I looked at Johnny and he looked at me. I think we both felt that we were taking an irrevocable step which could end very badly for us. Sophie was excited, but also exhausted, and was riding on my shoulders.

Suddenly Johnny said: 'Clothes!'

I realised at once what he meant. We were hardly in a seemly condition for meeting the occupants of the hut. We had been away from civilisation for so long that nakedness had become our natural state. There was, however, a barn to our right, so we went towards that, and entered, hoping to find something with which to clothe ourselves.

The sweet smell of hay filled our nostrils; another sign that we were back in civilised society.

We looked around and immediately saw a row of kangaroo and wallaby skins hanging high, to dry. Whilst Sophie played on the hay, we took a quick survey of the building, but found nothing else of interest except some twine. We tied pieces of that around our waists, as belts, and then fetched down a wallaby skin and, in the absence of any knives, used a hatchet to cut the skin into rough pieces. With these we improvised loincloths.

Sophie was becoming querulous again, so we resumed our march towards the log cabin.

With each step my trepidation grew. I could not imagine the reaction of settlers in these wild parts when a couple of escaped convicts, dressed in nothing but animal loincloths, came to their door. Only Sophie's presence would likely save us from the blast of a musket. I glanced back to where she was trailing fifty yards behind me, and felt the compassion I should have felt for her earlier. She had been lost for some considerable time, judging by her condition. It was a miracle she had survived, and now she was almost asleep as she walked. I stopped and waited for her. 'You look silly with that fur,' she said as she came up to me.

'Do you want me to carry you?'

She held up her arms, so I picked her up and swung her around my shoulders. She didn't seem to weigh much more than the wallaby skin. I reflected on the circumstances of our finding her. I was sure she had been in a sleep from which she would never have awakened had we not caught a glimpse of that patch of white. I found it disturbing that profound events could be determined by such slight chances. I wanted the world to be structured and logical; instead of which I had the Book of Job chronicling the apparent capriciousness of God. 'Doth God pervert Judgement? Or doth the Almighty pervert Justice?' Bildad the Shuhite asked Job. I was not sure that I could give the answer the Revd Mr Grimwade would have required of me.

We reached the cabin at last. It was bigger than it had first appeared. I felt unutterably tired myself, and I put Sophie down. As I did, a woman came out of the front door, carrying an infant on her hip. She took one look at us, screamed, and ran back inside crying: 'Nathaniel! Nathaniel!' I was not sure that she had even noticed Sophie. Johnny and I stood there irresolute. Sophie sat down in the mud and started sobbing. Her attitude towards mud seemed as capricious as God's attitude towards Job.

A man came out of the front door, slowly, cautiously, with a musket held to his shoulder and trained on us. 'Who are you? What do you want?' he growled.

'We've brought back a lost child,' Johnny said wearily.

For the first time the man seemed to see Sophie. He hesitated. The woman must have been watching from inside the darkness of the doorway, for suddenly she came flying out, calling: 'Sophie! My God! Sophie Collins!'

Sophie cried all the louder. The woman snatched her up and held her, at the same time touching her, checking her. 'She's all right, missus,' I said. 'She just needs food.'

Suddenly a shadow seemed to come over the woman's face. Her eyes narrowed as she looked at me, then she stared at Johnny. She addressed him. 'How long have you had her?' she asked. 'What have you done with her?'

We were both dumbfounded. 'We saved her,' I said blankly. 'We found her close to dying, miles back up there in the hills. Two days ago, after the big storm.'

'She's been missing a week,' the woman said. 'She couldn't have survived that long on her own. How do we know you didn't snatch her away yourselves? You look a right pair of ruffians.'

I broke out into a sweat. 'Sophie,' I said, 'tell them how we found you.'

Sophie, whimpering and sucking her thumb in the woman's arms, did not answer, did not even look at me. The man raised his musket again, threateningly. I looked at Johnny helplessly. 'Well here's a pretty pass,' I said to him. 'Not the welcome we expected.'

Behind me came a noise I had not heard for a long time: the drumming of a horse's hooves. I looked around. A horse and buggy had come through the last gate and was approaching the cabin. 'It's the new chaplain,' said the woman. 'He'll know what's to be done.'

We waited in silence. I felt that my doom was about to be pronounced. The buggy pulled up, and a big man in clerical garb swung himself awkwardly to the ground. He looked at Johnny, at the woman holding Sophie, at the grim-faced man with the musket, and then at me.

'Well, Barnaby Fletch,' he said warmly, 'we meet again. I always had the feeling we might. But my dear child, you look as though you have suffered greatly.'

My knees buckled under me; I struggled to stay upright. It was the Revd Mr Haddock.

Chapter 47

ALTHOUGH HE NEVER SAID SO, a few veiled allusions by the Revd Mr Haddock gave me the distinct impression that he might have requested a posting to New South Wales to escape the oppressive atmosphere of St Martin's. His concept of religion as a comfort, a source of hope, a sustenance and consolation for saints and sinners alike, was at odds with the beliefs of the rector, the Revd Mr Cartwright, and the Revd Mr Grimwade, who seemed more interested in endless predictions of eternal damnation for the wicked. Of course for them the wicked included almost everyone but themselves.

Or perhaps the ill-tempered advice of the Revd Mr Grimwade that he would be better suited to a position in St Luke's Asylum had planted a seed in his mind. At any rate, the Revd Mr Haddock shipped out to the chaos of the new colony, accompanied by his new young wife Amelia, who gave birth to a baby girl during the voyage. I just hoped that their daughter would not grow up to be as querulous and spoiled as Sophie.

Sophie's miraculous emergence from the forest was the talk of the colony for many a long day. This was a country of strange and marvellous things. It seemed impossible that a child so young could be in the wilderness for so long and yet survive. But after all, why should it be deemed impossible? As far as anyone could tell, there were no predators in New South Wales. The weather was getting colder and in consequence the snakes seemed to be making themselves more scarce. A child can go a week or more without food if she has to. If Sophie had not become so cold in the thunderstorm, and provided she did not slip over the edge of a waterfall or stand under a falling tree or aggravate the Indians, she might have survived even longer. I had managed to raise myself on the streets of London, which in many ways were more dangerous than the forests of New South Wales.

There were some who speculated that native tribes must have helped Sophie, but in the weeks that followed her return to the bosom of her family, she spoke of seeing no one but Johnny and me.

To my astonishment she attached herself to me with every evidence of great fondness. Nothing could have startled me more. I saw a good deal of her, because her parents and she lived less than a mile from the Revd Mr Haddock and Amelia, and their baby Clarissa. And I lived with the Revd Mr Haddock and his young family, because he arranged for me to be assigned to his household as a servant.

Johnny's gamble had succeeded. When we told the story of how we had found Sophie, how we had ridden logs down the flooded river in order to reach her, how we had revived her when she appeared to be beyond reviving, how we had fed her and carried her and brought her back to her loving parents – and here I confess that we did not mini-mise our account of our heroic efforts on her behalf – women wept and men pressed money upon us whilst dabbing their eyes with their hand-kerchiefs. Sophie's father petitioned the Governor for a pardon for us both, and whilst the Governor did not so far acquiesce as to remit our sentences entirely, he did absolve us for our escapes from lawful custody, and for Johnny's assault on the woman from whom he had stolen the food. Johnny told me he was no murderer, and he was right: the woman had been only stunned and had made a full and speedy recovery.

It was not only the fortunate resolution of her case which helped him, though. His expectation that the rescue of Sophie would work in our favour was better founded than he himself could have realised, for Sophie's father, the kind man who petitioned the Governor on our behalf, was none other than the deputy judge advocate of the colony, Mr David Collins. I sometimes wondered what would have become of us had Sophie been the daughter of a convict. Judge Collins was highly regarded, as a man who always urged moderation, who used common sense as the chief basis for his decision-making, and who often pleaded the case for the original inhabitants of New South Wales, so cruelly swept aside by the arrival of the Europeans.

I will remain discreet about the identity of Sophie's mother, for certain it is that Mrs Collins never made the long journey out from England to the colony, and yet her husband fathered two children in Sydney, Sophie and her brother George.

Although the Governor did not see fit to set Johnny Piggott free, he did in his gubernatorial wisdom commute the original sentence. Johnny was ordered to serve a further eighteen months. He was not treated well however, being assigned to roadwork, one of the least favoured jobs among the convicts. Furthermore, his movements were strictly curtailed, as he was confined to barracks when not in the road gang. I was at least permitted to see him every Sabbath Day, which I did without fail.

He was a changed man in so many respects. He had but one purpose, one burning desire, and that was to return to the country of his birth and seek out his loving parents, in order to acquaint them with the miracle of his return from the grave. This ambition assisted him to restrain himself when provoked by the overseers, who, considering the Governor to have been too indulgent towards him, were inclined to deal with him harshly.

I offered to write his parents a letter on his behalf, to let them know the facts of his situation, but Johnny was afraid of the effects upon them of receiving the news in such a way. 'And besides,' he said, 'with the greatest respect to you, Barnaby, and your powers of eloquence when you take up your pen, how are they to believe you? The only proof that will satisfy them is if I can stand before them once more and take them in my arms. I must pray that they will live long enough for us to have that meeting.'

I had my doubts about the practicality of his intentions, for there was much official and unofficial resistance to the idea of men who had served their sentences being allowed to go back to England upon their release. Some were successful, as the presence of the returnee in the Pie and Peas testified, but they were few in number.

I did not press the suggestion of a letter further with Johnny however, as it occurred to me that were he to die out here in New South Wales, as was most likely, it might be kinder for his parents never to know. They believed him to be at the bottom of the cold ocean off the coast of Scotland and they had, as much as humanly possible, reconciled themselves to his loss. It would be cruel to subject them a second time to such bitter grief.

Johnny's story however reminded me of the Lord's treatment of his servant Job. For Job, having suffered the loss of his sons and daughters, was then recompensed with a new complement of children. Job 1:21, 'The Lord gave, and the Lord hath taken away; blessed be the name of the Lord.' Silas and Abigail Piggott seemed to be God-fearing, righteous people, and yet the Lord had allowed their precious eldest son to be as one dead to them. When I pressed the Revd Mr Haddock about this he replied in the same terms he had used at St Martin's, that it was not for us to question these mysteries. Yet this was not enough for me. Being always of a restless and inquiring mind I found myself unable to show such meek compliance, much as I admired it in the Revd Mr Haddock. Though I fear the possibility that life is determined by random chance rather than divine intervention, yet I am forced to consider it a possibility. Should it prove to be so, I must find the strength to bear the dreadful burden of being a bark adrift on a capricious ocean; but if I am wrong I can only pray that the Lord will forgive my arrogance, for surely I would merit far worse sufferings than were meted out to Job – or the Piggotts.

The course of my life during this period was in marked contrast to the grinding hardship of quarrying and crushing rock that Johnny experienced. Working in weather which, in the course of a year, ranged from fierce heat to sharp frosts proved deleterious to the health of many a man on the road gangs. The Revd Mr Haddock's cottage, on the other hand, was quite an elegant affair, built of brick, with a tiled roof, whilst I was allotted a wattle-and-daub hut with thatched roof out the back. Although this leaked prodigiously when I moved in, I soon learned how to seal the gaps and felt much delight in occupying my own quarters for the first time in my life. Indeed, I was well content.

I spent most evenings in the company of the Revd Mr Haddock and his small family. Amelia, Mrs Haddock, was a demure, rather shy young lady, devoted to her husband and her infant. The baby had been endowed with the formidable name of Clarissa Josephine Emma Millicent Florence Muriel Haddock, after her grandmothers and great-grandmothers, and she thus epitomised the desire of the Haddocks to give pleasure to all, to cause distress to none. Better to burden the child with the names of half-a-dozen forebears, whether deceased or no, than to risk causing offence to any. This was how they lived their lives, seeking to satisfy all about them, in which endeavour, I hardly need to say, they failed dismally, for certain it is that the more we seek to placate our neighbours the more they take pleasure in criticising us.

I asked Mrs Haddock one evening: 'How did you determine the order of the names you gave Clarissa?' and she put down her knitting, sighed deeply, and said 'Alas, we unwittingly caused great disharmony among our dear family, for we placed them in the order we thought most pleasing to the ear, only to find that Great-Grandmother Clarissa was the only one satisfied by our choice.'

Rough and ready as I was, and hardened by the life I had led, I found it difficult to accustom myself to the gentleness of the Haddocks' manners, and even thought them somewhat innocent in their understanding of the world. On a number of occasions I intervened to stop them being swindled by rascally shopkeepers, and twice I chased thieving convicts out of the house. In turn, however, the Haddocks softened me somewhat by their influence. My learning continued apace under their tuition. They were both well-educated and well-read, and they seemed to take pleasure in my progress, and I in turn learned to share their appreciation of fine literature. I do not believe any lad or lass in the colony could have been better instructed.

During the day I worked as best I could, cleaning the house, chopping wood, tending the garden, running errands, and, my favourite task, taking care of Clarissa. I was moved beyond measure that on so many occasions the Haddocks entrusted me with she who was most precious to them.

It is at this point that I find I must lay down my pen. The telling of these early years of my life has been, as I said, at the request of the colony's chief chaplain, the Revd Mr Johnson, whom the Revd Mr Haddock serves as assistant chaplain. I did not expect to take so long about the narrative. It has awoken many memories for me, and many of them are painful. Yet I am still here, unlike a number of those whose paths crossed mine, and I am grateful for that. Despite my fears that we are subject to the random and mysterious workings of the universe, I nonetheless believe in the providence of the Divine Creator who watches over us, and I place my trust in the benevolence of His intentions for me.

I am tired now, and so will leave the telling of subsequent stages of my life, and indeed of Johnny's further adventures, until another time.

Author's Note

THE HISTORICAL DETAILS IN this story are accurate, although occasionally liberties have been taken with the truth. Among the books consulted in the preparation of this story were:

A Narrative of the Expedition to Botany Bay and *A Complete Account of the Settlement at Port Jackson* by Watkin Tench

The Colony: A history of early Sydney by Grace Karskens

Bound for Botany Bay by Frank Clune

Their Chastity Was Not Too Rigid: Leisure times in early Australia by J. W. C. Cumes

Sydney Cove 1788: The First Year of the Settlement of Australia (original diaries), edited by Dr John Cobley

For the Term of His Natural Life by Marcus Clarke

Orphans of History: The forgotten children of the First Fleet by Robert Holden

The Diary of Joseph Sams, edited by Simon Braydon and Robert Songhurst

The Journal of John Sweatman, edited by Jim Allen and Peter Corris

The Oxford Book of Australian Letters, edited by Brenda Niall and John Thompson

The Long Farewell: The perilous voyages of settlers under sail in the great migrations to Australia by Don Charlwood

Phillip of Australia: An account of the settlement at Sydney Cove by M. Barnard Eldershaw

Botany Bay by Charles Nordhoff and James Norman Hall

Joseph Mason: Assigned convict, 1831–1837, edited by David Kent and Norma Townsend

Guilty Wretch That I Am: Echoes of Australian bushrangers, from the death row memoirs of Richard Burgess with historical notes by Ken Byron

Dancing With Strangers by Inga Clendinnen

Early Australian History: Convict life in New South Wales and Van Diemen's Land by Charles White

The 1811 Dictionary of the Vulgar Tongue, foreword by Max Harris

Farewell to Old England by Hugh Anderson

Sources of Australian History, selected and edited by Manning Clark

For the description of the treatment, cooking and distribution of animals by some Australian Aboriginal groups, and for information about the play of Aboriginal children, I am indebted to the book *Children of the Desert* by Géza Róheim, based on observations made by Róheim in 1929. Several paragraphs in my book that relate to animal cooking and distribution are merely paraphrases of Róheim's descriptions.

Many websites, too numerous to list, were also consulted. Outstanding among these were www.londonlives.org and www.oldbaileyonline.org.

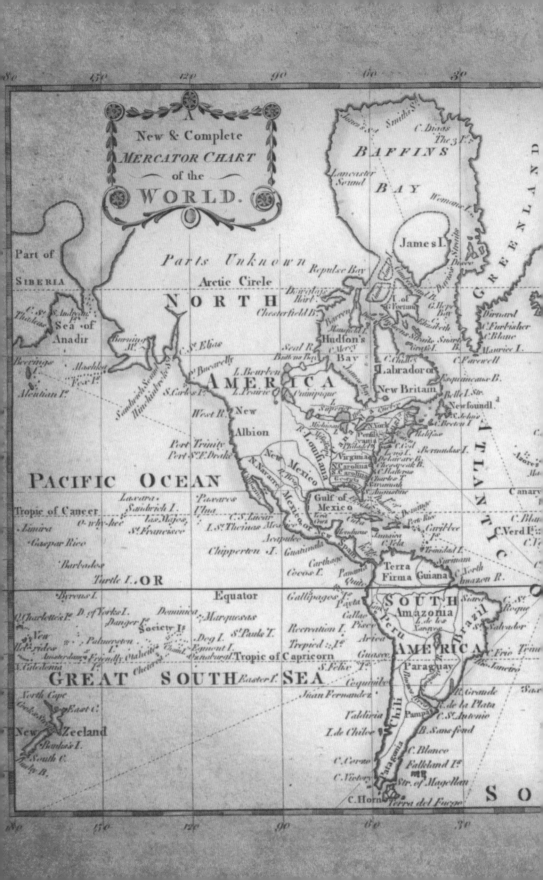

A
New & Complete
MERCATOR CHART
of the
WORLD.

Part of
SIBERIA

Parts Unknown

Arctic Circle

NORTH

BAFFINS

BAY

C. Dixas
The St.

GREENLAND

Lancaster
Sound

James I.

Repulse Bay

C. St Andrew
Thaddeus

Sea of
Anadir

Devrday's
Burk

Chesterfield B.

I. of
Fortune

G. Hope
Bay

Dirnard
M.Furbisher
C. Blanc

Maurice I.

Burning
Mt.

St Elias

Seal R.
Baffins Bay

Hudson's

Bay

C. Challes

Labrador or

C. Farewell

Esquimause B.

Beerings
I.
Maskhot
Fox I.

L. Bourbon

New Britain

Belle I. Str.

Azores

Aleutian I.

Sandwich Sound
Hinchinbrooke

St Carlos P.

West R.

AMERICA

L. Treurie

Superior

Newfoundl.

St Johns
C. Breton I.

New

Albion

R. Mississippi

L. Louisiana

Michigan

York
Pensil vania

Halifax

C. Cod
Long I.

Bermudas I.

Canary

PACIFIC   OCEAN

Port Trinity
Port St F. Drake

N. Navarel
California

New Mexico

R. Bravo

Virginia
N. Carolina
S. Carolina

Delaware R.
Chesapeak B.
St Mathias

Georgia
St Augustine

Tropic of Cancer

Lavara
Sandwich I.
O-why-hee

Pararos
Una

Mexico, or New

Gulf of
Mexico

Cuba

Bahama

Bermuda

C. Verd I.

Limira

St Francisco

C. St Lucar

Vera Cruz

Porto Rico

Caribbee
Is.

C. Blanc
C. Verd I.

Gaspar Rico

I. St Thomas

Mes

Spain

Honduras

Jamaica
C. Lela

Barbadoes

Acapulco
Clipperton I.

Guatimala

Trinidad I.

Turtle I. OR

Cocos I.

Carthagena

Porto

Panama

Cadix

Terra
Firma

Surinam
Guiana

C. North
Amazon R.

Byreus I.

Equator

Gallipagos I.

Payta

SOUTH

C. St
Roque

St Charlottes I.
D. of Yorks I.

Dominica

Marquesas

Recreation I.

Callao

Amazonia
L. de los Xarayes

Brazil

St Salvador

New
Hebrides

Danger I.

Society Is

Palmerston

Dog I.
Egmont I.

St Pauls I.

Trepiced I.

Arica

Pisco
Peru

AMERICA

C. Frio
Rio

Amsterdam
Friendly

Otaheite
Chain

Chili

S. Felix I.

Guasco

Tropic of Capricorn

Paraguay

Janeiro

N. Caledonia

Cheteri

GREAT   SOUTH

Easter I.

SEA

S. Felix I.

Juan Fernandez

Coquimbo

Pampas

R. Grande
R. de la Plata
C. St Antonio

North Cape

East C.

Valdivia

Zeelan d

I. de Chiloe

B. Sans fond

New

Bawks's I.

South C.
Twly B.

Patagonia

C. Blanco
Falkland Is.

C. Cerro

C. Victory

Str. of Magellan

C. Horn

Terra del Fuego

SO